Understanding Cancers

This publication forms part of an Open University course SK123 *Understanding cancers*. Details of this and other Open University courses can be obtained from the Student Registration and Enquiry Service, The Open University, PO Box 197, Milton Keynes MK7 6BJ, United Kingdom: tel. +44 (0)845 300 60 90, email general-enquiries @open.ac.uk

Alternatively, you may visit the Open University website at http://www.open.ac.uk where you can learn more about the wide range of courses and packs offered at all levels by The Open University.

To purchase a selection of Open University course materials visit http://www.ouw.co.uk, or contact Open University Worldwide, Walton Hall, Milton Keynes MK7 6AA, United Kingdom for a brochure. tel. +44 (0)1908 858793; fax +44 (0)1908 858787; email ouw-customer-services@open.ac.uk

The Open University
Walton Hall, Milton Keynes
MK7 6AA

First published 2010

Edited and designed by The Open University.

Typeset by SR Nova Pvt Ltd, Bangalore, India

Printed and bound in the United Kingdom by Halstan Printing Group, Amersham.

ISBN 978 1 8487 3278 0

1.1

THE SK123 COURSE TEAM

Course Team Chairs and Academic Editors

Sotiris Missailidis, Department of Chemistry and Analytical Sciences, Faculty of Science

Kerry Murphy, Department of Life Sciences, Faculty of Science

Course Managers

Simone Pitman, Department of Chemistry and Analytical Sciences, Faculty of Science

Rosie Meade, Department of Life Sciences, Faculty of Science

Course Team Assistant

Helen Copperwheat, Department of Life Sciences, Faculty of Science

Course Team Authors

Basiro Davey, Department of Life Sciences, Faculty of Science (Chapters 1 and 12, Host Chapter 11)

Ignacio Romero, Department of Life Sciences, Faculty of Science (Chapters 2, 3, 4, 6 and 12, case studies)

Sotiris Missailidis, Department of Chemistry and Analytical Sciences, Faculty of Science (Chapter 12, Host Chapter 5)

Kerry Murphy, Department of Life Sciences, Faculty of Science (Chapter 12, Host Chapters 7 and 8)

Elizabeth Parvin, Department of Physics and Astronomy, Faculty of Science (Chapters 6, 9 and 12)

Li XiuHui, Peking University School of Distance Learning for Medical Education (case studies)

Yao-Zhong Xu, Department of Chemistry and Analytical Sciences, Faculty of Science (Chapters 10 and 12)

Academic Readers

Duncan Banks, Department of Life sciences, Faculty of Science

Claire Rothwell, Staff Tutor, Faculty of Science

Mark Hirst, Department of Life Sciences, Faculty of Science

Multimedia Coordinator

Duncan Banks, Department of Life Sciences, Faculty of Science

External Course Assessor

Professor Karol Sikora, Professor of Cancer Medicine and Honorary Consultant Oncologist at Imperial College School of Medicine, Hammersmith Hospital, London

Production Team

Martin Chiverton (Producer)

Lydia Eaton (Media Assistant)

Emily Fuller (Media Assistant)

Sarah Gammon (Contracts Executive)

Rebecca Graham (Media Developer)

Sarah Hofton (Media Developer)

Chris Hough (Media Developer)

Martin Keeling (Media Assistant)

Corinne Owen (Media Assistant)

Jonathan Owen (Media Developer)

Judith Pickering (Media Project Manager)

Will Rawes (Media Developer)

Consultants

David Shuker, Visiting Research Professor, Department of Chemistry and Analytical Sciences, Faculty of Science (co-author Chapter 5)

Paul Rogers, Consultant Oncologist, Royal Berkshire NHS Foundation Trust (co-author Chapter 7)

Arjun Takhar, Specialist Registrar Surgery, University Hospitals Coventry and Warwickshire Hospitals NHS Trust (co-author Chapter 8)

Vinod Menon, Consultant Surgeon, University Hospitals Coventry and Warwickshire Hospitals NHS Trust (co-author Chapter 8)

Alison Prust, General Practitioner, Isle of Jura (co-author Chapter 11 and case studies)

Clare Sansom, Associate Lecturer, part-time lecturer Birkbeck College and freelance science writer (case studies)

Other Contributors

The Course Team would like to thank the following people for their involvement in the production of SK123:

Andrew J. Doggart, Principal Physicist, Royal Berkshire NHS Foundation Trust

Tom Goodfellow, Consultant Radiologist, University Hospitals Coventry and Warwickshire Hospitals NHS Trust

Richard Wellings, Consultant Radiologist, University Hospitals Coventry and Warwickshire Hospitals NHS Trust

Nigel Williams, Head of Nuclear Medicine, University Hospitals Coventry and Warwickshire NHS Trust

The SDK125, SK195, S807 and S819 Course Teams.

Developmental testers: Peter Culleton, Ann McCrory, Lisette Nixon and Eileen Newman.

CONTENTS

CHAPTER 1   A GLOBAL HEALTH PROBLEM   1

1.1   Cancers ancient and modern   1
1.2   A brief survey of global cancer statistics   4
1.3   Concluding remarks   17
1.4   Summary of Chapter 1   18
Questions for Chapter 1   18
References   19

CHAPTER 2   CELLS AND CANCERS   21

2.1   Introduction   21
2.2   What are cells?   21
2.3   Cells are made from a few types of molecules   25
2.4   A 'typical' human cell   30
2.5   A brief overview of the basic properties of normal
       and neoplastic cells   32
2.6   Cell metabolism   33
2.7   Cell proliferation   34
2.8   Cell differentiation   39
2.9   Changes in cellular function in response to
       the cell's environment   44
2.10   Concluding remarks   50
2.11   Summary of Chapter 2   51
Questions for Chapter 2   52
Further reading   54

CHAPTER 3   GENES AND CANCERS   55

3.1   Introduction   55
3.2   The structure of DNA   56
3.3   Genes and proteins   58
3.4   Cancers and mutations   60
3.5   How do mutations arise?   64
3.6   Can you inherit cancer?   71
3.7   Concluding remarks   73
3.8   Summary of Chapter 3   73
Questions for Chapter 3   74
Further reading   75

CHAPTER 4   THE HUMAN BODY AND CANCERS   77

4.1   Introduction   77
4.2   Benign and malignant tumours   77
4.3   Tumour cells require a blood supply to grow into larger
         tumours   80
4.4   How do tumour cells spread?   83
4.5   Cancers and the immune system   89
4.6   Symptoms of cancers   90
4.7   Maintaining the whole: body homeostasis   96
4.8   Concluding remarks   98
4.9   Summary of Chapter 4   98
Questions for Chapter 4   99
Further reading   100

CHAPTER 5   RISK FACTORS FOR CANCERS   101

5.1   Introduction   101
5.2   What is a risk factor for cancers?   102
5.3   Identifying and quantifying risk factors for cancers   104
5.4   Genetics and cancer risk   110
5.5   Some environmental risk factors for cancers   113
5.6   Lifestyle, environment and cancers   121
5.7   Cancer prevention   123
5.8   Concluding remarks   125
5.9   Summary of Chapter 5   125
Questions for Chapter 5   126
References   127

CHAPTER 6   DIAGNOSIS AND SCREENING   129

6.1   Introduction   129
6.2   An overview of the diagnostic process   130
6.3   Physical examination   132
6.4   Laboratory tests   135
6.5   Imaging tests   138
6.6   Biopsies   160
6.7   Screening for cancers   168
6.8   Concluding remarks   172
6.9   Summary of Chapter 6   173

Questions for Chapter 6		174
References		175
Further reading		175

CHAPTER 7 INTRODUCTION TO CANCER THERAPY — 177

7.1	Introduction	177
7.2	The diagnosis	177
7.3	The multidisciplinary team	180
7.4	Treating the cancer	186
7.5	How is a treatment chosen? The patient and the oncologist	190
7.6	Consent	192
7.7	How do we know which treatments work best? Clinical trials	193
7.8	Concluding remarks	198
7.9	Summary of Chapter 7	198
Questions for Chapter 7		199
References		199

CHAPTER 8 SURGERY IN CANCER TREATMENT — 201

8.1	Introduction	201
8.2	Surgical approaches in the treatment of cancer	201
8.3	Surgery: open or minimal	208
8.4	Special techniques in cancer surgery	211
8.5	The process of surgical therapy in the treatment of cancer	214
8.6	Risks of cancer surgery	220
8.7	Tissue transplantation	222
8.8	Cancer surgery: a global perspective	223
8.9	Concluding remarks	223
8.10	Summary of Chapter 8	223
Questions for Chapter 8		224
References		224

CHAPTER 9 RADIOTHERAPY — 225

9.1	Introduction	225
9.2	How does radiotherapy work?	226
9.3	Teletherapy	231
9.4	Brachytherapy	239
9.5	Unsealed source radiotherapy	243
9.6	Radiation protection	245

9.7   Radiotherapy around the world   246

9.8   Concluding remarks   248

9.9   Summary of Chapter 9   248

Questions for Chapter 9   249

References   249

Further reading   250

CHAPTER 10   CHEMOTHERAPY AND BIOLOGICAL THERAPY   251

10.1   Introduction   251

10.2   Chemotherapy drugs   253

10.3   Alkylating drugs   256

10.4   Antimetabolite drugs   259

10.5   Other types of chemotherapy drugs   265

10.6   Biological therapies   267

10.7   Cancer growth inhibitors   267

10.8   Immunotherapy   269

10.9   Hormone therapy   274

10.10 Gene therapy   275

10.11 Other issues related with anticancer drugs   276

10.12 Concluding remarks   280

10.13 Summary of Chapter 10   281

Questions for Chapter 10   282

Further reading   282

CHAPTER 11   LIVING WITH CANCER   283

11.1   Introduction   283

11.2   Psychological adjustment to living with cancer   284

11.3   Managing cancer symptoms and side effects   286

11.4   Effects on lifestyle   294

11.5   Returning to normal life   297

11.6   Facing the end of life   305

11.7   Concluding remarks   312

11.8   Summary of Chapter 11   312

Questions for Chapter 11   312

References   314

CHAPTER 12   CANCERS IN THE FUTURE   317

12.1   Introduction   317

12.2   Cancers: a worsening global health problem?   317

12.3   The biology of cancer   319

12.4   Cancer prevention   321

12.5   Early detection and diagnosis   322

12.6   Advances in cancer treatments   324

12.7   Quality of life for people with cancer   326

12.8   Concluding remarks   327

References   327

ANSWERS TO QUESTIONS   A1

APPENDIX   A17

ACKNOWLEDGEMENTS   A19

INDEX   A23

CHAPTER I

A GLOBAL HEALTH PROBLEM

Learning outcomes

After studying this chapter and its associated activity, you should be able to:

1.1 Define and use in context, or recognise definitions and applications of, each of the terms printed in **bold** in the text.

1.2 Interpret epidemiological data demonstrating that cancers are a major global health problem, using or identifying examples of cancer incidence, prevalence, mortality and survival presented in graphs and tables.

1.3 Describe some differences in the distribution of cancers in different parts of the world, and comment on variations between age-groups, genders, ethnic groups and between richer and poorer populations.

1.4 Summarise the issues of reliability and comparability that must be kept in mind when interpreting epidemiological data on cancers.

1.1 Cancers ancient and modern

This course is about the science underlying cancers – a complex group of over 100 diseases, which physicians have been diagnosing for at least 3500 years, as demonstrated by the earliest record describing eight cases of breast cancer in ancient Egypt. No-one knows how commonly cancers occurred in ancient times, but lifespans were much shorter than they are today (Figure 1.1) and cancers are more likely to develop as we age, so it is safe to predict that they were not as prominent as they are in modern populations. In 2005, cancers were responsible for 7.6 million deaths worldwide, accounting for 13% of all deaths in that year – more than the total dying from HIV/AIDS, tuberculosis and malaria combined. Over 11 million new cases of cancer developed in 2005 and at least 25 million people were living with the disease (WHO, 2006).

Later in this chapter, you will see examples of variations in how the commonest cancers are distributed in different parts of the world, and how they vary with age, ethnicity, and between males and females, rich and poor. The principal aim is to illustrate the impact of cancers on human health by examining data from different populations and, in the process, to discuss difficulties in assembling accurate data from many parts of the world. We also explain why data on the occurrence of cancers are often several years old by the time they are published. (So, for example, at the time of writing in 2008, the most recently published estimates of the total number of cancers worldwide come from 2005.) Along the way we will preview the topics to be covered in later chapters of this book.

Figure 1.1 The mummified remains believed to be those of Queen Hatshepsut, who ruled Egypt between 1503 and 1482 BC, show evidence that she died at the age of about 50 from cancer which had spread to her bones. (Source: Brando Quilici/AP/PA Photos)

The fact that there are so many different types of cancer, with different symptoms, treatments and **prognoses** (singular: prognosis; i.e. the probable course and outcomes of the disease), explains why we have chosen to use the plural 'cancers' throughout this course. The variation between different cancers means that a number of different ways of classifying them are in use, but the simplest refers to their site of origin in the body, as in lung or breast cancer. Even this categorisation obscures the fact that there are, for example, four main types of lung cancer, each originating in a different type of lung cell. You will learn about other classification systems in later chapters.

Despite their differences, all cancers have one thing in common, highlighted in the World Health Organization (WHO)'s definition, which states that **cancers** are characterised by 'the rapid creation of abnormal cells which grow beyond their usual boundaries, and which can invade adjoining parts of the body and spread to other organs' (WHO, 2006). Chapters 2 to 4 explain how these abnormal cells are generated, the role of genes in cancer initiation and how cancer cells spread around the body and interfere with the normal function of body organs.

The causes of cancers are as varied as the cancers themselves. Chapter 5 looks at the risk factors associated with an increased likelihood that a cancer will develop. The term **risk factor** is often misunderstood. Exposure to a risk factor (for example, the chemicals in tobacco smoke) does not mean that an exposed individual *will* develop the associated cancer; it simply means that in a *population* the cancer is found to occur more frequently in those who have been exposed to the risk factor than in those who have not, or not as much. Note that some exposed individuals never develop a cancer and some who weren't exposed do – so the association between the risk factor and the cancer refers to the level of *probability* of cancers occurring in the exposed population, not the risk to any particular individual.

Physicians in ancient civilisations may have had some notions of possible risk factors for certain cancers, but they knew nothing about 'cells' (abnormal or otherwise). However, they would have recognised most of the definition of cancers given by the WHO. The term 'cancer' is derived from the Greek *karkinos* – the crab – a term credited to Hippocrates (born around 460 BC), which suggests the 'sideways creeping' of cancers away from their original site and into other parts of the body.

Hippocrates made an important distinction that remains in current medical teaching. A solid mass of new cells growing in an inappropriate location is known as a **tumour** (or colloquially, a growth), but Hippocrates recognised that tumours could be either 'benign' or 'malignant' and that this had a crucial impact on the person's chances of survival. Most **benign tumours** are not life-threatening, though some may, over time, grow very large and eventually prove fatal if they damage the functioning of a vital organ. But the cells of which the original **primary tumour** is composed do not spread around the body, or (if they do) they do not lodge in distant locations and begin to generate new **secondary tumours**. The habit of spreading to other parts of the body is the defining characteristic of **malignant tumours** or cancers, and it is this property that can make some of them difficult to treat. Chapter 6 of this book describes the methods used to detect cancers 'early' by screening for signs of disease and the diagnostic techniques commonly employed to identify the cancer accurately.

- Can you suggest why diagnosis of a cancer as early as possible might have a bearing on the prognosis?

- If the primary cancer is detected soon enough, cancer cells may not have spread away from the original site; treatment is likely to be more successful if the cancer is confined to a single location.

Chapters 7 to 10 explain and illustrate the main types of cancer treatment, beginning with an overview of the general principles of therapeutic interventions and then focusing in turn on surgery, radiotherapy (the use of radiation), and chemotherapy (the use of drugs). If these treatment strategies fail, and the illness enters the terminal phase, much can now be done in countries with adequate palliative care services to alleviate the physical and psychological pain and discomfort of dying with cancer, as Chapter 11 explains. But most people with cancer are living with the disease and Chapter 11 discusses ways in which quality of life can be improved if the necessary support is available. The book closes in Chapter 12 by gazing into the future and speculating about some experimental ways of tackling cancers that may prove to be valuable in years to come.

Fictional case studies of individuals with cancer from around the world have been woven into all the chapters except the first and last in the book. They are based on elements of real people's stories, chosen to illustrate some of the variation in the experience of being diagnosed and treated for different cancers in a wide range of personal, cultural and medical contexts. As you encounter each case study, bear in mind that everyone's experience is unique and these examples only give a glimpse of the much wider variation in the real world. Below we have included a summary of the main distinguishing features of these seven case studies that will help you follow their progression throughout the book (Table 1.1).

Table 1.1 Summary of case studies in the course and where they occur in the book.

Family name, first name	Age (at diagnosis)	Type of cancer	Ethnicity and sex	Location	Sections in the book
Bayler, Dave	42	Colon cancer	African-American, male	USA	3.6, 6.3, 6.6.2, 8.3, 11.4, 11.5.1
De Groot, Anneke	62	Lung cancer	Caucasian, female	Netherlands	5.3, 6.8, 8.5.6, 11.6, 11.6.3, 11.6.4, 11.6.5
Jones, Naheed	55	Colon cancer	Middle Eastern, female	UK	4.6.3, 8.4
Ming, Lin	51	Liver cancer	East Asian, male	China	5.5.3, 6.5.3, 10.11.2, 11.6.3
Moloney, Terri	67	Skin cancer	Caucasian, female	Australia	2.9.4, 4.4.2, 7.3.1, 7.7, 10.8.2
Rodrigues, Jôao	76	Prostate cancer	African-American, male	Brazil	6.7, 7.5, 9.4.2, 11.5.3, 11.5.5
Shah, Trupti	5	Cancer of immune cells	South Asian, female	UK	2.8, 4.6.3, 6.6.1, 10.4, 10.11.5
Simpson, Julie	23	Thyroid cancer	Caucasian, female	UK	4.7, 8.2.2, 9.5, 11.5.2

1.2 A brief survey of global cancer statistics

As you will see throughout this course, the experience of being diagnosed and treated for a cancer can be very different in richer and poorer countries, and in the affluent and impoverished sectors of any society. Cancers also vary with age and with ethnicity, and in the extent to which treatment is curative or increases survival. It requires a huge database to summarise the data on cancer diagnoses and deaths for every type of cancer in defined populations around the world (if you wish to access it, see Curado et al., 2007); here we will simply give you an insight into some key variations in the global impact of cancers.

1.2.1 Cancer prevalence, mortality and incidence

At the start of this chapter it was stated that 25 million people were estimated to be living with a cancer in 2005. This is the cancer **prevalence** for that year – the total number of people estimated to be living with the condition at a particular date. However, knowing the global prevalence doesn't tell you anything about where people with cancer are living, what types of cancer they have, how many of them die each year, or how many new cases are diagnosed. This is the territory of a branch of science called **epidemiology** – the study of the occurrence, distribution, causes and control of diseases, disorders and disabilities in populations, based on numerical data collected from a range of sources, including national disease registers, medical records and research studies.

In most countries of the world it is easier to count deaths than to count existing cases, and a great deal of epidemiological evidence is based on **mortality data**, i.e. the number of deaths occurring in a given period, usually one calendar year. Figure 1.2 gives a 'snapshot' of what proportion of cancer deaths worldwide in 2002 was due to each of the main types of cancer in males and in females (WHO, 2004). (These were the most recent global estimates, for each type of cancer separately, available in 2008.) Pie charts enable you to see at a glance which cancers accounted for most deaths in each sex from the size of each 'slice' of the pie.

● Which cancers apart from those of the breast, cervix, uterus and ovary among females and of the prostate among males show the *largest* difference between the sexes in terms of the proportion of cancer deaths worldwide? Can you suggest an explanation for this sex difference?

● Cancers of the trachea (windpipe), bronchus (the main branching airways) and lung account for *twice* the proportion of deaths in males as they do in females (24.6% compared to 12.2%). Most of this is due to differences in tobacco smoking between the sexes; smoking was uncommon among women until relatively recently in Western industrialised nations like the UK and USA and it remains rare among most women in Africa, Asia, South America and the other less affluent countries of the world (a point returned to later in the chapter).

However, many more people develop cancer than die of it and this is reflected in another commonly published statistic, the **incidence**, i.e. the number of *new* cases arising in a given period, also usually one calendar year. But just comparing the *number* of deaths or new cases in different countries isn't a good basis for comparing the impact of cancers in those countries.

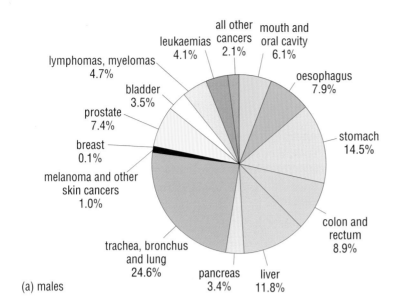

(a) males

Figure 1.2   Pie charts showing the proportion of deaths from cancers worldwide in 2002 for each of the major types of cancer (a) in males, and (b) in females. In that year, there were almost 4 million deaths from cancers among males, and just over 3 million among females. (Percentages do not sum to exactly 100% due to rounding of decimal places. Data derived from WHO, 2004, Statistical Annex, Table 4.)

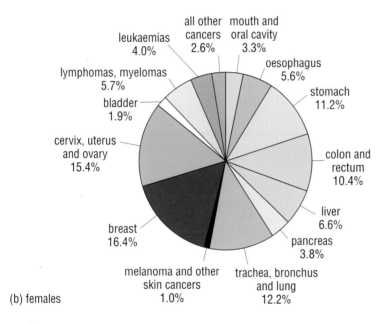

(b) females

● Can you suggest why not?

● If the countries you want to compare have different population sizes (to take one example, China with around 1.33 billion people and the UK with around 60 million), you would expect there to be a much larger *number* of cancers in China than in the UK, just because there are a lot more people. Comparing the number of deaths or new cases couldn't tell you whether the Chinese experienced more or fewer cancers 'per head' of population than their UK counterparts.

The solution is to express the number of deaths as a **mortality rate** per 100 000 population, and the number of new cases as an **incidence rate** per 100 000 population. This allows you to compare, for example, how many new cases of lung cancer arose or how many died from it in every 100 000 people in China and in the UK in the same year. With these ways of measuring the impact of cancers it's possible to take a more detailed look at how they are distributed around the world and within populations.

Sometimes you will see mortality rates or incidence rates expressed per 1000 people, or per 10 000 or per million; it doesn't matter as long as comparisons are made on the same basis.

1.2.2 The influence of age, poverty, geography and gender

Life expectancy has been increasing for several decades around the world in all but the countries in Sub-Saharan Africa most affected by HIV/AIDS. The risk of developing most cancers rises with age so, as the world's population 'ages', the incidence of cancers has been increasing everywhere. In 2005, around 70% of all deaths from cancers and almost 50% of new cases occurred in the populations of *low-* and *middle-income countries*, a categorisation based on a country's gross national product (GNP) and how much money on average each person has to live on. The level of industrialisation and the proportion of the population with access to education and health care, adequate housing, employment, clean water and sanitation is significantly lower in these less affluent countries than in the *high-income countries* of Europe, North America, Australia, New Zealand and Japan. These features of daily life have significant impacts on health, including the rates of incidence and prevalence of cancers and cancer mortality. However, the relative wealth of a country as a whole is not the only economic indicator of cancer risk: the relative wealth of individuals within each population is highly significant. Cancer rates in the most affluent countries are highest among the poor in the society, and in countries where the majority are poor the wealthier individuals are at the lowest risk.

Many sources of data on disease and disability refer to the low- and middle-income countries as 'developing' and the high-income countries as 'developed' but these terms are gradually falling out of use.

● What do you think is the most significant challenge posed by the high proportion of people with cancers being located in low- and middle-income countries?

● The diagnostic and treatment options available to them are far less than in the richer nations of the world, and in some cases they are non-existent.

For example, a report by Wakabi (2007) of evidence presented at the 6th International Congress of the African Organisation for Research and Training (AORTIC) noted that around 80% of people with cancers in the continent of Africa were being diagnosed 'late' relative to their counterparts in high-income countries, with adverse consequences for survival. In some countries more than 50% of those with cancer *never* saw a health professional. Treatment for malignant tumours in many poorer countries is heavily reliant on surgery (the subject of Chapter 8 of this book), yet there are crucial shortages of surgeons; for example, the Ugandan population of 27 million were served by about 75 surgeons in 2007 (Ozgediz et al., 2008). There is also relatively poor availability of radiotherapy (Chapter 9) and chemotherapy (Chapter 10). In 2006, for example, 22 African and Asian countries had no radiotherapy machines (Barton et al., 2006) and only 5% of people with cancer in Africa had access to chemotherapy (Wakabi, 2007).

Table 1.2 puts more detail on how cancers were distributed in 2002 in the various regions of the world. It shows two statistics for each geographical region: the first is the number of deaths from cancers in 2002 and the percentage this contributed to the total of just over 6.7 million cancer deaths that year. The second statistic is the cancer incidence, the number of new cases in 2002 and the percentage this contributed to the total of just over 10.8 million new cases that year.

Table 1.2 The distribution of deaths from cancers and the number of new cases in different regions of the world in both sexes combined in 2002, together with the percentage of all cancer deaths and the percentage of all cancer incidence in each region.

World region	Number of deaths	% of all cancer deaths	Number of new cancer cases	% of all cancer incidence
North America	631 900	9.4	1570 500	14.5
Central and South America and the Caribbean	479 900	7.1	833 100	7.7
Northern, Western and Southern Europe	1064 600	15.8	1917 400	17.7
Central and Eastern Europe	637 000	9.5	903 400	8.3
North Africa and the Middle East	224 000	3.3	319 800	3.0
Sub-Saharan Africa	412 100	6.1	530 100	4.9
Asia	3224 900	48.0	4676 700	43.0
Oceania*	49 500	0.7	111 400	1.0
Total	**6723 900**		**10 862 400**	

*Australia, New Zealand and the Pacific island states.

● From Table 1.2, which region of the world had the highest percentage of cancer deaths and which had the highest percentage of cancer incidence in 2002? (If you are new to reading data from tables, run your eye down the two columns with % at the top.)

● Asia had 48% of all cancer deaths and 43% of all new cases of cancer.

Table 1.2 underlines the point made earlier about less affluent countries lacking adequate resources to deal with large numbers of cancers. As people live longer and industrialisation and urban lifestyles expose them to greater risks, you can see why organisations like the WHO are predicting a cancer epidemic in the near future. By 2030, there are expected to be 20–25 million new cases annually and 13–16 million deaths worldwide, the majority in the poorer countries of the world (IARC, 2008).

● Figure 1.3 (overleaf) shows the 'top three' cancers, i.e. those with the highest incidence, in each region in Table 1.2 for males and females in 2002. Spend a few minutes studying it. What do you notice about the pattern of lung cancers?

● Lung cancers rank in the top three for males everywhere except Sub-Saharan Africa, and they are in the top three cancers among females in North America, Northern and Western Europe, and Eastern Asia.

The best known **cancer trend** (i.e. changes over time) in the 20th century has been the rise and then fall of lung cancer incidence and deaths among men in most of the high-income countries, as tobacco smoking became widespread among males after World War II and then gradually declined from about the 1970s. At the time of writing, lung cancer rates were still rising among men in Spain and Japan (Devesa et al., 2005), and also in many low- and middle-income countries, most obviously in China (Figure 1.4a, overleaf) where smoking has become increasingly popular among women (Figure 1.4b) and the young (Figure 1.4c). But there are noticeable variations in the trends in female lung

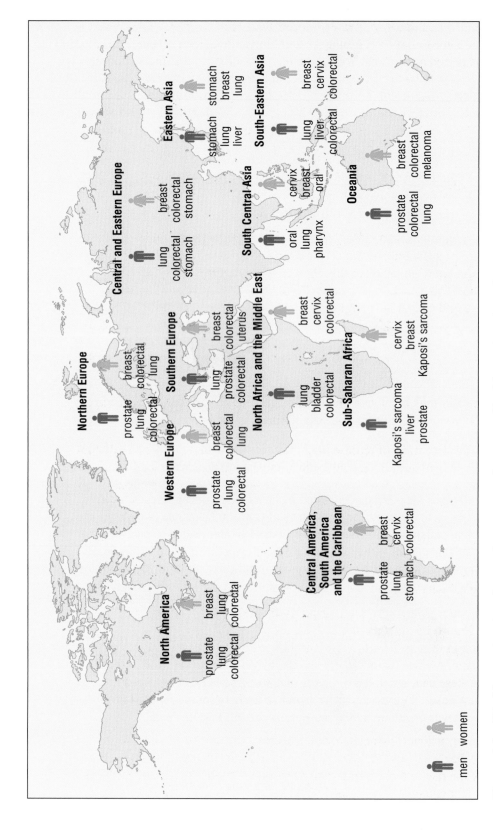

Figure 1.3 World map showing the top three cancers in terms of incidence (number of new cases) in different regions of the world in adults (aged 15 or over) in each sex in 2002. Colorectal refers to cancers of the colon and rectum. (Data from WHO and IUAC, 2005, pp. 4–5)

cancer, even between countries that are close neighbours, suggesting significant differences in the cultural acceptability of smoking among women (Levi et al., 2007). In the period after World War II, the rise was most rapid in the UK but it peaked around 1970. Figure 1.5 (overleaf) compares the mortality rates among women in four European countries since 1970. In Poland, the peak came later than in the UK, around 1996, and female lung cancer deaths have declined slowly thereafter. This is in sharp contrast to Spain and France where mortality rates for younger women were still rising at the end of the period covered by this research.

Activity 1.1   Interpreting epidemiological data in graphs

Allow about 45 minutes in total for this activity

If you are unfamiliar with interpreting data from graphs, particularly those with a vertical scale like the one in Figure 1.4, then the next time you come to a 'natural break' in studying this chapter, go to Activity 1.1, where you will find more explanation and examples to help develop your skills and enable you to demonstrate an important course learning outcome.

●   Look at Figure 1.3. What does it suggest is the most common cancer among women in different parts of the world?

●   Breast cancer ranks first or second in female cancer incidence in every major region of the world. (Note the trend in China, Figure 1.4d.)

Notice that different ways of representing international patterns in the distribution of cancers have been used in this discussion. Table 1.2 presents the total *number of deaths* and the *incidence* (number of new cases) in a single year, without taking into account either the sex of the individuals or the relative size of the populations; Figure 1.4 presents the *trend over time* in the number of *new cases* in each sex in a single city expressed as a rate per 100 000 men or women of all ages; and Figure 1.5 presents the *trend over time* in the number of *deaths* per 100 000 women in a particular *age group* in four countries. When you look at epidemiological data it is very important to take note of aspects such as these.

A few other patterns in world cancer distribution are worth highlighting before moving on. Figure 1.3 shows that cancers either of the stomach, or of the colon or rectum, are in the top three for incidence in both sexes everywhere except for Sub-Saharan Africa. Factors in the diet are believed to be involved in the causation of these cancers, and changes in diet are implicated in the steady decline in new cases of stomach cancer in countries like China (Figure 1.4a and b) where it was once much more common.

Cervical cancer, which is associated with infection with the human papilloma virus (HPV), has been pushed out of the top three for incidence in high-income countries by the rise in female lung cancers (Figure 1.3), but it remains common everywhere (for example, Figure 1.4d) and ranks high on the list among women in less affluent countries; for example, more new cases of cervical cancer occur among women in South Asia (principally India) and Sub-Saharan Africa than any other type of cancer. Prostate cancer among men is another cancer that is rapidly increasing in populations around the world; there are now more men with prostate cancer than with lung cancers in both American continents, and in Northern and Western Europe, and Oceania.

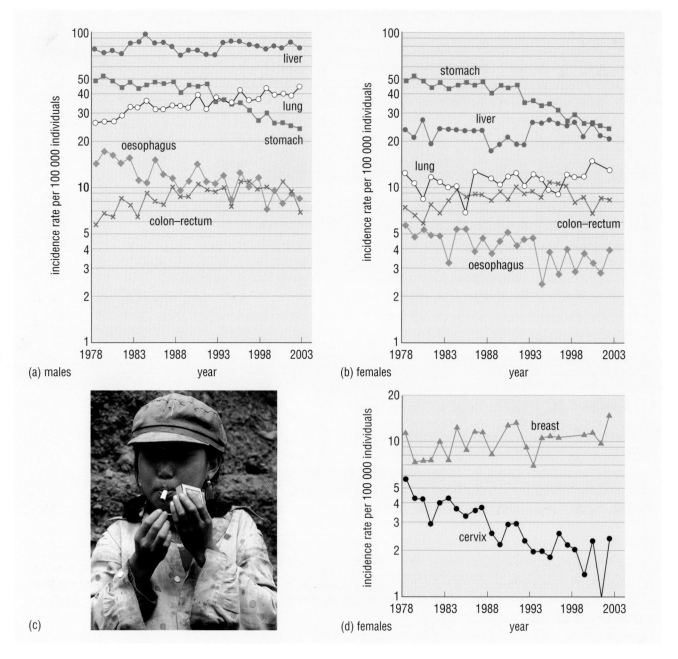

Figure 1.4 Trends in incidence rates of the major cancers (a) per 100 000 males and (b) and (d) per 100 000 females (all ages combined) between 1978 and 2002 in Qidong, China – a city of 1.16 million people. Notice that the vertical axis of the graph has the same distance between an incidence rate of 1 and 10 per 100 000 as it does between 10 and 100 per 100 000 people. This type of scale is used when a graph has to cover a very wide range of values; without it, the vertical axis would either have to be very 'tall' or the trends near the top and bottom would be compressed and much harder to see. Activity 1.1 includes an example of how Figure 1.4a would look if the vertical scale was linear, i.e. with evenly spaced intervals. The data in parts (a), (b) and (d) are age-standardised; this will be explained in the next section. (c) A Chinese child lights a cigarette. (Sources: Data for (a), (b) and (d) from Chen et al., 2006, Figure 2, p. 1450; photo for (c) Gang Fen Wang/Panos Pictures)

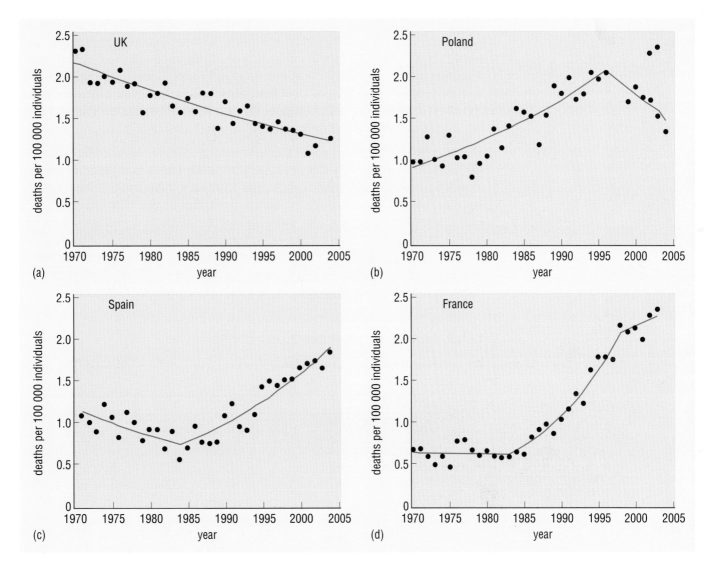

Figure 1.5   Variations in the trend in deaths from lung cancers among younger women (aged 20–44 years) in four major European countries between 1970 and 2004 (or nearest date) expressed as a rate per 100 000 women in that age group. The red line represents the 'best fit' trend based on the data collected at different times (black dots). (Data from Levi et al., 2007, Figure 1, p. 463)

Sub-Saharan Africa is the only region of the world where an unusual cancer called Kaposi's sarcoma is in the top three for both sexes. This normally slow-growing and rarely fatal cancer originates in the walls of lymphatic vessels (part of the immune system that collects the fluid draining from cells and returns it to the bloodstream). Before infection with the human immunodeficiency virus (HIV) became widespread in the region, Kaposi's sarcoma was relatively common in Africa before the rise in infection with HIV, which promotes the development of this cancer and explains its high prevalence in countries where HIV infection is widespread.

Finally, consider two types of cancer that (like Kaposi's sarcoma) have specific regional distributions illustrated in Figure 1.3. Cancers of the liver, which are strongly associated with hepatitis virus infections, are most common in

South-Eastern Asia (e.g. Indonesia, Thailand, Vietnam) and Sub-Saharan Africa, where they are in the top three cancers among males. Cancers of the oral cavity (mouth, lips and tongue) are the most prevalent cancers in men in South Central Asia, and they come third among women in this region, largely due to factors such as the chewing of tobacco and betel nuts. In Chapter 3 you will learn about how environmental factors can trigger the development of cancers; Chapter 5 discusses the evidence that implicates them as risk factors.

This discussion may have caused you to wonder if there are some differences in the *susceptibility* to certain cancers among particular ethnic groups, quite apart from their exposure to specific risk factors. There are some cancers like Kaposi's sarcoma, which (in the absence of additional risk factors like HIV infection) have higher distributions in particular ethnic groups; for example, a particular form of breast cancer is more common among Ashkenazi Jewish women. But ethnicity is a relatively minor factor in the incidence of most types of cancer, swamped by the greater impact of socioeconomic position (i.e. relative wealth or poverty) on an individual's chances of developing a cancer and being successfully treated.

1.2.3 Cancer in younger age-groups

We have made the point several times that the risk of developing most cancers increases with age, but there are some relatively rare cancers that mainly affect infants and children. The so-called **childhood cancers** include certain types of leukaemia, and cancers originating in the bones, kidneys, muscles and nervous system. Reliable data on the incidence of these cancers only exists in countries where there are good registration systems to record each diagnosis. The rarity of childhood cancers across Europe as a whole, is illustrated by the most recent study at the time of writing (Stiller et al., 2006): the annual cancer incidence rate among children aged 0–14 years averaged around 14 cases per 100 000 children in the age group. This contrasts with the much higher adult incidence rate of 338 cases per 100 000 population in Eastern Europe and 447 per 100 000 in Western Europe (quoted in Verdecchia et al., 2007).

Earlier we reviewed some differences in the lung cancer death rates among relatively young women aged 20–44 years in four countries (Figure 1.5). Figure 1.6 illustrates a striking cancer trend among young men and also the importance of distinguishing between incidence and mortality. Testicular cancer rose in incidence throughout Europe (Bray et al., 2006) in the second half of the 20th century and by the 1990s it had become the most common cancer among males aged 15–34 years (data for some European countries are given in Figure 1.6a). But advances in treatment during the same period produced rapid declines in mortality (Figure 1.6b).

It is worth pausing for a moment to focus on why **age standardisation** (as in Figures 1.4 and 1.6) is so important when comparing data on cancers in different countries. The incidence rate of most cancers rises as people age, so the proportion of older people in a population can have a distorting effect on comparisons between countries with different **age-structures**, i.e. different proportions of people in different age groups.

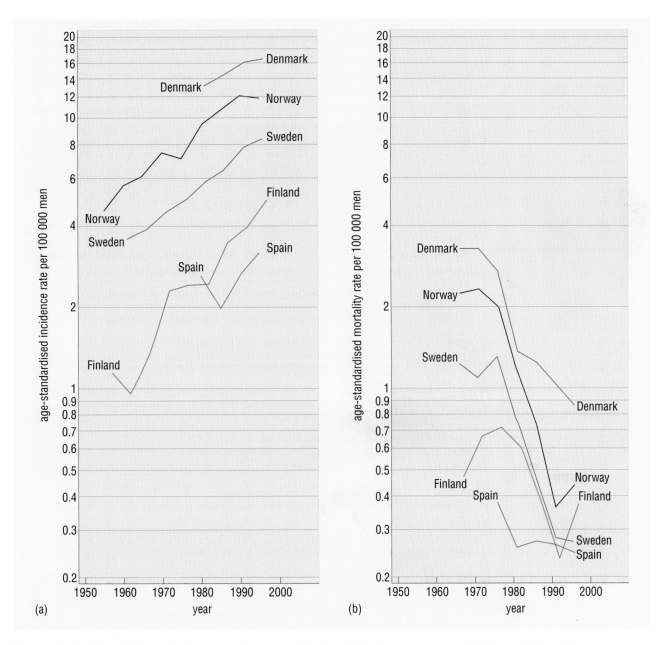

Figure 1.6   Trends in testicular cancer between 1955 and 1997 (or nearest available year) in various European countries: (a) incidence per 100 000 males; (b) mortality per 100 000 males. The data have been 'age-standardised', a statistical procedure that allows for differences in the proportion of people in different age groups in each population, and are expressed per 100 000 males in each population because this cancer does not affect females. (Note the scale on the vertical axis, which is similar to that for Figure 1.4.) (Data from Bray et al., 2006, Figure 1)

● How would you characterise the age-structure of a Western industrialised country such as Germany or the USA? How does this differ from the age-structure of less affluent countries such as Indonesia, Bangladesh or Nigeria?

● The wealthier industrialised countries have so-called 'ageing' populations, with relatively high proportions of older people (because the average life expectancy keeps increasing) and relatively small proportions of younger people (because the birth rate is steady or falling). This contrasts with the age-structure of most low- and middle-income countries where birth rates are much higher, so the proportion of young people in these populations is relatively large; but life expectancy is shorter, so the proportion of people who survive into old age is less than in the high-income countries.

Comparisons of disease rates from countries with even slightly different age-structures would give a distorted picture unless these differences were taken into account. This is what the mathematical adjustment known as age standardisation achieves and it is particularly important for diseases like cancers, which predominantly affect a particular section of the population age-structure – in this case, mainly older people.

Figure 1.6 also illustrates the importance of expressing cancer data as *rates* per 100 000 when tracking changes over time in the impact of a disease in particular countries. This means that the cancer trends are not distorted by changes in the number of people in the comparison populations from year to year. This is particularly important if one country's population has been growing rapidly over time, whereas another's might have changed very little in that period.

- What variations do you notice in the trends in testicular cancer incidence (Figure 1.6a) between different countries?

- There are quite large differences even between countries that are geographically close, e.g. Norway has a higher incidence than Sweden, and Finland's rate of new cases is lower still.

In the case of testicular cancer, the differences in incidence in males in different European populations (Figure 1.6a) suggest that young men in these countries have been exposed to different levels of risk factors in their environment.

- What do the differences in the mortality rates from testicular cancer (Figure 1.6b) suggest?

- The most likely explanations are variation in the time taken to diagnose the disease and/or the quality of treatment available to young men with testicular cancer in these countries.

1.2.4 Survival rates and disease-free statistics

As we said earlier, more people are living with a cancer than are dying with one, and this raises the question of how the impact of treatment on survival can be measured. The most commonly published statistic is the **five-year relative survival**, i.e. the percentage of people who remain alive five years from a cancer diagnosis, after excluding the number of deaths expected from other possible causes in that population. Figure 1.7 shows the percentage of males and females in England and Wales who survived for five years after a specific cancer was diagnosed between 1996 and 1999. (Data such as these can only be collated and published retrospectively after the five years have elapsed, so at the time of writing in 2008 these are among the most recent survival data available for part of the UK.) Notice the very wide variations between the prognoses for different cancers.

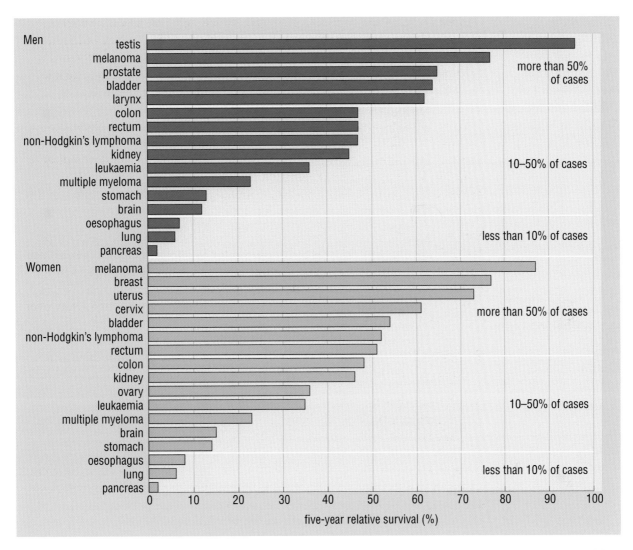

Figure 1.7 Five-year relative survival (percentages) for males and females in England and Wales with a cancer diagnosed between 1996 and 1999. (Data from Cancer Research UK, 2008)

Trials of new treatments for a cancer often use an outcome measure called **disease-free survival**, based on the number of years after treatment in which no signs of the disease can be detected. It is often expressed as the percentage of the trial participants who are still alive and disease-free a certain number of years (usually five or ten) after the treatment was completed. Measures such as these enable comparisons to be made between survival data for the same cancer in different countries, and reveal which countries are more successful at treating cancers than others. Figure 1.8 (overleaf) shows that even among the countries of Europe there are sharp differences in the survival chances for people diagnosed with the same type of cancer (Berrino et al., 2007).

Of course, there are factors other than treatment that might be relevant to survival, for example, the speed with which the cancer is diagnosed, but 'league tables' based on data such as those in Figure 1.8 can indicate whether countries are using their health resources most effectively on behalf of people with cancer.

Figure 1.8 Variations in the five-year relative survival from prostate cancer among men aged 15 years or more who were diagnosed between 1995 and 1999 in different European countries. (Data from Berrino et al., 2007, Figure 3, p. 777)

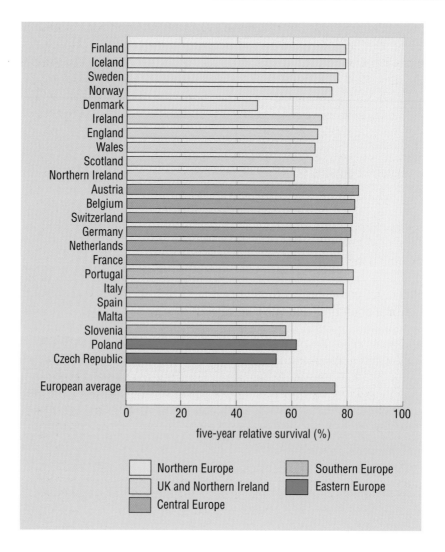

The good news is that – at least in Europe – the five-year relative survival has been increasing over time for cancers of the colon and rectum, breast, prostate, thyroid and certain types of lymphoma (Verdecchia et al., 2007). Although differences between European countries have narrowed in recent years, survival rates are worst in Denmark and the UK and best in Finland (Berrino et al., 2007); and cancer survival is generally better in the USA than in Europe as a whole.

1.2.5 The accuracy of cancer statistics

You may have been wondering about the accuracy of the data presented in this chapter and how a global institution such as the WHO could collect reliable information about cancers from all over the world, including in countries with poorly resourced health services. And you would be right to wonder!

In 1838, England was the first country in the world to introduce mandatory death certification by doctors attending the deceased, systematically recording the cause of death in a national registry for the first time. In 2008, 170 years later, less than 0.1% of the population of Africa and only 8.5% of Asian populations were covered by medically certified cause-of-death schemes (IARC, 2008). In the 20th century it became a legal requirement for doctors in many industrialised countries, including the UK and the USA, to inform national disease registries of every case they diagnosed on a list of so-called *notifiable diseases*, including all cancers. But in 2008 these countries recorded and reported the cancer diagnoses of less than 20% of the world's population.

So the data presented in global statistics on cancer incidence, prevalence, mortality and survival involve *estimates* for many countries based on complex mathematical modelling, extrapolating national rates from data collected in small-scale surveys and applying the evidence gained from reliable cancer registries where these exist. For example, cancer statistics have been collected from Qidong (Figure 1.4) since 1972 and are considered to be among the most accurate and complete in China (Chen et al., 2006).

- Survival data are particularly difficult to estimate for cancers in low- and middle-income countries. Can you suggest why?

- If more than 50% of those with a cancer never see a health professional in some low-income countries, the onset of their cancers and the amount of time they remain alive cannot be recorded. And if around 80% of cancers that *are* diagnosed in many low-income countries are detected 'late', then the percentage surviving after (say) five years will be reduced by the later onset of treatment for cancers that had reached a more advanced stage when they were detected.

The need to construct mathematical models to estimate cancer data for so many parts of the globe is the main reason why international statistics may appear to be rather 'old' by the time they are published. It takes a great deal of detailed and painstaking work over a number of years to generate estimates that command confidence among cancer experts. Several graphs in this chapter use data from 2002 because when the book went to press in 2008 this was the most recent year for which the WHO had published internationally comparable statistics on cancers. When you reflect on cancer statistics from around the world, bear in mind where the data have come from and that the published results are likely to *underestimate* the true picture in low-income countries where so many cancers go unreported.

1.3 Concluding remarks

It sometimes happens that people studying a disease like cancer for the first time become more anxious about their health as a result of thinking about the risk factors they might have been exposed to, or about the statistics on incidence and survival. The authors of this course encourage you to consult your family doctor if you have any symptoms that concern you, but otherwise put your anxieties into perspective. Despite the importance of cancers in terms of global health, the majority of people, even in the 'ageing' populations of the world's high-income countries, will never develop a cancer.

1.4 Summary of Chapter 1

1.1 Cancers are a complex group of over 100 diseases, originating in different sites in the body, with the common characteristic of uncontrolled growth of cells and a tendency to spread away from the original site.

1.2 The most important cancers worldwide in terms of mortality among males are those of the lung, stomach, liver, colon and rectum, oesophagus and prostate; among females they are cancers of the breast, lung, stomach, colon and rectum, and cervix.

1.3 Variations in the incidence of the same cancers in different countries can give clues to the possible underlying causes; variations in the prevalence, mortality and survival rates can indicate differences in the quality of diagnosis and treatment.

1.4 The trends over time for some cancers (e.g. testicular and breast cancers) in many countries show a rising incidence rate per 100 000 population, but a falling mortality rate as diagnosis and treatments improve.

1.5 Data from countries with different age-structures must be age-standardised before comparisons of cancer rates are made.

1.6 The majority of the world's population living with a cancer are in low- and middle-income countries where health services are frequently inadequately equipped to treat them.

1.7 There is a degree of uncertainty about the accuracy of cancer data estimated for countries where registration of cases and death certification covers only a minority of the population, but the published statistics are more likely to *under*estimate the true rates.

Questions for Chapter 1

Question 1.1 (Learning outcomes 1.1 and 1.2)

Figure 1.6 shows that the incidence rate of testicular cancer in several high-income countries was rising at the same time as the mortality rate was falling. What impact would this have on the prevalence rate and why?

Question 1.2 (Learning outcomes 1.2 and 1.3)

In 2002, the continent of Africa contained just under 11% of the world's population and almost 6% of all cancer deaths. By contrast, the continent of Europe contained 14% of the world's population and just over 25% of all cancer deaths. Suggest an explanation for these differences.

Question 1.3 (Learning outcomes 1.2 and 1.3)

Look again at Figure 1.8. Which region of Europe has the best survival characteristics for prostate cancer and which has the worst? Are there any notable exceptions to this pattern? Estimate the gap between the two countries with the highest and the lowest five-year relative survival.

Question 1.4 (Learning outcomes 1.2 and 1.4)

The trends in cancers in Qidong, China, between 1978 and 2002 (Figure 1.4), were age-standardised incidence rates per 100 000 individuals. Explain why it increased the accuracy of the data to age-standardise the incidence rates even though they came from the population of a single large city.

References

Barton, M.B., Frommer, M. and Shafiq, J. (2006) 'Role of radiotherapy in cancer control in low-income and middle-income countries', *The Lancet Oncology*, vol. 7, pp. 584–95.

Berrino, F., De Angelis, R., Sant, M., Rosso, S., Lasota, M.B., Santaquilani, M. and the EUROCARE Working Group (2007) 'Eurocare-4 studies bring new data on cancer survival', *The Lancet Oncology*, vol. 8, pp. 773–83.

Bray, F., Richiardi, L., Ekhom, A., Pukkala, E., Cuninkova, M. and Müller, H. (2006) 'Trends in testicular cancer incidence and mortality in 22 European countries: continuing increases in incidence and declines in mortality', *International Journal of Cancer*, vol. 118, pp. 3099–111.

Cancer Research UK (2008) [online], Figure 1.1 in http://info.cancerresearchuk.org/cancerstats/survival/latestrates/ (Accessed February 2008).

Chen, J-G., Zhu, J., Parkin, D.M., Zhang, Y-H., Lu, J-H., Zhu, Y-R. and Chen, T-Y. (2006) 'Trends in the incidence of cancer in Qidong, China, 1978–2002', *International Journal of Cancer*, vol. 119, pp. 1447–54.

Curado, M.P., Edwards, B., Shin, H.R., Storm, H., Ferlay, J., Heanue, M. and Boyle, P. (eds) (2007) [online], 'Cancer Incidence in Five Continents', vol. IX, IARC Scientific Publications No. 160, Lyon, IARC. http://www-dep.iarc.fr/ (Accessed February 2008).

Devesa, S.S., Bray, F., Viscaino, A.P. and Parkin, D.M. (2005) 'International lung cancer trends by histologic type: male:female differences diminishing and adenocarcinoma rates rising', *International Journal of Cancer*, vol. 117, pp. 294–9.

IARC (2008) [online], World Cancer Day 2008, Press Release No. 182, International Agency for Research on Cancer, Lyon. http://www.iarc.fr/ENG/Press_Releases/pr182a.html (Accessed February 2008).

Levi, F., Bosetti, C., Fernandez, E., Hill, C., Lucchini, F., Negri, E. and La Vecchia, C. (2007) 'Trends in lung cancer among young European women: the rising epidemic in France and Spain', *International Journal of Cancer*, vol. 121, pp. 462–5.

Ozgediz, D., Kijjambu, S., Galukande, M., Dubowitz, G., Mabweijano. J., Mijumbi, C., Cherian, M., Kaggwa, S. and Luboga, S. (2008) 'Africa's neglected surgical workforce crisis', *The Lancet*, vol. 371, no. 9613, pp. 627–8.

Stiller, C.A., Marcos-Gragera, R., Ardanaz, E., Pannelli, F., Almar-Marquès, E. and Cañada Martinez, A. (2006) 'Geographical patterns of childhood cancer incidence in Europe, 1988–1997', Report from the Automated Childhood Cancer Information System Project, *European Journal of Cancer*, vol. 42, no. 13, pp. 1952–60.

Verdecchia, A., Francisci, S., Brenner, H., Gatta, G., Micheli, A., Mangone, L., Kunkler, I. and the EUROCARE-4 Working Group (2007) 'Recent cancer survival in Europe: a 2000–02 period analysis of EUROCARE-4 data', *The Lancet Oncology*, vol. 8, pp. 784–96.

Wakabi, W. (2007) 'Africa's increasing efforts to control cancer', *The Lancet Oncology*, vol. 8, p. 1057.

WHO (2004) [online], *World Health Report 2004: Changing History*, World Health Organization, Geneva. http://www.who.int/whr/2004/en/index.html (Accessed February 2008).

WHO (2006) [online], *Cancer*, Factsheet No. 297. http://www.who.int/mediacentre/factsheets/fs297/en/ (Accessed February 2008).

WHO and IUAC (2005) *Global Action Against Cancer*, World Health Organization and International Union Against Cancer, Geneva.

CHAPTER 2

CELLS AND CANCERS

Learning outcomes

After studying this chapter and its associated activities, you should be able to:

2.1   Define and use in context, or recognise definitions and applications of, each of the terms printed in **bold** in the text.

2.2   Demonstrate an understanding of the basic components of cellular life, paying particular attention to the structure of DNA and proteins.

2.3   Describe the basic structural features of a typical animal cell, including those of a tumour cell.

2.4   Outline the major functions of normal cells with particular emphasis on how they differ from those of tumour cells.

2.5   Describe the biological process of cell division.

2.6   Explain, with examples, the basic principles underlying the changes in regulation of cell growth, differentiation, signalling, ageing, adhesion and death observed in tumour cells.

2.1   Introduction

As mentioned in Chapter 1, cancer is not just one disease, but a complex collection of over 100 illnesses. Having established the diversity of cancers, you should consider the common biological basis that underlies these diseases. Why do people usually refer to 'cancer' as a unique entity? The answer is that all cancers share similar biological features. The type of cancer may determine how it is treated and its outcome. In addition, its location in the body and where it spreads to, may result in the multitude of different symptoms that characterise a particular type of cancer. However, all cancers originate in similar ways. Cancers are formed by cells that, unlike normal cells, grow out of control, forming a lump or cell mass (Figure 2.1). In this chapter, you will learn about many factors that regulate the life of a normal cell in multicellular organisms, and how (and to some extent, why) these cellular processes malfunction in cancer cells.

When clinicians and scientists speak of tumour growth, they refer to an increase in the number of cells, not to an increase in the size of a single cell.

A multicellular organism is a form of life that contains more than one cell such as an animal or a plant.

Activity 2.1   Cell city

Allow about 90 minutes in total for this activity

Now watch the video sequence *Cell City* which will introduce some of the key aspects of Chapter 2.

2.2   What are cells?

All living organisms including microorganisms (e.g. bacteria), plants and animals are organised into distinct functional and structural units termed cells, a property that differentiates them from non-living materials such as rocks. A cell is formed by a 'bag' or membrane that separates the inside from the external environment.

Figure 2.1 (a) Cells are usually organised and do not grow beyond their normal boundaries in a multicellular organism. (b) Cancer cells grow uncontrollably forming a mass with undefined boundaries.

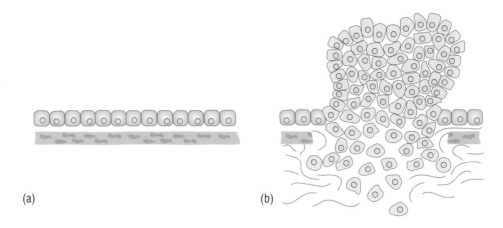

(a)　　　　　　　　　(b)

Inside the cell membrane there are a number of substances and subcellular structures with specific functions arranged in a particular way. Whereas the function of cells may be very different (e.g. that of lung cells compared to the bacterium that causes tuberculosis in the lung), their basic life processes are remarkably similar. They (usually) reproduce by dividing into new cells (a process also known as **cell proliferation**), they convert nutrients into chemical energy and they adapt to changes in their environment by changing their activity.

Cells come in a huge variety of shapes and sizes (Figure 2.2), and as a general rule, these variations in structure reflect the specialised properties of a particular cell. All cells are built on one of only two basic plans. The simpler of the two is characteristic of all bacteria (Figure 2.2a), which are believed to have evolved before other cells. The more complex is found in all animal cells (Figure 2.2d), plant cells (Figure 2.2c) and fungal cells, and in some

Figure 2.2 Cell diversity. (a) A bacterium (in this case a rod-shaped bacterium, but there are several other basic shapes). (b) An amoeba – a single-celled organism capable of independent life. (c) A plant cell. (d) An animal cell (in this case a skin cell). (e) Although viruses (in this case HIV) are not cells, they depend on cells for their survival. You will learn about the structures within a cell in Section 2.3. Note that the cells and virus are not drawn to scale. (DNA and RNA will be explained in the next chapter.)

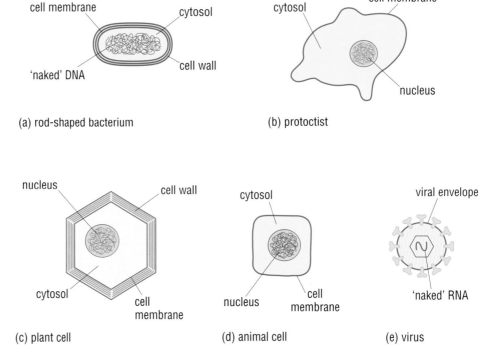

single-celled organisms capable of independent life (Figure 2.2b shows one of the best known examples of the latter, an amoeba). You may have wondered why viruses have been left out, but viruses are not cells at all and are generally referred to as virus particles. They are minute 'boxes' containing little more than one or two strands of genetic material (Figure 2.2e). They are not capable of independent life but survive by invading a living cell and taking control of the basic life processes going on in that cell, subverting them to the production of new virus particles. Nevertheless, it is important to mention viruses at this stage of the course since infection by some of them is known to cause specific cancers, as you will learn in Chapter 5.

Cancer is a disease of multicellular organisms. As such, cancer can affect not only humans but also other animals and plants. If you are fond of gardening you may have heard of crown galls, which are cancers on the trunks of certain trees, caused by a bacterium (Figure 2.3). Whereas single-celled organisms compete individually with other life forms in order to survive and reproduce (or indeed die in the process), this is not the case for each cell that constitutes a multicellular organism. Rather, all cells in multicellular organisms collaborate with each other within a 'social' context. The cells send, receive and interpret an elaborate set of signals that tell them to act in a particular manner and in doing so they collectively maintain the health of the whole organism.

Table 2.1 shows the hierarchy of components that make up a multicellular organism. Note that similar cells are associated with each other to form **tissues** and that **organs** comprise more than one type of tissue. You will learn more about each component in the structural hierarchy of multicellular organisms later in the course. For the moment, you should focus on the notion that each individual cell within a tissue and/or organ performs a specific function determined by its environment. As a result of signals between cells, a cell in the body may divide, or increase its energy requirements, or even die, for the sake of the whole organism. These actions support other cells such as the sperm and egg cells (collectively known as **germline cells**) which alone are the only cells that propagate copies of the organism's hereditary information to form new individuals or, in other words, are the only cells that truly reproduce.

In a way, cancer as a disease results from the disruption of the cellular equilibrium necessary for the survival and reproduction of a multicellular organism. Changes in the communication properties of a cell may make it divide more vigorously than its neighbours giving rise to a population of cancer cells which also grow outside the restricted controls of normal cells (Box 2.1). Although the growth of a population of cells may in itself appear not to be harmful to the health of an organism, cancer cells do so at the expense of nearby cells; indeed, they use up the available resources (i.e. nutrients), send out incorrect signals and may even physically press against normal cells disturbing their functions. Their uncontrolled growth may also lead them to spread by invading other parts of the body where they disrupt the specialised

roots

crown gall

Figure 2.3   A crown gall on the trunk of an eastern red cedar. (Source: E.L. Barnard, Florida Department of Agriculture and Consumer Services)

cellular function of their new neighbours. As a result, the precisely coordinated functioning of all cells within a multicellular organism is altered leading to an imbalance that may jeopardise the individual's health and ultimately be responsible for their death.

Table 2.1 The hierarchy of biological organisation in a multicellular organism.

Level of organisation	Definition	Examples in the human body	Discussed in this book
Element, atom	Elements cannot be reduced to simpler substances by normal chemical means. Atoms are the smallest individual units of elements	The most abundant elements in the human body are oxygen, carbon and hydrogen	Section 2.3
Molecule	Two or more atoms of the same or different elements, held together by chemical bonds	Simple molecules include oxygen gas (chemical formula O_2) and water (chemical formula H_2O). Large macromolecules such as proteins and DNA are an assembly of simpler molecules	Section 2.3
Organelle	A structure within a cell that performs a specific function	Mitochondrion, nucleus	Section 2.4
Cell	The smallest individual unit of an organism	Neurons, muscle cells, blood cells	This chapter
Tissue	A group of similar cells with a common function	Nerve tissue, muscle tissue	Section 2.8
Organ	A group of tissues that form into a distinct structure which performs a specialised task	The brain, the heart, skin	Section 2.8
Organ system (or biological system)	A group of organs that work together as a unit	The nervous system (brain, spinal cord and peripheral nerves, sensory organs), the cardiovascular system (heart and blood vessels), the respiratory system (e.g. trachea and lungs)	Chapter 4
Organism	A form of life composed of mutually interdependent parts that maintain the processes of life	The entire human body	Chapter 4

Box 2.1 Cancers, tumours and neoplasms

The scientific term used to describe the uncontrolled proliferation of cells is **neoplasia**, which is from the Greek meaning new (*neo-*) growth (*-plasia*). The end result of this abnormal and progressive cell growth in a tissue or organ is the formation of a **neoplasm** which, if it is solid and forms a mass or a lump, is also called a tumour. (For a definition of tissue and organ see Table 2.1 – these terms will be further discussed in Section 2.8.) Although, strictly speaking, cancerous cells that do not form solid tumours should only be described as 'neoplastic' cells, you will often come across the term 'tumour cells', either in the general press or in scientific articles, somewhat incorrectly applied to cells that are not fixed within a tissue (e.g. leukaemic cells; leukaemias are neoplasms of the white cells of the immune system which do not form a solid mass as they are found circulating in the blood). In this course, the common terms 'tumour cells' or 'cancer cells' will often be used, as well as the more scientific 'neoplastic cells', when the general biological principles that underlie the abnormal proliferation of cells within a tissue or an organ are described.

2.3 Cells are made from a few types of molecules

All matter, whether it is in a living organism like a tree or a person, or in non-living material such as the rocks and the atmosphere, is composed of **chemical elements** (Table 2.1). Cells are no different in this respect. There are about 100 different elements in nature and among the most familiar are the most abundant constituents of living things: oxygen, carbon, hydrogen and nitrogen, which together form over 90% of the mass of every organism.

Elements are not commonly found in their pure form but in combination with each other to form **compounds**. For example, water, the most abundant compound in living matter, is formed by two elements, hydrogen and oxygen. However, this definition is not very informative about the proportion of elements within each compound, an important issue because many compounds are formed by the same elements but in different amounts. For example, ethanol (also known by the generic term, alcohol) and sucrose (table sugar) are compounds formed exclusively by the same three elements, carbon, oxygen and hydrogen, but obviously the consequences for a person of ingesting table sugar or alcohol are quite different!

In order to understand how elements combine to form different compounds it is necessary to define two terms, atoms and molecules. Each element exists in the form of extremely small 'particles' known as **atoms**, which can be joined together by chemical bonds. Thus, chemical elements can be defined as substances that contain only one type of atom. Two or more atoms, of the same or different element, joined together by chemical bonds constitute a **molecule** (a common representation of a water molecule is shown in Figure 2.4). A pure compound comprises many identical molecules which themselves consist of atoms. For example, a single raindrop contains as many as 100 000 000 000 000 000 000 water molecules because they are very small (about 0.000 000 0002 metres across) (Box 2.2).

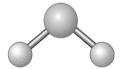

Figure 2.4 A ball-and-stick representation of a water molecule, consisting of two atoms of the element hydrogen (small grey sphere) attached to one atom of the element oxygen (large red sphere).

Box 2.2 Scientific notation

While referring to the number of water molecules in a raindrop and the size of a water molecule, you may have noticed how cumbersome (and even confusing) it was to read either a very large or a very small number in the text. One could express the number of molecules in a raindrop as the number 1 followed by twenty zeros (as above) or as one hundred billion billion. A method used for making very large or small numbers easier to express is called **powers of ten** notation (also known as **scientific notation**). Powers of ten notation enables us to express the number above as 10^{20}, which in many ways is more manageable. How do we pass from one notation to another? It makes sense to start this explanation with a smaller number, a hundred. The number 100 is the same as 10×10 and this can be written 10^2, i.e. ten multiplied twice or ten 'squared'. The ten in 10^2 is called the *base number* and the superscript 2 is called the *power*. This can be spoken aloud as 'ten to the power two' or 'ten to the two' for short. Of course, there isn't any point in calling a number such as a hundred, ten to the two, but the number of molecules in a raindrop contains many more zeros and scientific notation makes it a more convenient form of the number. As mentioned above, the number of molecules in a raindrop is 1 followed by twenty zeros. This is the same as

$$10 \times 10 \times 10 \times 10 \times 10 \times 10 \times 10 \times 10 \times 10 \times 10 \times 10 \times 10 \times 10 \times 10 \times 10 \times 10 \times 10 \times 10 \times 10 \times 10$$

Using powers of ten notation, this can be written as 10^{20}.

● How would you say the number of molecules in a raindrop aloud?

● 10^{20} can be spoken aloud as 'ten to the power twenty' or 'ten to the twenty'.

Numbers such as 10^2 and 10^{20} should, strictly speaking, be multiplied by one and be written as 1×10^2 and 1×10^{20} in scientific notation. In this case the power of ten shows how many times 1 has been multiplied by 10. This is to differentiate them from more complicated numbers which can also be expressed as multipliers of ten. For example, 200 could be expressed as 2×100 or 2×10^2 whereas 3500 is the same as 3.5×1000 or 3.5×10^3. The way you would say these numbers aloud would be 'two times ten to the two' and 'three point five times ten to the three', respectively.

● How would you express the number of 235 000 in scientific notation?

● 2.35×10^5.

This is fine for expressing numbers larger than 10, but what about numbers smaller than one? These can be also expressed using powers of ten notation by dividing 1 by the power of ten. For example, the number 0.1 is the same as $\frac{1}{10}$ and the number 0.01 is the same as $\frac{1}{100}$ and so on. The fraction $\frac{1}{100}$ can also be expressed as $\frac{1}{10 \times 10}$ or $\frac{1}{10^2}$. Another way of expressing these numbers is by writing them down as negative powers of 10 with a minus sign in front. So, $\frac{1}{10}$ is written as 1×10^{-1} and $\frac{1}{10^2}$ as 1×10^{-2}.

● How would you express the size of a water molecule in metres (abbreviated as m) using scientific notation?

● A water molecule is 0.000 000 0002 m across. This is the same as $2 \times 0.000\,000\,0001$ m or $2 \times \dfrac{1}{10\,000\,000\,000}$ m. Using the negative powers of ten notation, the size of a water molecule is 2×10^{-10} m or, spoken aloud, 'two times ten to the minus ten'.

As in the case of water, most molecules contain atoms of more than one element and each element is represented by a one- or two-letter symbol. The symbols for carbon, hydrogen and oxygen are C, H and O, respectively, whereas the symbol for calcium, an important constituent of bone, is Ca. The proportion of each element, i.e. the number of atoms of an element, that constitutes a single molecule is designated by a subscript number following the chemical symbol. Water, ethanol and table sugar may then be written in chemical notations as H_2O, C_2H_6O and $C_{12}H_{22}O_{11}$, respectively, which tells us about the number of atoms and their relative amounts within a particular molecule. You can see now the different proportions of C, H, and O in ethanol and table sugar. In order to illustrate the chemical structure of a molecule, the chemical bonds that join the different atoms that form molecules are usually represented by one or more lines (Figure 2.5).

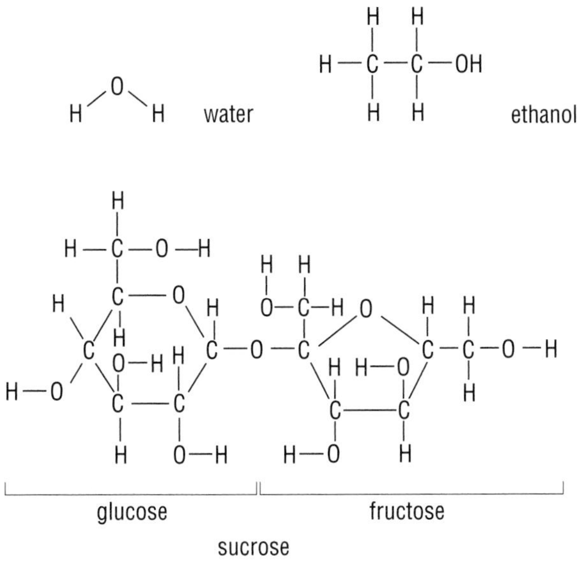

Figure 2.5   The chemical structure of water, ethanol (alcohol) and sucrose (table sugar). Note that sucrose is formed from two subunits called glucose and fructose.

Water, ethanol and even table sugar, although of increasing size, are still small molecules (a molecule of table sugar contains only 45 atoms), but molecules can be millions of times larger than this and contain many atoms of different elements. These are called macromolecules. Macromolecules are large molecules that are made from smaller molecule units that repeat themselves and are joined together as very long chains. There are four types of biological macromolecules that are integral for living organisms, namely **carbohydrates**, **protein**, **nucleic acids** and **lipids**.

1   Carbohydrates are made from smaller units called sugars. For example, the carbohydrate sucrose (table sugar) is formed by two sugars, glucose and fructose (Figure 2.5) but other larger carbohydrates such as starch (found in potatoes and cereals) are made of a complex network of glucose chains joined together. Generally speaking, sugars provide an energy source for cells.

2   All proteins in living matter, whether they form part of animals, plants, fungi or bacteria, consist of long chains of molecule units called **amino acids**. There are 20 different types of amino acids. Different combinations of these amino acids give rise to different proteins. An example of a protein is haemoglobin, the protein that transports oxygen and carbon dioxide in red blood cells.

3   Nucleic acids consist of long chains combining four different molecule units termed nucleotides. An example of a nucleic acid is **deoxyribonucleic acid** or **DNA**, which contains the hereditary information in all cells. (You will learn more about DNA in Chapter 3.)

4   Lipids are any fat-soluble molecules. The best-known types of lipid are fats and oils (also called triglycerides), which serve as food storage molecules in animal tissues and some plant seeds, respectively. These molecules are composed of three long-chain fatty acids combined with the small molecule glycerol, hence the name triglycerides. Although strictly speaking lipid molecules are not formed by molecule units that combine with each other into chains, they do cluster together to form huge molecular aggregates, which we shall refer to here as macromolecules: for example, phospholipid molecules (which comprise fatty acids, glycerol and also a phosphate unit) aggregate in sheets to form the membrane of the 'bag' that separates the outside of the cell from the inside. (You will learn more about membranes in the next section.)

These four types of macromolecules together with water are the main chemical components of all cells, whether normal or cancerous (Table 2.2). Both macromolecules and their small molecule subunits are essential for cellular life. Some functions of carbohydrates and lipids have been listed above but we should examine proteins and nucleic acids in more detail in order to understand what makes cancer cells different from (as well as similar to) normal cells. If we exclude water, proteins constitute most of a cell's mass (Table 2.2). Proteins are extremely important because they execute every single process of any cell; that is, they are the molecules that mediate whether (and how) a cell divides, that maintain the shape of a cell, that drive chemical reactions to provide energy, and so on. The combination of amino acids that a particular protein contains is determined by the nucleic acids in that cell, in particular, by the sequence of the four different types of nucleotides in specific regions of DNA called **genes** (Figure 2.6). Each sequence of amino acids in a protein determines its three-dimensional (3D) shape and this in turn dictates its unique function within the cell. There are many types of protein, which we shall not attempt to catalogue, but you should keep in mind that much of the variation in function between cells and how they respond to their environment – for example, the different responses of a tumour cell and a normal cell – stems from differences in the nature of the proteins they contain.

Table 2.2 Chemical composition of a typical cell.

Type of molecule	Amount of matter/% of total
water	70
proteins	18
lipids	5
carbohydrates	2
nucleic acids	1
others	4

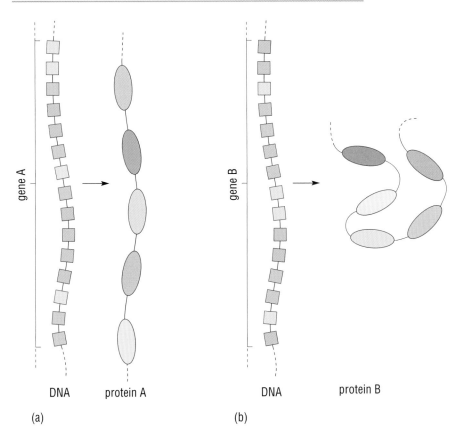

(a)

(b)

Figure 2.6 The sequence of nucleotides in a region of DNA called a gene determines the sequence of amino acids in a particular protein which, in turn, determines its three-dimensional shape. Nucleotides are represented as squares and amino acids as ellipses. Note that proteins may contain hundreds of amino acids and genes, thousands of nucleotides. Simplified versions of genes and proteins have been drawn here.

The sequence of events linking DNA to the synthesis of a specific protein is extremely complex but, for the moment, you should focus on the concept that genes instruct (or 'encode') the building of numerous different proteins in a cell. So a particular sequence of nucleotides in a gene will be decoded to build a specific sequence of amino acids of the protein it encodes.

- Can you suggest a possible consequence of a change in the sequence of nucleotides in a gene for the function of the protein it encodes?

- A change in the sequence of nucleotides in a gene may result in a change in the sequence of amino acids in the protein. If this is the case, the shape, and hence the unique function, of that protein may be altered.

2.4 A 'typical' human cell

A typical cell found in the human body is shown in Figure 2.7. All cells are bounded by an outer layer, the **cell membrane**. The cell membrane is a highly complex structure that allows the passage of certain substances into the cell and others out of the cell. Cell membranes consist of a double layer of phospholipids, or in other words, two sheets of fatty molecules composed of an outer water-soluble region and an inner water-insoluble region formed by fatty acids (Figure 2.8). The two sheets are not fixed together and the phospholipid molecules can move laterally within each sheet. Another fatty molecule, cholesterol, which is interspersed within the cell membrane, makes the membrane less fluid. Bobbing about in the membrane are proteins, which can move laterally within the membrane in all directions. Some of them protrude out of the membrane and/or inside the cell. Membrane proteins have a variety of functions: some enable the cell to take in nutrient molecules and others can detect (chemical or electrical) signals from outside the cell delivering information or instructions.

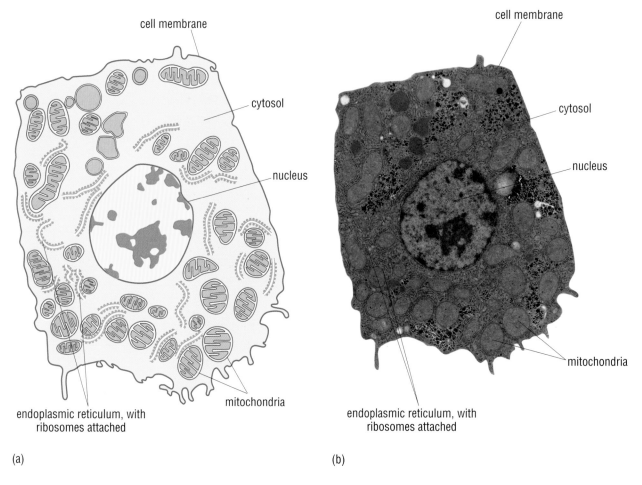

(a)

(b)

Figure 2.7 (a) Schematic drawing of a typical human cell, showing some common structural features. Compare this with (b) a photograph of a liver cell taken through an electron microscope and magnified 8000 times. (An electron microscope is a microscope that makes use of a beam of electrons instead of light.) (Source: (b) Heather Davies/Open University)

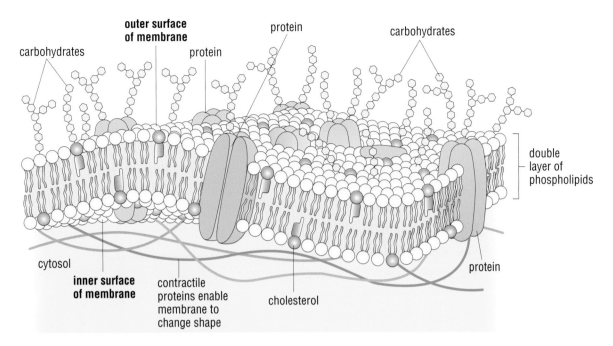

carbohydrates

outer surface of membrane

protein

protein

carbohydrates

double layer of phospholipids

cytosol

inner surface of membrane

contractile proteins enable membrane to change shape

cholesterol

protein

Figure 2.8 Representation of the basic structure of the cell membrane of an animal cell. Membranes surrounding the organelles within cells are also built on the same basic plan.

A vast number of small carbohydrate molecules, predominantly attached to proteins and lipids, also cover the outer surface of the cell membrane forming an additional barrier.

Attached to the inside of the cell membrane there are protein filaments that can contract and expand, so enabling cells to change shape. (Note, these contractile proteins form the scaffolding of the cell called the cytoskeleton.) These proteins 'bathe' within a watery fluid, the **cytosol**, rich in dissolved molecules, including many proteins. The cytosol also contains individual structures collectively known as **organelles**, each bounded by a membrane similar to the cell membrane. There are many different kinds of organelle; here we will do no more than point out some of the principal ones and give a 'thumbnail sketch' of their functions.

The largest organelle in any cell is usually the **nucleus**, surrounded by a nuclear membrane. The nucleus contains most of the DNA in the cell. Cells typically have one nucleus though certain kinds of cell (e.g. muscle cells) have more and others, for example red blood cells, have none. Within the nucleus, the DNA is arranged into a number of single threads with proteins attached to them forming the structures called **chromosomes**. There are 46 chromosomes in human cells (do not attempt to find them in Figure 2.7 as they usually cannot be seen under the microscope unless stained with dyes).

Another important structure is the ribosome, where proteins are assembled from amino acids. Ribosomes are often attached to the endoplasmic reticulum which is a vast canal system of membranes, on which a huge number of chemical reactions occur – some creating new molecules (i.e. proteins), others breaking down existing molecules. Cells would not be able to survive without mitochondria which are the 'engines' where most of the energy is generated from chemical reactions to fuel all the processes that go on inside the cell.

You should now look at the cellular structures of a tumour cell, shown in Figure 2.9. How different is a tumour cell in terms of cellular structures from a typical normal cell? The short answer is not very much. A tumour cell contains a cytosol, in which several organelles are immersed, and is surrounded by a cell membrane. In order to survive, tumour cells require energy, as normal cells do, so they also contain mitochondria. Tumour cells need proteins that execute cellular functions so they have ribosomes attached to the endoplasmic reticulum to produce them. Finally, the DNA of a tumour cell also lies within the nucleus, which in appearance does not differ much from that of a normal cell (if anything, it is larger and somewhat irregular in tumour cells).

Figure 2.9 A photograph of a tumour cell of the thyroid gland taken through an electron microscope and magnified 3500 times. Note that normal thyroid cells are generally twice as large as normal liver cells (Figure 2.7). (Source: Steve Gschmeissner/Science Photo Library)

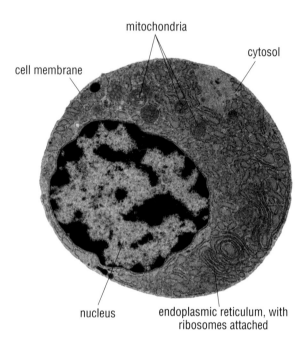

At this point, you may be asking yourself why tumour cells grow in an uncontrolled fashion if they contain the same types of molecules and cellular structures as normal cells. The most important thing to remember here is that although tumour cells are very similar to their 'normal' counterparts in both chemical composition and cellular structures, they differ in only the sequence of nucleotides of a few genes that encode a subset of proteins. These gene alterations may result in an abnormal pattern of proteins which, sometimes, may change the behaviour of cells in such a way that they progress towards becoming a tumour cell.

2.5 A brief overview of the basic properties of normal and neoplastic cells

You now have a working knowledge of what a typical normal (and tumour) human cell looks like (in reality, all animal cells look similar to the plan depicted in Figure 2.7). But, how do cells function? What are the different functional responses of normal and tumour cells? Cells are not inert building blocks of living organisms. Rather, they are complex entities that, to some extent, are self-sufficient – many processes go on within cells independently of what is happening in other cells – but the environment they live in also influences their behaviour. In some instances, normal and neoplastic cells function in much the same way, whereas in others the properties of neoplastic cells are quite distinct from those of normal cells. Here, we will briefly outline some general properties of cells that are important to understand the biology of cancers. These properties are summarised for both normal and neoplastic cells in Table 2.3. You should be aware that the cellular properties listed in this table are very simplified accounts and they will be unravelled as we proceed through the rest of this chapter.

Table 2.3 The basic properties of normal and neoplastic cells.

Normal cells	Neoplastic cells
Require energy to fuel chemical reactions	Require (more) energy to fuel chemical reactions
Reproduce themselves only when the appropriate signals are received	Reproduce themselves even in the absence of appropriate signals
Acquire specialised functions	Lose part or all of their specialised functions
Age after a limited number of cell divisions	May not age following unlimited cell divisions
Commit 'suicide' when the appropriate signals are received	May not kill themselves even when the appropriate signals are present
Are usually fixed in a location within tissues and/or organs	May escape from their normal location in tissues and/or organs and reproduce in other ones

2.6 Cell metabolism

All cells require energy to fuel the huge number of chemical reactions necessary to maintain life. It is necessary to define here what scientists understand by 'metabolic activity' or, in the context of a cell, what **cell metabolism** means. The term covers all the chemical reactions that go on in a cell from moment to moment, either building up molecules or breaking them down, and including the molecular interactions occurring on (and through) the cell membranes and in the cytosol. In an organism made up of many cells such as a human, it is conventional in science and in medicine to speak of 'metabolic activity' or simply 'metabolism' of an individual, meaning the sum total of all chemical reactions going on in all cells of the body.

In much the same way as humans at the organism level require oxygen and nutrients in their diet to live, all cells use oxygen and break down macromolecules (particularly carbohydrates) in a complex sequence of chemical reactions that yields energy together with carbon dioxide and water – these reactions occur mostly in the mitochondria of cells. The 'energy' is trapped in the structure of a molecule called ATP (adenosine triphosphate, a name you need not remember). ATP can be transported anywhere in the cell and the energy it contains can be released in controlled amounts wherever energy is required to drive a chemical reaction.

You will learn more about how enzymes work in Chapter 10.

You may be wondering what regulates these complex chemical reactions. The short answer is a type of protein called an **enzyme**. Enzymes catalyse (i.e. speed up) very specific chemical reactions in living organisms. Although you may have heard of enzymes digesting food in the cavity of the gut, the cytosol of cells is also rich in enzymes and some of them are even present in the cell membrane and in the membranes surrounding organelles.

Millions of different interlinked chemical reactions are taking place in every cell all the time. As a rule of thumb, the more 'active' a cell is, i.e. the more chemical reactions occurring in that cell at any one time, the more energy in the form of ATP it will need. Tumour cells also require ATP to fuel chemical reactions and are metabolically very active – even more so than most normal cells. Why is this? The reason lies behind the high proliferation rate of tumour cells compared to normal cells. Cell proliferation involves many chemical reactions involving enzymes and other proteins. The metabolic activity, and hence the requirements for ATP, of a tumour cell that divides often and uncontrollably is much higher than that of a normal cell that divides only when the correct signals are transmitted. High levels of ATP are thus essential to drive the huge number of complex chemical reactions involved in controlling cell division, a topic that will be discussed in the next section.

2.7 Cell proliferation

A fundamental property of most cells is their capacity to reproduce themselves or, in other words, to proliferate. All of the cells in your body are descendants of a fertilised egg, i.e. a cell composed of an egg cell and the nucleus of a sperm cell, shown at the left-hand side of Figure 2.10a. As they derive from a single cell (the fertilised egg), all cells (with a few exceptions) of an individual contain exactly the same genetic material, regardless of what type of cell it is.

● From what you have learnt so far in this course, can you think of any cells in the human body that may not contain genetic material that is identical to that in the other cells in the same organism?

● Tumour (neoplastic) cells differ from the normal cells they derive from in the nature of some of the proteins they contain (Section 2.2): therefore at least some of their genes (those that encode these proteins) must be altered so are not exactly the same as the equivalent genes in other cells of the body. You may have also thought of red blood cells which do not contain nuclei (Section 2.4).

In much the same way, as the cells of an organism formed from a fertilised egg, all cancer cells derive from a single cell that undergoes many cycles of cell division (Figure 2.10b). At one point, the genetic material of this 'parent' cell somehow changed enabling it to outgrow its neighbours. This alteration in the cell's DNA sequence is called a **mutation**. The consequence of a mutation, if it occurs in a gene, may be an alteration in the structure of the protein it encodes

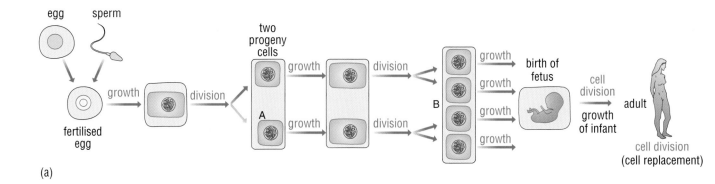

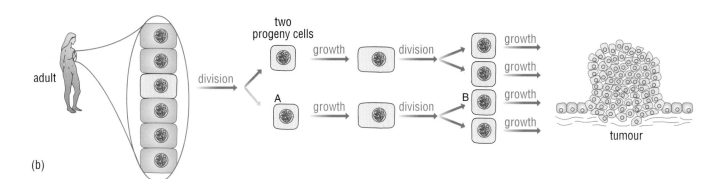

Figure 2.10 A sequence of cell divisions. (a) All of the cells in the body are descendants of a fertilised egg. This cell produces two progeny cells when it divides, and so on. The letter A represents the start and the letter B the finish of one cell cycle. (b) All of the cells in a tumour are derived from a single aberrant cell (itself a descendant of a fertilised egg) whose DNA has mutated.

and therefore in that protein's function, thereby resulting in a cell with slightly altered behaviour. Mutations and how they relate to the formation of tumours will be explained in detail in Chapter 3, but for now you should keep in mind that all progeny cells derived from this abnormal parent cell will carry the same mutation (and some new ones that they acquire along the way) in their genetic material, setting them apart from most other cells within the same organism.

Progeny refers to a genetic descendant or offspring. The term progeny is used in the context of both cells and whole organisms.

2.7.1 The cell cycle

To explain how cancer forms, we need to consider first the **cell cycle** in some detail. This process is fundamentally the same for both normal and tumour cells, even though the rate at which it occurs is generally much higher in tumour cells than in normal cells. In essence, a cell enlarges and makes copies of everything it contains; it then divides to give two progeny cells, each of which receives a complete set of all the molecules and structures that the 'parent' cell contained. The original parent cell itself effectively disappears leaving only the two progeny cells. The new cells grow before the cycle starts again. The sequence of cell growth followed by cell division repeats again and again, so one cell becomes two, two become four, and so on, as shown in Figure 2.10.

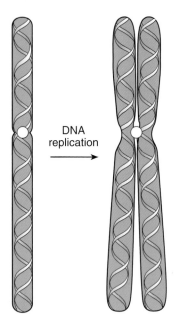

Figure 2.11 A chromosome before and after DNA replication.

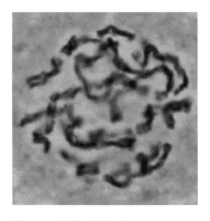

Figure 2.12 The chromosomes become conspicuous under the microscope at the beginning of cell division. The photograph shows chromosomes in a white cell of the immune system, magnified approximately 1000 times. (Source: Biophoto Associates)

Cell growth

During the phase of **cell growth**, the chromosomes within the nucleus exist as very long thin threads of DNA, and at this stage cannot be seen under the microscope (Figure 2.11). It is during this phase that each chromosome is copied along its length, to produce an identical copy. Somewhere along their length, the original chromosome and its copy are joined together forming a 'double' chromosome. Note that scientists often refer to 'a chromosome' regardless of whether it is in its 'single' or 'double' form. Because chromosomes are composed of DNA (and other molecules, e.g. proteins), this phase involves copying the DNA, a process called DNA replication. (DNA replication will be explained in more detail in Chapter 3.)

Cell division

The other phase of the cell cycle, **cell division**, involves two events. Cell division begins when each long thin 'double' chromosome arranges itself into a coil, and then again into a supercoiled structure, which, at this stage, is visible under the microscope (Figure 2.12).

Figure 2.13 shows the main stages of cell division. First, the nuclear membrane disappears so that the cell no longer has a nucleus (Figure 2.13a). The chromosomes can then move within the cell in an unrestrained way. (For simplicity, cell division is described here for a cell with just four chromosomes, but the same principles apply when there are 46 chromosomes, as in the case of human cells.) In the next stage, the 'double' chromosomes line up in the centre of the cell (Figure 2.13b), and then separate, each generating a chromosome in its own right (Figure 2.13c). One copy of each chromosome migrates to opposite ends of the cell (Figure 2.13d). Alignment and separation of chromosomes into two sets is mediated by large proteins called **microtubules**, which essentially function as 'ropes' pulling apart the double chromosomes. Once separated, the chromosomes gradually uncoil and elongate again (eventually becoming invisible again under the microscope) and a nuclear membrane forms around each chromosome cluster so that the cell has temporarily two nuclei (Figure 2.13e).

The next event in cell division involves the formation of two cells from the original parent cell. This is achieved by constriction of the membrane across the middle of the cell, dividing it and its contents equally into two (Figure 2.13f). Each of the two daughter cells contains exactly the same DNA as the parent cell, and enough cytosol and organelles for normal cell metabolism to occur. The new cells enter into a growth phase until the time comes for them to divide in their turn; hence the term cell cycle.

● Based on what you have learnt so far, does the cell cycle differ between normal and tumour human cells?

● No. The cell cycle is essentially the same process for normal and tumour cells. In both cases, one 'parent' cell will replicate its DNA and give rise to two 'daughter' cells.

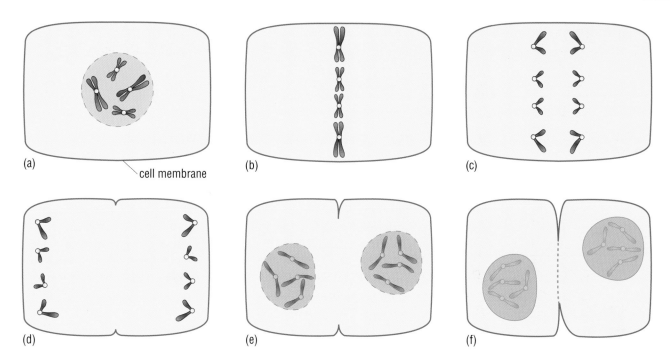

Figure 2.13   The essential features of cell division. (a) Once the DNA has been replicated in the phase of cell growth (the four chromosomes consist of two identical copies), the nuclear membrane starts to disappear. (b) The four chromosomes line up in the centre of the cell. (c) The 'double' chromosomes separate generating two identical copies of each chromosome. (d) Each single chromosome migrates to opposite ends of the cell forming two identical sets of chromosomes and (e) a nuclear membrane starts forming around each cluster of chromosomes. (f) The cell membrane squeezes into itself dividing all cellular contents into two identical daughter cells.

Activity 2.2   Cell division

Allow about 30 minutes in total for this activity

Now watch the video sequence *Cell Division* which summarises the key aspects of Section 2.7.1.

2.7.2 When do cells divide?

Cells divide when they receive signals to do so and stop dividing when these are absent or when they receive signals that inhibit cell division. Cell division is obviously important during the growth of an embryo, which is formed from a fertilised egg, into a fetus (Figure 2.10), and during childhood, to enable growth of the organism. However, even when a person has reached adult size many types of cells continue dividing during their lifetime, mainly to replace worn-out cells or cells that have died. A clear example of this type of process is the skin cells that provide a mechanical barrier for the rest of the organism. As part of this external barrier, skin cells are continually being damaged by rubbing against clothes, soap, bacteria and exposure to the sun. As a result, skin cells continue to divide throughout life with new cells replacing those that die, which then form an outer layer on the surface of the skin (the cellular structure of the skin's outer layer is further explained in Section 2.8.2). Skin cells have a lifetime of approximately a month but cell division to replace dead cells occurs at different rates in different parts of the body. While some cells, such as nerve cells, may survive for the entire life of the organism, others have a very short lifespan. For example, cells in the lining of the gut are replaced every few hours whereas those in the liver and kidney live for weeks.

● Can you think of another example in which cell division is a frequent cellular process?

● Cancer, which involves sustained division of neoplastic cells.

Indeed, a type of actively dividing cell called an **epithelial cell**, which forms the lining of the gut, the skin, etc., is at the origin of the most common types of cancer in humans. This is because the more often a cell divides, the more chances there are that errors arise when copying the DNA that is passed to the daughter cells – although there are mechanisms to prevent these errors, as you will learn in Chapter 3. By contrast, there are also cells in adult organisms that do not divide at all, such as nerve cells and the cells that form the muscles used for movement (termed skeletal muscle). As these cells do not undergo cell division, no errors in DNA replication occur. Thus, even though gene alterations caused by external agents may still happen in these cells, the chances of skeletal muscle and nerve cells giving rise to cancers are nil as they do not divide (although the 'parent' cells that divide into and generate nerve and muscle cells may do so, particularly in children).

2.7.3 Cell ageing

Cells do not divide infinitely. It seems as if cells have the ability to divide only a finite number of times, after which cells withdraw from the cell cycle, i.e. they stop dividing, and enter a phase termed **cell senescence** (also known as replicative senescence as it concerns DNA replication). Cell senescence is characterised by changes in metabolic activity and cell structure (senescent cells are larger and have larger nuclei) and by modifications in the nature of the proteins that a cell contains. Cell senescence is an extremely complex process, and is still a subject of intensive research in biology and medicine, as it has enormous implications for ageing of the whole organism, in other words, for how we humans age and die.

Some structures at the end of the chromosomes called **telomeres** appear to be important in the cell ageing process (Figure 2.14). Telomeres stabilise the structure of chromosomes. Each time a cell divides, the telomeres on the chromosomes of the daughter cells shorten. After a certain number of cell cycles, the telomeres at the ends of the chromosomes become so short that they may become completely eroded. As a result, and for reasons that we need not explain here, the chromosomes become unstable and tend to get damaged in some way, either cut from the ends or sometimes even breaking into two. This event obviously affects the normal production of proteins in a cell and is a signal for it to stop dividing. That is, a cell with short telomeres enters senescence and can also die.

In up to 90% of cancers, tumour cells are able to overcome senescence, an acquired property that allows them to grow into even bigger tumours. They do this by reactivating the production of an enzyme called telomerase that is usually present in the cells of the developing embryo but not in adult cells. Telomerase restores telomeres to a length that maintains chromosome stability so that the cell may carry on dividing. So in some tumours such as human breast and colorectal cancers, and especially at an advanced stage, telomerase production allows cancer cells to

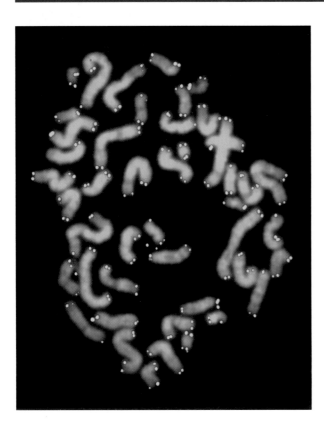

Figure 2.14 Human chromosomes (blue) with the telomeres showing in yellow at the ends of each chromosome. Scale: 1 cm = 10 μm. (Source: Courtesy of Peter Lansdorp, Terry Fox Laboratories)

continue dividing and avoid senescence – in a way, making tumour cells become somehow 'immortal' even if the whole organism that they derive from is not. For example, many scientists use tumour cells in laboratory culture dishes to study many aspects of cell biology, including tumour biology. The most commonly used tumour cells were originally obtained from a woman called Henrietta Lacks who had cervical cancer – hence, the name of these cells, HeLa. Although Henrietta died in 1951 from her cancer condition, HeLa cells, which produce a very active version of telomerase, have been propagated ever since in laboratories all over the world. In fact, it is said that the collective biomass of HeLa cells nowadays is larger than Henrietta ever was herself! This extensive use of HeLa cells, however, has greatly advanced research into tumour biology and cancer treatments.

2.8 Cell differentiation

In the previous section, you were introduced to a few different types of cell. There is in reality a great deal of variation in size, shape and function of cells within the human body (Figure 2.15). In reading Section 2.7, you may have asked yourself how a single fertilised egg, following many rounds of cell division, develops into a multicellular organism such as that of a human with a variety of different cell types, instead of developing into an organism in which all the cells are identical. In fact, cells become *specialised* during development; that is, they acquire specific cellular properties so that each cell carries out only some of the functions required for the survival and reproduction of the whole organism. Within the body, some cells are involved in digesting food, other cells collect and excrete waste products, and so on. The process by which a cell becomes specialised is known as **differentiation**.

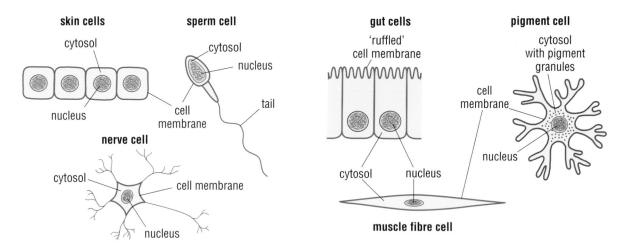

Figure 2.15 Examples of human cells illustrate the variety of shapes and structures evolved by cells with specialised functions.

Cell differentiation occurs during development and in normal adult life because cells receive signals from neighbouring cells. As a result of these signals, each cell produces specific proteins involved in the specialised function of that cell. For example, there are proteins that link epithelial cells of the skin tightly together so that they form the sheets that constitute a protective layer on the outside of the body. Another example is **leukocytes**, the white cells of the immune system, which produce proteins that bind to and destroy infectious agents. You will learn in Chapter 3 how proteins are produced in a cell by 'decoding' the DNA in the nucleus. It is nevertheless worth reiterating here that most normal cells in the body contain the same genetic material (with exceptions, e.g. red blood cells; eggs and sperm cells) as they all are derived by cell division from a single fertilised egg, but each cell activates and decodes only a part of the full genetic material to produce a pattern of proteins characteristic of a particular cell type.

Case study 2.1   Trupti Shah and her family

Mr and Mrs Shah are second-generation UK Asians, living in London; they both have parents who came to the UK as children and teenagers in the 1950s. Mr Shah works as a minicab driver; Mrs Shah stays home to look after their family, occasionally taking short-term cleaning jobs when money is particularly tight. They have three children between the ages of eight and three. Mrs Shah is 20-weeks pregnant and she has just returned, accompanied by her husband, from having an ultrasound scan at the nearest hospital. They were told the likely sex of the baby and have decided on a name for the unborn baby, Trupti. They are very excited about hearing their youngest daughter's beating heart and have also brought home a scan photo which shows the shape of her head and body. From a single cell, the fertilised egg, and after many rounds of cell division, most of the tissues and organs formed by different cell types such as heart muscle cells are already in place in Trupti's body. Many more cell divisions and differentiation processes are yet to occur in her body before she's born as a healthy baby.

2.8.1 Tissues and organs

In Section 2.2 you learnt that, in multicellular organisms, similar cells or, more aptly, cells that have differentiated into the same type, associate to work together forming tissues. There are several types of tissue in the human body (Figure 2.16), including muscle tissues, which allow movement, nerve tissues, which provide inbuilt communication and control of function throughout the body, fatty or adipose tissues, which store energy as fat, connective or supportive tissues,

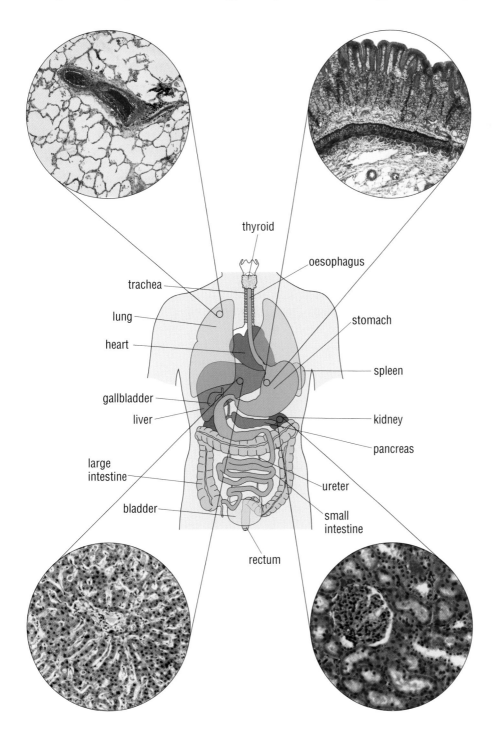

Figure 2.16 Examples of human organs and the tissues that form them. (Source: lung: CNRI/Science Photo Library; liver: Astrid and Hanns-Frieder Michler/Science Photo Library; kidney and stomach: Steve Gschmeissner/Science Photo Library)

which as their name indicates hold tissues together (bone and blood are types of connective tissues) and lymphoid tissues, which are responsible for fighting infections. In addition, epithelial tissues form layers of cells that cover surfaces of internal organs or in contact with the outside world, and hence confer protection or form an interface that allows the exchange of molecules (e.g. nutrients).

● Can you suggest two examples of organs in the human body composed of epithelial tissues?

● The skin (protective function) and the lining of the gut (involved in the absorption of nutrients as well as being a protective barrier) are composed of epithelial tissues. You may well have thought of other examples such as the lining of the lung and other internal and external surfaces of the body.

As explained in Table 2.1, organs are a collection of two or more tissues that perform a specific function. For example, the heart is an organ composed of muscle, nerve and connective tissues. Examples of human organs are shown in Figure 2.16.

Many differentiated cells within tissues and organs lose the ability to undergo cell division (e.g. skeletal muscle cells) but interspersed within tissues there are usually immature cells, also known as **stem cells**, which can divide and ultimately replace specialised cells that have been damaged or have died. In cancers, cells that would normally have all the characteristics of a particular cell type (a gut epithelial cell, for example) lose their specialised structure and functions and become undifferentiated. Undifferentiated cancer cells resemble unspecialised stem cells in many ways (either the ones that existed in the early embryo or those interspersed within tissues). As such, tumour cells lose the pattern of cell division characteristic of the cell type they are derived from and proliferate more vigorously, like immature cells.

2.8.2 Types of cancers

Human cancers are often classified according to the organ/tissue and/or cell type from which they are derived (Table 2.4). **Carcinomas** are tumours derived from epithelial cells and are the most common types of cancer in humans, accounting for around 85% of all human cancers. As there are different types of epithelial cells depending on the tissue and organ they are in and the exact function they perform, there are many types of carcinomas. So, for example, epithelial cells that form a flat surface in the skin (Figure 2.17), lungs, digestive system, etc. are called squamous cells and thus give rise to squamous cell carcinomas, whereas those cancers derived from epithelial cells that form part of glands and secrete substances are called adenocarcinomas. In order to distinguish the type of carcinoma further, the organ in which the tumour originated usually accompanies these names. So doctors speak of skin squamous cell carcinoma, breast adenocarcinoma, etc.

Table 2.4 Types of cancer.

Cancer	Definition
carcinomas	tumours that arise in epithelial cells that line external and internal body surfaces
sarcomas	tumours that originate in cells forming supportive or connective tissue (bone, muscle, cartilage, fibrous tissue or fat)
leukaemias	cancers of immature immune cells in the blood or in blood-forming organs
lymphomas	affect cells of the lymphatic system, a network of vessels and nodes that forms part of the immune system (Chapter 4)
melanoma	cancer of melanocytes, the pigmented cells in the skin (Figure 2.17)
nervous-tissue cancers	affect cells that form part of nervous tissue (e.g. brain)

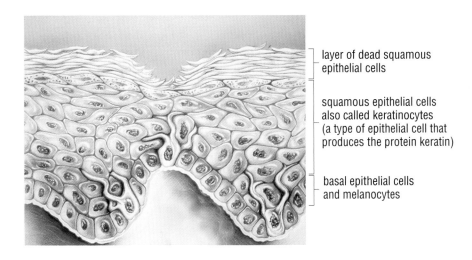

layer of dead squamous epithelial cells

squamous epithelial cells also called keratinocytes (a type of epithelial cell that produces the protein keratin)

basal epithelial cells and melanocytes

Figure 2.17 Cell types in the outer layer of the skin (epidermis). The epidermis contains squamous epithelial cells (also called keratinocytes: orange) that produce keratin, a protein that helps in the skin's barrier function. Dead keratinocytes (yellow) form a layer on the outer surface of the epidermis and are replaced by cell division of basal epithelial cells that form the innermost layer of the epidermis. (Note that the immature keratinocytes are shown in pink.) Melanocytes (green) are interspersed between basal epithelial cells and produce melanin, the brown pigment of the skin. These three cell types give rise to the three major types of skin cancer, skin squamous cell carcinoma, skin basal cell carcinoma and skin melanoma. (Source: BSIP, Gilles/Science Photo Library)

The next broad category of cancers, with the second highest number of cases in the world, is **sarcomas**. Sarcomas are cancers of connective or supportive tissue (bone, cartilage, fat, muscle, fibrous tissue, blood vessels). Similar to the nomenclature of carcinomas, an osteosarcoma is a cancer of bone cells whereas a liposarcoma is a cancer of fat cells. Other cancers that, although relatively common, do not fall within these categories are **melanoma** (a cancer of the melanocytes, the pigmented cells in the skin), **lymphomas** and **leukaemias**, the neoplasms of lymphoid tissue and leukocytes, respectively, and cancers that originate in nervous tissue (e.g. neuroblastoma). All these categories together, carcinomas, sarcomas, leukaemias and lymphomas, skin melanoma and nervous-tissue cancers, accounted for about 95% of all cancer cases and 90% of cancer deaths in the USA in 2000.

It is important to realise that, although usually undifferentiated, in most instances, tumour cells retain some aspects of the behaviour of the original cell type. For example, melanoma cells, like melanocytes (Figure 2.17), continue to make pigment. Even when tumour cells barely resemble the normal cells they derive from, cancers originating from different cell types give rise to very different diseases, even if they are originally located within the same organ. Skin melanoma, if left untreated, is an aggressive cancer and tends to become fatal by spreading from the skin to other organs such as the lungs, brain and liver (where the melanoma cells continue to be pigmented). By contrast, basal cell carcinoma, the most common skin cancer, is usually restricted in growth and localised to the skin, where it may turn into a nasty ulcer if it is not removed.

2.9 Changes in cellular function in response to the cell's environment

Thus far, cells have been discussed as single living entities but, as you learnt in the previous section, cells are also members of complex interactive networks with other cells of the same or a different type and in the same or in another tissue and/or organ. The environment surrounding cells is constantly changing. Cells respond to these changes by sending and responding to signals across their outer membrane, which either change the conditions outside the cell or modify the activity inside. In response to these signals, cells may, for instance, start dividing or may differentiate into a particular cell type.

2.9.1 Cells communicate with each other by signalling molecules

Cells can secrete a variety of different **signalling molecules** into the fluid in which they are immersed. A signalling molecule is a substance involved in transmitting information between cells. Each of these molecules has a highly specific three-dimensional shape so that it exactly fits into a particular region of another molecule called a **receptor** on the surface of the target cell membrane (Figure 2.18a). The two surfaces fit together so precisely that – like a key in a lock – their interaction will result in the transmission of the correct signal (i.e. opening the door or locking it).

Many of the proteins that stick out of the cell membrane are actually receptors (Figure 2.8). When a receptor encounters a signalling molecule to which it can bind (i.e. it forms a very close though transient contact), the binding event sets off a chain of chemical reactions inside the cell which leads ultimately to a change in the behaviour of the receiving cell (Figure 2.18b). In fact, when a signalling molecule binds a receptor and a signal is transmitted, it is said that the receptor has been activated. Inside the cell, the signal is 'decoded' by means of other molecules termed **intracellular signalling molecules**. These are usually (but not always) proteins whose function changes in response to the activation of the receptor by a signalling molecule. Receptor activation leads to activation of an intracellular signalling molecule, which in turn activates another intracellular signalling molecule, and so on. As a result, a chain of intracellular events triggered by receptor activation leads to specific cellular responses (e.g. cell division and/or the production of a specific protein).

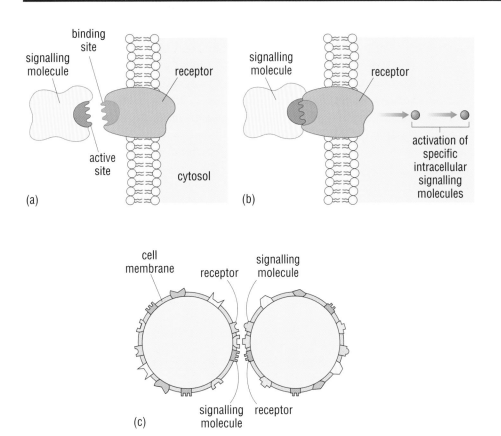

Figure 2.18 (a) A receptor on the membrane of the cell. (b) A secreted signalling molecule binds to a receptor on the outer membrane of a target cell and triggers a response in the target cell by activating intracellular signalling molecules. (c) Cells in close contact can send and receive signals via receptors and signalling molecules embedded in the cell membrane. There are many different signalling molecules and receptors on the same cell. Note that there are two major types of signalling molecules. Those inside the cell are called intracellular signalling molecules and those outside the cell are extracellular signalling molecules. For simplicity we will refer to the extracellular signalling molecules as just 'signalling molecules'.

In the example shown in Figure 2.18b, only the receptor is part of the cell membrane whereas the signalling molecule is 'free-floating', secreted into the outer fluid by cells either in their vicinity or even in other tissues or organs and transported by the blood to the target cell. However, both receptor and signalling molecule can be embedded in cell membranes providing a mechanism to transmit information between adjacent cells, a process termed cell-to-cell communication (Figure 2.18c). Other types of receptors are proteins located inside the cell so that the signalling molecule has to cross the cell membrane to interact with it. This is the case for some hormone receptors such as the oestrogen receptor whose activation induces proliferation in breast epithelial cells (thus contributing to the development of breasts in puberty).

2.9.2 Signals that control cell proliferation

Many signalling molecules trigger cell division in cells that have the appropriate receptors. These signalling molecules are generally called **growth factors** and their receptors, aptly, growth factor receptors. (However, these are not the only compounds that induce cell proliferation; other substances that do not fall within this category, such as the hormone oestrogen described above, may also do so.) Growth factors are usually small proteins. If a growth factor binds to its receptor on the surface of a normal cell, the cell will respond by initiating cell division. However, in the absence of the growth factor, the signal will not be transmitted via its receptor and the cell will not divide. In many tumour cells, the interactions between growth factors and their receptors are abnormal. These abnormal interactions are discussed below and summarised in Figure 2.19b to e.

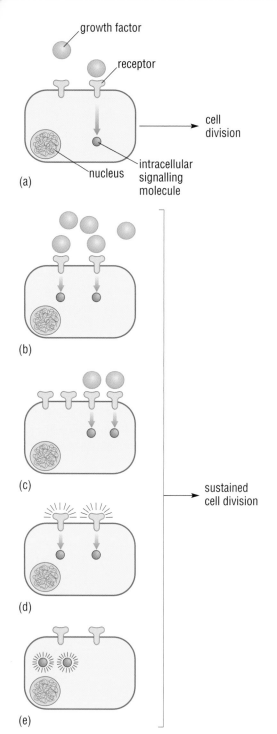

growth factor

receptor

cell division

nucleus

intracellular signalling molecule

(a)

(b)

(c)

sustained cell division

(d)

(e)

Figure 2.19 Abnormal growth-inducing signals in tumour cells. (a) A normal cell responds to a growth factor binding to its receptor and activating intracellular signalling molecules by initiating cell division. (Note, for simplicity, only two of the many receptors are shown on the membrane.) In the absence of growth factors, no cell division is induced. There are four major mechanisms involving mutations by which cell division may be increased in tumour cells. (b) Tumour cells show increased production of growth factors, thereby activating receptors and intracellular signalling molecules to a higher extent than normal cells. (c) Tumour cells produce higher levels of growth factor receptors or (d) normal levels of a mutated receptor that is constantly activated, thereby increasing the activation of intracellular signalling molecules. (e) Tumour cells produce normal levels of a mutated intracellular signalling molecule that is constantly activated. The end result for pathways (b), (c), (d) and (e) is an increased rate of cell division compared to (a).

In some instances, mutations in tumour cells lead to the release of growth factors in much higher amounts than in normal cells (Figure 2.19b), resulting in increased tumour cell division and hence proliferation. This is the case of some brain tumours called gliomas, which overproduce a growth factor called PDGF or platelet-derived growth factor (names you do not need to memorise). In other cases, there are many more growth factor receptors on the surface of tumour cells than on normal cells (Figure 2.19c) or, even if receptor levels are similar in both tumour and normal cells, the structure of the receptor protein in tumour cells is altered so that it becomes activated all the time (Figure 2.19d) – the receptor transmits to the cell the signal to proliferate even in the absence of the growth factor. There are many examples of cancers with abnormal communication between cells involving growth factor receptors. One of them is a proportion (approximately 25%) of human breast carcinomas whose cells overproduce a receptor termed HER2; an inhibitor of this receptor, called Herceptin®, is currently being used to selectively treat this type of cancer, as you will learn in Chapter 10. Finally, some tumour cells contain intracellular signalling proteins involved in 'decoding' growth-inducing signals whose activity is modified so that they are continuously active (Figure 2.19e), even in the absence of receptor activation by the growth factor. This is the case in at least 50% of human colorectal carcinomas, in which an intracellular signalling protein called RAS is constantly activated.

● In what way would mutations involving growth factors, their receptors, or their intracellular signalling components affect the proliferative behaviour of a tumour cell?

● Mutations resulting in either hyperactive proteins or overproduction of normal proteins would lead to the tumour cell persistently receiving signals to initiate cell division even in the absence of the correct signals. Consequently, these mutations would lead to sustained cell proliferation.

So, in many ways, tumour cells are hypersensitive to signals that increase proliferation or, more precisely, tumour cells will continue dividing regardless of whether signals that induce the growth of normal cells are about or not. This property of tumour cells is called self-sufficiency in growth signals.

There are also other signalling molecules that inhibit cell division called **growth-inhibitory factors**, to which many tumour cells are insensitive. Growth-inhibitory factors are also small proteins and have the opposite effect of growth factors on normal cells. If a growth-inhibitory factor binds to its receptor on the surface of a normal cell, the cell will not divide. By contrast, tumour cells are insensitive to growth-inhibitory signals, that is, tumour cells continue dividing even in the presence of growth-inhibitory signals.

● Can you suggest possible changes in the activity of growth-inhibitory factors, their receptors or their intracellular signalling components or in their rate of synthesis that may result in increased proliferation of tumour cells?

● These will include the opposite changes described for growth factors, i.e. a decrease in the production of growth-inhibitory factors compared to normal cells, a decrease in the levels of growth-inhibitory factor receptors (or in their activity) and/or a decrease in the activity of intracellular signalling proteins that 'decode' the message of growth inhibition.

A combination of both properties of tumour cells, self-sufficiency in growth signals and insensitivity to growth-inhibitory signals, underlies the unrestrained proliferative behaviour of many cancers.

2.9.3 Cell adhesion

Another important feature of cells is their ability to adhere to each other, a cellular property that is abnormal in many tumour cells. Although single-celled organisms may move about in order to find nutrients, this is not the case for most cells in multicellular organisms. After all, differentiated cells form tissues and/or organs that are pretty much fixed in position within the body of an adult human (Figure 2.16). Indeed, interactions between adjacent cells of the type described in Section 2.9.1 (cell-to-cell communication) are crucial in signalling cells when to stop dividing, so that organs like the eyes end up of a certain size and shape and not, for example, too big for the eye socket or of an irregular form so that it does not fit in.

● What kind of signals are communicated to cells to stop them dividing?

● Growth-inhibitory signals.

The molecules on the cell membrane responsible for fixing cells within a specific tissue are called **cell adhesion molecules**. These adhesion molecules allow cells to interact with each other and locate themselves within a tissue and/or organ. In addition to their roles in positioning cells and communicating to them to stop dividing, cell adhesion molecules have two other functions. First, they attach to a complex network of proteins and carbohydrates in which cells are embedded, generally known as the **extracellular matrix**, so that they become immobile within the tissue. Second, they communicate 'survival' signals. If normal cells are displaced from their position by, for example, tissue damage, they usually die as they do not receive the 'survival' signals from their neighbouring cells.

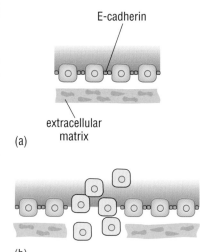

E-cadherin

extracellular
matrix

(a)

(b)

Figure 2.20 (a) A stomach epithelial barrier is joined together by the protein E-cadherin on the surface of cells. (b) In stomach carcinoma, tumour cells do not produce E-cadherin and divide in a disorganised way.

Tumour cells, especially in the late stages of cancer, have lost their ability to adhere to other cells. An example of this is human stomach carcinoma, a cancer of epithelial cells which do not produce an adhesion molecule termed E-cadherin (Figure 2.20). E-cadherin holds epithelial cells together in a neat row of single cells so that the inside of the stomach (which contains acid and digestive enzymes) is separated from the rest of the body. (Note that E-cadherin has the same function in other epithelial barriers covering most organs.) However, because stomach carcinoma cells have lost E-cadherin on their cell surface, they are free to divide as they no longer receive growth-inhibitory signals from nearby cells. They also disassemble themselves from other cells and the extracellular matrix so that they can move about and infiltrate the surrounding tissue. This property of tumour cells is called **invasion**, a normal occurrence in advanced cancers. Invasive tumour cells that have moved into the adjoining tissue may also encounter blood vessels then migrate through the vessel wall and circulate in the blood. Then, it is possible that some of them may be transported by the blood to other tissues and organs in the body where they form new tumours, a process called **metastasis**. In Chapter 4, you will learn in more detail about the processes of invasion and metastasis and how they impact on human health.

● Can you suggest a possible outcome in terms of survival for invasive or metastatic tumour cells that have become dislodged from the solid tumour?

● Invasive or metastatic tumour cells may have an increased rate of cell death as a result of them not receiving correct 'survival' signals from neighbouring cells.

However, in many cancers, tumour cells have evolved the ability to persist even in the absence of these 'survival' signals, a topic that will be discussed in the next section.

2.9.4 Cell death

The notion of cell death as one of the basic properties of cells in multicellular organisms may sound peculiar, but there are many situations in which it is advantageous, or even essential, that certain cells are destroyed to maintain the health of the organism. To start with, there are many instances in which cells are required at a particular point in development and then may become obsolete in later stages. An obvious example in human development is when the cells forming the webbing between fingers die, leaving separated digits, during the growth of the fetus. In the adult organism, cell death is often also part of ordinary cellular life in order to maintain the tissue functioning normally.

● Can you think of an example of cell death in normal tissue maintenance?

● You may have thought of cells like those of the skin or the gut that have short lifespans and are continuously being replaced (Section 2.7.2) or of cells that die because they have become displaced from their position in a tissue and do not receive 'survival' signals (Section 2.9.3).

A distinction must be made here between cells that die 'accidentally' (i.e. by exposure to high levels of toxins or by direct mechanical injury), a process by which cells simply swell and burst, and those cells that die 'predictably' – for example, in development and normal tissue maintenance. In the latter, cells are eliminated in a regulated way, and the surrounding tissue is not damaged. This process is termed **apoptosis** (sometimes called **programmed cell death**) and can be defined as the controlled 'suicide' of a cell, which, as for most cellular properties, is mediated by a specific set of the cell's own proteins.

Apoptosis acts as an inbuilt quality control mechanism whereby the body disposes of abnormal cells such as, for example, tumour cells. Even when a cell receives all the correct 'survival' signals, programmed cell death may be triggered when a cell detects anomalous processes going on within itself (which leads to cell 'suicide') or, sometimes, when abnormal cells send incorrect signals that are somehow detected as such by immune cells (which then signal the defective cells to kill themselves). Apoptosis enables the removal of cells whose DNA is damaged by, for example, exposure to radiation and some types of drugs, and of stressed or virus-infected cells. Scientists differentiate 'survival' and 'death' types of signals that control cell death signals and classify them into anti-apoptotic and pro-apoptotic signals, respectively.

Case study 2.2   Terri in 1962

Australian Terri Moloney turned 21 in 1962. She always seemed one of those who fortune favoured: born into a wealthy and caring family, she was intelligent, and was able to take full advantage of an expensive education. After picking up her degree – a First in Law – she has a whole summer to play with before deciding what to do with the rest of her life, and that is what she does. She spends many hours every day on the beach, swimming, surfing, or (more often than not) just lying in the glorious sunshine.

Terri would like her body to turn a very fashionable shade of brown. She is not particularly bothered if she burns to achieve this objective. While she toasts herself, the intense rays of the Australian mid-day sun are penetrating deep into her skin. Melanocytes in the epidermis of Caucasians, like Terri, produce less of the protective pigment, melanin, than those of people with naturally darker skins. Melanin can help block UV light to a certain extent. When UV rays do penetrate Terri's epidermis, they can cause damage to the DNA of her skin cells. Many of the sun-overexposed skin cells (mainly squamous epithelial cells) have gross DNA damage and, therefore, undergo programmed cell death or apoptosis. During the following days, the extent of cell death is such that the layer of dead cells on the surface of Terri's skin thickens considerably and Terri entertains herself by peeling this visible layer to reveal the long-awaited bronzed skin. What Terri does not know is that in order to renew her damaged skin, the basal epithelial cells of her epidermis have undergone many more rounds of cell division followed by differentiation into squamous epithelial cells than they would normally do. At the same time, the melanocytes in Terri's epidermis have increased the production of melanin which is then released in order to protect the skin from further damage by UV light. Melanin gives the characteristic tanned appearance to her skin. Melanocytes, as they are located deeper in the epidermis, may still undergo some degree of DNA damage but this is usually not sufficient to trigger apoptosis. Alternatively, melanocytes that are closer to the surface such as those forming a mole are more likely to be damaged by UV light. Terri's twenty-second summer may well have set the scene for more than just a successful career in the law.

Changes in the normal regulation of apoptosis, in particular too little cell death, contribute to the progress from abnormal cell growth to rapidly growing tumours.

● By comparison with what you learnt of the two signalling mechanisms by which tumour cells increase their proliferation rates, suggest two ways that would enable tumour cells to decrease their rate of apoptosis.

● In order to have increased cell proliferation, tumour cells may become insensitive to growth-inhibitory signals and self-sufficient in growth signals (Section 2.9.2). Assuming that cellular mechanisms are similar in the context of cell death, tumour cells may become self-sufficient in anti-apoptotic ('survival') signals and insensitive to pro-apoptotic ('death') signals.

These are in fact the two main processes by which tumour cells acquire the ability to escape apoptosis. The mechanisms leading to evasion from apoptosis are in a way similar to those resulting in uncontrolled cell division (Section 2.9.2). In a nutshell, evasion from apoptosis is mediated by alterations in a subset of the cell's proteins that are implicated in regulating cell death. These proteins with altered function may include signalling molecules, their receptors or intracellular signalling molecules that control cell death and survival. In principle, a tumour cell with abnormal growth as a result of alterations in its DNA sequence (and therefore with aberrant proteins) should be programmed to die. However, tumour cells may survive if these DNA alterations directly modify the activity of proteins involved in apoptosis. As a result, tumour cells that evade apoptosis continue dividing, transferring their own genetic alterations to their progeny cells.

2.10 Concluding remarks

While reading this chapter, you may have noticed two underlying themes. First, there appear to be many different mechanisms by which a normal cell may first turn abnormal and then become a tumour cell. Whereas tumour cells divide and use energy in much the same way as their normal counterparts (albeit at a higher rate), tumour cells are characterised by the abnormal control of signals regulating cell division, ageing, adhesion and death, summarised in Table 2.3. It is important to realise here that there is not a single 'common' path that normal cells follow to progress to tumour cells. Rather, normal cells may acquire at one point a characteristic that leads to increased cell division and, later, their progeny may gain other features (e.g. irregular cell adhesion properties or cell death mechanisms) that favour the uncontrolled proliferation of tumour cells, becoming, at every stage, more and more aggressive in their growth properties.

Second, the alterations in the behaviour of tumour cells are the result of changes in the levels and/or activity of the proteins that are responsible for these responses within a cell. You may recall from Section 2.3 that the production of proteins by cells is determined by small regions of the DNA called genes. A single faulty protein molecule may not have any consequences for a normal cell (as there are many copies of the same protein that function correctly). However, in a tumour cell, all copies of the particular protein that a mutated gene encodes will be abnormal. As such, cancers can be considered, at their origin, as genetic diseases.

To finish this chapter, you should be aware that irregularities in cell division are more common phenomena in the human body than you may have thought, due to two factors:

1   Humans are constantly being exposed to external agents that cause DNA damage.

2   At least 10^{16} cell divisions take place in the human body during the lifetime of an average person.

As a result, the number of mutations in genes occurring during DNA replication is enormous, of the order of 10^{10}, in the average life of a human being. From this point of view, it is a feat of the human body that cancers do not occur more frequently than they actually do. Even when cancers arise, although some are still fatal, recent advances in medical science mean that many cancers are treatable with high and increasing success rates (particularly in high-income countries).

2.11 Summary of Chapter 2

2.1   Cells are the functional and structural units of all living organisms. Cancers are diseases of multicellular organisms and are formed by cells that, unlike normal cells, grow out of control.

2.2   All matter is formed by chemical elements in the form of atoms which combine to form molecules. Compounds are formed by many molecules.

2.3   The four main types of macromolecules in cells are carbohydrates, proteins, nucleic acids and lipids. Macromolecules are made from smaller molecule units which include, for example, amino acids, which form proteins, and nucleotides, which form nucleic acids.

2.4   Cancers arise from cells that progress from normal to cancerous as a result of changes in their cellular functions. Changes in the activity of tumour cells derive from alterations in the nature of proteins that they contain which, in turn, result from gene mutations.

2.5   Both normal and tumour cells show similar chemical composition and cellular structures. They are formed by a cell membrane that surrounds the cytosol and organelles. DNA in the nucleus is arranged into single threads with proteins attached to them forming the structures called chromosomes.

2.6   Energy is required to maintain cell metabolism, which is the sum of all the chemical reactions that are necessary to maintain cellular life. Tumour cells are metabolically more active, i.e. they require more energy than normal cells.

2.7   Cell proliferation is the reproduction of cells both during development and in adult life. The cell cycle involves two phases, cell growth and cell division. In essence, the cell cycle involves a cell growing in size, then making copies of all the molecules and structures it contains, including the DNA in the nucleus, and subsequently dividing into two daughter cells. The rate of cell proliferation in tumour cells is higher than in normal cells.

2.8   Normal cells become senescent after a limited number of cell divisions. Tumour cells may overcome senescence by maintaining the length of telomeres at the ends of chromosomes.

2.9   Cells differentiate into different types to form tissues and organs. Tumour cells usually lose their specialised functions and structure. Human cancers are often classified according to the tissue and/or cell type from which they are derived. The most common human cancers are carcinomas, sarcomas, leukaemias, lymphomas, melanoma and brain tumours.

2.10   Cells communicate with each other by signalling molecules, which activate receptors on the cell membrane of a target cell. Receptor activation, in turn, initiates a series of activation events of intracellular signalling molecules, leading to a change in the cell's function.

2.11   Changes in the activity and/or levels of signalling molecules, their receptors and intracellular signalling molecules that control cell proliferation underlie the abnormal rate of cell division in many tumour cells. Tumour cells are self-sufficient in growth signals and insensitive to growth-inhibitory signals.

2.12   Tumour cells in advanced cancers lose the ability to adhere to each other; they invade nearby tissue and/or metastasise to distant tissues and/or organs.

2.13   Changes in the activity and/or levels of signalling molecules, their receptors and intracellular signalling molecules that control cell death enable some tumour cells to evade apoptosis. Tumour cells are self-sufficient in cell survival signals and insensitive to cell death signals.

Questions for Chapter 2

Question 2.1 (Learning outcomes 2.1, 2.2 and 2.3)

Complete each of the phrases (a)–(h) with one of the answers selected from 1–8 below.

(a)   Carbohydrates …

(b)   The mitochondria …

(c)   The endoplasmic reticulum …

(d)   A receptor …

(e)   The nucleus …

(f)   Genes …

(g)   The cytosol …

(h)   Molecules …

1... is a canal system of membranes that are studded with ribosomes, the structures responsible for the synthesis of proteins within a cell.

2... are segments of DNA which 'encode' for specific proteins.

3... is a type of protein which is inserted in the cell membrane and is activated by extracellular signalling molecules.

4... are macromolecules formed by smaller molecule units termed sugars.

5... are the 'powerhouses' of the cell.

6... contains the genetic information of the cell.

7... are formed by combinations of atoms joined by chemical bonds.

8... is the fluid that is contained within the cell membrane and surrounds the intracellular organelles.

Question 2.2 (Learning outcome 2.2)

(a)   List the four main types of biological macromolecules and their molecule units giving one example of each.

(b)   Are all four types of macromolecules 'true' macromolecules? Explain your answer.

Question 2.3 (Learning outcomes 2.3, 2.4 and 2.6)

Which of the following statement(s) are true?

(a)   The nature of the proteins that a tumour cell produces is essentially the same as that of the normal cell it derives from.

(b)   A tumour cell and a normal cell comprise a cell membrane, the cytosol and the same types of intracellular organelles.

(c)   Energy is necessary to fuel chemical reactions in all cells, whether normal or cancerous.

(d)   In tumour cells, the shortening of telomeres at the end of chromosomes allows them to divide an unlimited number of times.

(e)   Tumour cells maintain the structure and functions of the differentiated cells they derive from.

Question 2.4 (Learning outcome 2.5)

How many chromosomes would there be in each progeny cell of a human cell that has divided? And how many nuclei?

Question 2.5 (Learning outcome 2.6)

(a) Draw a diagram to describe abnormal responses to growth-inhibitory signals in tumour cells, similar to that drawn for growth-inducing signals in Figure 2.19, specifying any changes in the levels and/or activity of the molecules involved.

(b) If you were to draw another diagram to describe abnormal responses to anti-apoptotic signals in tumour cells, would the changes in the levels and/or activity of the molecules involved resemble those in Figure 2.19 or those in the figure you drew for Question 2.5a (i.e. Figure 2.21)? Justify your answer.

Further reading

If you would like to read further about this topic, please refer to the following publications.

Alberts, B., Johnson, A., Lewis, J., Raff, M., Roberts, K. and Walter, P. (2000) Chapter 23: Cancer, in *Molecular Biology of the Cell* (4th edn), New York and London, Garland Science.

Alison, M.R. (2006) Cancer, in *Encyclopedia of Life Sciences*, Chichester, John Wiley & Sons Ltd; also available online at http://mrw.interscience.wiley.com/emrw/047001590X/home/ (Accessed 30 April 2008).

Hanahan, D. and Weinberg, R.A. (2000) 'The hallmarks of cancer', *Cell*, vol. 100, no. 1, pp. 57–70.

GENES AND CANCERS

3.1 Introduction

While learning the basic properties of cells and how these change in tumour cells, you may have observed that proteins hold the key to the unique character of each living cell in terms of both cell structure and its functions. Indeed, alterations in the nature of the proteins that a cell contains are essential to the transformation process from a normal cell into a neoplastic cell. Recall that in cells, enzymes and most receptors are proteins and that many signalling molecules (whether outside the cell like hormones and growth factors, or located intracellularly helping the cell decode signals) are also proteins. So changes in the nature of proteins will affect how a cell responds to its environment, whether it divides, or produces new signalling molecules, or dies. As genes instruct the cell how to make its own proteins, a normal cell must have acquired changes in its genes in order to be transformed into a tumour cell. In this context, and as mentioned in Chapter 2, cancers may be considered as genetic diseases of cells.

A great deal is already known about the genes involved in cancer, but there is still an enormous amount to learn. Thus, before we discuss how cancerous cells affect the workings of the human body in Chapter 4, we have to take a step back and look into the formation of cancers at the molecular level. In this chapter, we examine the relationship between genes and cancers, and describe the roles of genes in causing cells to become cancerous; in particular, we describe how cancer arises as a result of mutations in the molecule that directs the production of proteins in a cell, that is, the macromolecule called DNA.

3.2 The structure of DNA

The information required to manufacture all of the many thousands of proteins in the human body is contained in the DNA 'molecular' code. Recall from Chapter 2 that, in the majority of cells, most of the DNA is in the nucleus, tightly coiled around packing proteins in structures called chromosomes. In humans, there are 46 chromosomes in most cells. (Remember that red blood cells have no nuclei and note that germline cells, e.g. sperm and eggs, contain half that number of chromosomes (23) which will result in 46 chromosomes in the fertilised egg.) The number of chromosomes is characteristic of each species; for example, chimpanzee cells have 48 chromosomes whereas chicken cells have 78. Figure 3.1 shows the chromosomes in a cell of a human male. There are 22 pairs of *homologous* chromosomes – that is, two chromosomes of similar structure that contain analogous genetic information. Each homologous chromosome in a cell is derived from a germline cell of each parent. When displaying homologous chromosomes they are usually arranged in a conventional sequence and numbered 1 to 22. In addition, there are the two sex chromosomes (X and Y), so called because they play an important role in sex determination. Figure 3.1 shows the X and Y chromosomes of a human male; females would have a pair of homologous X chromosomes. Hence, males are described as XY and females as XX. It is important to mention here that each of the 24 different kinds of chromosomes that may occur in a human cell (i.e. chromosomes 1 to 22, plus X and Y) carries different genes arranged in a specific order along its length. However, both partners in a pair of homologous chromosomes usually carry the same genes in the same order.

Figure 3.2 represents DNA being unwound from a chromosome. You can see that its appearance is like two interwoven spiral staircases each coiled around each other or, in more scientific terms, DNA forms a double helix. The two strands are kept together by cross-pieces like the rungs of a ladder.

●   What are the building blocks that form the DNA macromolecule?

●   Nucleotides (Section 2.3).

A single DNA **nucleotide** consists of three linked components; a phosphate group, a sugar termed deoxyribose (hence the name deoxyribonucleic acid) and another type of molecule called a **base** (Figure 3.3a). Together, the sugar and the phosphate form part of the backbone of a DNA strand (the handrail of each spiral staircase), whereas the base points towards the centre of the helix forming weak bonds with the corresponding base on the opposite strand (the rungs of the ladder) (Figure 3.3b). There are just four kinds of bases in DNA, namely adenine, guanine, thymine and cytosine (names you need not memorise), which are also generally known

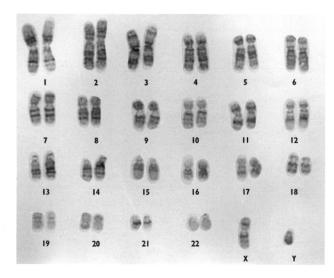

Figure 3.1 Photograph of the chromosomes of a human male arranged in a sequence and stained to reveal a characteristic banding pattern. Chromosomes 1 to 22 are present as homologous pairs. The sex chromosomes of a male are X and Y. (Source: Professor Ferguson Smith)

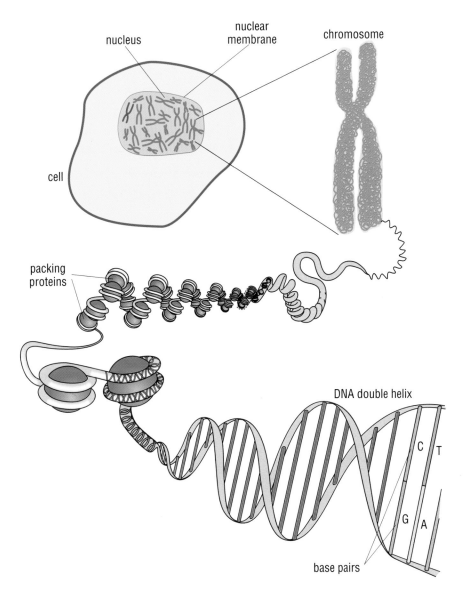

Figure 3.2 DNA wraps around special packing proteins to form tightly wound chromosomes in the nucleus of each human cell.

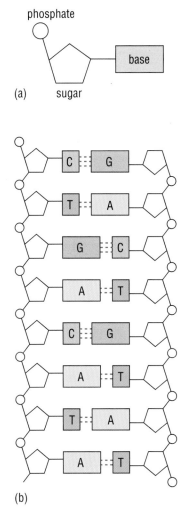

Figure 3.3 (a) A single nucleotide composed of a phosphate group, a sugar and a base. (b) A short portion of a DNA molecule with the helix unwound, showing a sequence of bases (represented as A, G, C and T) forming weak bonds (shown as red dashed lines) with complementary bases in the opposite strand. The sugar–phosphate backbone is shown in white. The base pair AT forms two bonds; GC forms three bonds. (You will learn more about the base pairs in Chapter 10.)

by the initial letters of their chemical names, **A**, **G**, **T** and **C**, respectively. DNA bases always pair up in the same way, A with T, and C with G, as each pair of bases complements each other due to their molecular shape. These interactions are known as **base-pairing**.

By convention, scientists write down the sequence of nucleotides in a segment of DNA, and indeed that of the whole structure of DNA, in a simplified manner, as a series of letters corresponding to the bases of one strand (since bases in one strand pair with their complementary bases, the sequence of nucleotides in the other strand can be easily inferred). The sequence of nucleotides in Figure 3.3b can be written down (starting from the top) as CTGACATA. As any position in the sequence can be occupied by one of four nucleotides, there are many possible permutations of the four bases in this short sequence. This can be worked out exactly in a stretch of DNA of only eight nucleotides; that is, there are $4 \times 4 \times 4 \times 4 \times 4 \times 4 \times 4 \times 4$ or, simply, $4^8 = 65\,536$ possible different sequences! In each human cell, there are approximately 6×10^9 nucleotides in all 46 chromosomes. The amount of DNA (i.e. the number of nucleotides) present in a single cell that contains all the genes necessary for life is called the **genome**. The human genome is half that number, 3×10^9 nucleotides, due to the pairs of homologous chromosomes that contain the same genes. Note that the sequence of nucleotides will not be exactly identical on each gene as we inherit one copy of a homologous chromosome from each of our parents (each of whom will have his or her unique version of the genome). As you may imagine, the variation in the sequence of this huge number of nucleotides represents a vast potential store of information.

3.3 Genes and proteins

Having examined the structure of DNA, we can now reiterate the concept of genes at the molecular level. Genes are the sequences of nucleotides that contain the coded instructions for a specific protein. In the human genome, there are more than 3×10^4 genes, which constitutes approximately 5% of the human genome. Each gene can be thought of as coding for a different protein or, in other words, there is a 'gene for insulin', a 'gene for haemoglobin', etc. Strictly speaking, however, some segments of DNA may be shared by different genes and some genes can be 'decoded' in slightly different ways so that several forms of the same protein are produced.

Note that genes in DNA are different from the hypothetical 'genes' for behavioural traits popularised by the media, such as the 'gene for compulsive gambling' or the 'homosexual gene', which refer to possible genetic components in these behaviours but have so far no scientific basis.

● How many copies of each gene will there be in a human cell?

● There will usually be two copies, i.e. one on each of the homologous chromosomes carrying that gene (with the exception of genes in the X and Y chromosomes of males where there will only be one copy).

Not all genes are active at the same time; there are mechanisms for switching genes on and off, i.e. for starting synthesis of a protein or for ceasing to do so. The synthesised protein is often described as a **gene product**, i.e. the product of an active gene.

However, information from DNA to protein does not flow directly; rather, the genetic information is carried by an intermediary molecule, a nucleic acid called messenger RNA or ribonucleic acid (Figure 3.4), or mRNA for short. There are therefore two steps in this information flow. First, mRNA is synthesised by assembling nucleotides using as a 'template' the sequence of nucleotides of one of the DNA strands that constitutes a gene. This process is called transcription and occurs in the nucleus. Second, protein molecules are assembled from amino acids using the instruction coded by the sequence of nucleotides in the mRNA. This process is called translation and occurs in the ribosomes located in the cytosol. When a specific gene is first transcribed and the transcription product, mRNA, then translated into a protein by a cell, it is said that the cell **expresses** that particular protein.

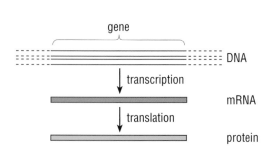

Figure 3.4 Information flow from DNA to mRNA to protein: the process of gene expression.

The complex cellular processes of transcription and translation will not be described here. However, in order to understand how mutations (and subsequently cancers) arise, it is necessary for you to understand the basic principles of how the DNA information is 'decoded'. In essence, the language of four characters of the DNA (the nucleotides A, T, G and C) has to be 'translated' into the 20-character language of proteins (the 20 essential amino acids). There is a particular relationship between the linear sequence of base pairs that makes up a gene and the linear sequence of amino acids that makes up the protein it encodes. We shall explore this concept with a particular example. Suppose that a sequence of bases in a particular stretch of a DNA molecule is:

… ATGCCTGCTGTTGGAAAG …

This DNA message is formed from a series of three consecutive nucleotides termed **codons**. In this example, they would be:

… ATG–CCT–GCT–GTT–GGA–AAG …

Each codon contains the information for a particular amino acid so that during protein synthesis in the ribosomes the correct amino acid is added to the emerging protein chain. So, in order to decode the DNA 'message' the linear series of nucleotides is read three at a time. Specific codons then specify the correct sequence of amino acids in the synthesised protein. The sequence of codons given above would give the following sequence of amino acids:

… methionine–proline–alanine–valine–glycine–lysine …

● How many possible combinations of three nucleotides are there in DNA, assuming that each nucleotide can occur, once, twice or three times in a codon?

● There are $4 \times 4 \times 4 = 64$ possible combinations of three nucleotides.

In fact, 64 is a higher number of possible codon combinations than those required for 20 amino acids but some amino acids are specified by more than one combination of three nucleotides in codons. For example, the amino acid *glycine* is specified by the following four different codons in DNA: GGT, GGC, GGA and GGG. In addition, cells use a series of complex mechanisms to identify where to start protein synthesis. An important feature is that protein synthesis always starts with the codon ATG which is called the **start codon**, and is terminated when specific codons are reached, the so-called **stop codons**, that 'tell' the protein synthesis machinery of the cell that its job is complete. Where start and stop codons are located in a gene is important to determine the length of the gene product, i.e. the synthesised protein.

In order to differentiate between the name of a gene and that of its product, scientists usually write by convention the gene name in upper-case letters in italics and that of the protein in upper-case upright letters. So, for example, the *RAS* gene encodes the RAS protein. Note that you will come across many exceptions to this convention.

Activity 3.1 DNA information

Allow about 60 minutes in total for this activity

Now watch the video sequence *DNA: the medium and the message* which summarises the key aspects of Sections 3.2 and 3.3.

3.4 Cancers and mutations

3.4.1 Genes and mutations

Recall that changes in the sequence of DNA nucleotides are known as mutations. Each time a mutation happens, a different version of DNA is created. Two examples of the changes in the DNA sequence that might occur following mutations are shown in the left-hand side of Figure 3.5b and c. For example, a single base may be replaced by another, such as an A where a C should have been, a type of mutation called a substitution (Figure 3.5b), or one or a few nucleotides may be lost, a type of mutation called deletion (Figure 3.5c). Alternatively, a few additional nucleotides might be added to the chain of nucleotides (a type of mutation called insertion). These types of mutations may happen anywhere in the DNA, and are essentially random events. However, a change in the sequence of bases within a gene might produce a change at the level of the functioning protein.

● Why would changes in the sequence of bases in a gene lead to protein changes?

● Because the sequence of nucleotides in the DNA of a gene determines the sequence of amino acids in the protein it encodes (Section 3.3).

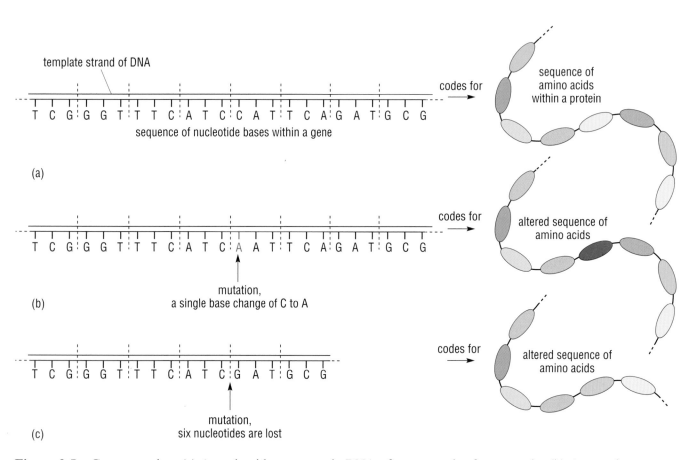

Figure 3.5 Gene mutation. (a) A nucleotide sequence in DNA of a gene codes for a protein. (b) A mutation resulting in a single base substitution in DNA of a gene gives rise to a protein with an altered sequence of amino acids. (c) A mutation resulting in the deletion of six nucleotides gives rise to a protein with two fewer amino acids in its sequence.

In the example shown in Figure 3.5b in which a single base is mutated, the resulting protein will have a different amino acid in the position determined by the codon where the mutation occurs – the rest of the sequence of amino acids in that protein will not be altered, though.

● Can you think of an example in which a single mutated base within a gene may *not* lead to changes in the sequences of amino acids in the protein it codes for?

● Some amino acids are specified by more than one codon (Section 3.3). If the 'new' codon with the mutation specifies the same amino acid as the 'original' codon, the sequence of amino acids in the encoded protein will not be altered.

This type of mutation in which the sequence of amino acids is not altered is called a **silent mutation**. Silent mutations are rare in the case of deletions or insertions. As stated earlier, deletions or insertions may result in the removal or addition of a few amino acids in the resultant protein, if the number of mutated bases is a multiple of three (Figure 3.5c). In a situation in which, for example, a single nucleotide has been added or deleted, then all the subsequent codons would be changed to the end of the gene.

● What is the probable outcome of the insertion of a single nucleotide for the sequence of amino acids of the encoded protein?

● By virtue of all codons being changed from the point of the mutation, the whole sequence of amino acids from where the mutation occurred until the end of the protein will be changed.

If we insert a nucleotide (shown in red below) in the example we saw previously in Section 3.3, then the series of codons from the point of insertion will be changed

>   … ATG–CCT–AGC–TGT–TGG–AAA–G …

Note that AAG and AAA both code for lysine. You do not need to worry about the names of the various amino acids.

and so will the sequence of amino acids in the resulting protein:

>   … methionine–proline–serine–cysteine–tryptophan–lysine …

● Do you think that the insertion of one nucleotide in a gene may alter the length of the encoded mutated protein?

● Yes. This situation may happen when new stop codons are created in the sequence of nucleotides that follow the mutation. As a result, protein synthesis may stop prematurely resulting in a shorter mutated protein. Alternatively, if stop codons are eliminated the resultant protein will be longer.

So DNA mutations in genes may or may not alter the sequence of amino acids or the length of the proteins they encode but in those mutated proteins whose structure has been changed, mutations may modify their biological function (as their three-dimensional shape will also be changed). In Chapter 2, you learnt that each specialised cell type has its own characteristic set of proteins. Thus, the change in the nature or activity of proteins within a cell may result in an altered cellular function. Some mutations may confer a change in a particular property of that cell (such as an increased rate of cell division); some can have harmful consequences (such as cell death); and, yet again, some may have no effect whatsoever. Why some mutations are harmful and others are not depends on how much they disrupt the normal function of the protein.

It is appropriate to examine here an example of a mutated protein that is commonly present in tumour cells of many cancers (about 25% of all cancers). RAS, briefly mentioned in Section 2.9.2, is an intracellular signalling protein which 'decodes' signals that promote cell division. When growth-inducing signalling molecules from outside the cell act on their specific receptor, RAS changes its shape from an inactive to an active form, and only the active form signals the cell to divide. By switching between these two forms, the protein RAS is able to control cell division, as shown in Figure 3.6a.

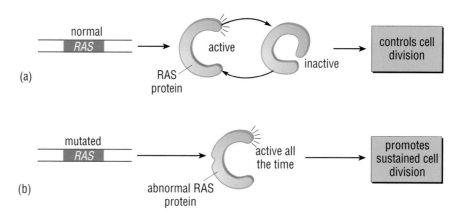

(a)

(b)

The *RAS* gene and RAS protein are so named because they were first identified in <u>ra</u>ts with <u>s</u>arcoma.

Figure 3.6   The *RAS* gene and the RAS protein: (a) in a normal cell; (b) in a cancer cell.

A comparison has been made between the DNA sequences of the *RAS* gene in normal cells and the *RAS* gene in tumour cells from a number of different people with colon carcinoma. The results revealed that normal cells in all patients had an unmutated *RAS* gene but the gene had an altered nucleotide sequence, i.e. it was mutated, in cancer cells of about 50% of the patients. In cancer cells, the mutations consisted of a few nucleotides being misplaced so that only one or two amino acids were changed in the mutant protein. Nevertheless, the effect of the change of the amino acid sequence was such that the mutated RAS protein was locked permanently in the active form (Figure 3.6b). As a result, the RAS protein constantly signals the cell to prepare to divide, regardless of whether the receptor is activated by signalling molecules outside the cell or not. This is why a mutated *RAS* gene promotes enhanced cell division.

3.4.2 Chromosomes and mutations

In addition to small changes at the DNA level, mutations can also occur at the chromosome level. It is possible that a whole section of DNA, including part of a chromosome or even a whole chromosome, is gained or lost. In either case of chromosome mutation, many genes are involved. Occasionally, a portion of a chromosome can be excised and then wrongly reattached to another chromosome. This inappropriate rearrangement of chromosomes is termed **chromosomal translocation** and underlies the mutations detected in some cancers such as chronic myeloid leukaemia (or CML for short), which is a cancer of a type of leukocyte called a B cell. CML cells have exchanged a segment of DNA between chromosomes 9 and 22 resulting in a longer mutated chromosome 9 and a shorter mutated chromosome 22 (Figure 3.7a). The shorter chromosome 22 is called the 'Philadelphia' chromosome after the city where it was first discovered. This translocation of chromosomes would have no serious consequences were it not for a gene called *ABL*, originally located at the breakpoint of the translocated region of chromosome 9.

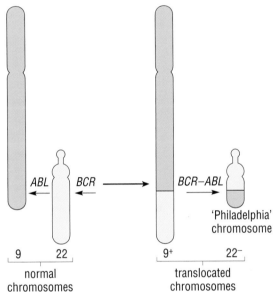

(a)

(b)

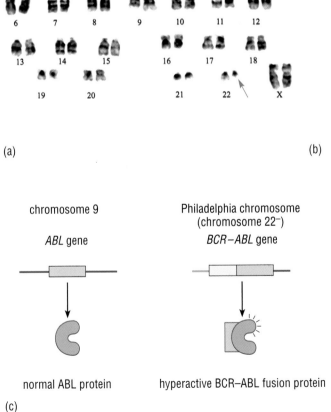

(c)

Figure 3.7 (a) Photograph of the chromosomes of cancer cells in a woman with chronic myeloid leukaemia. The Philadelphia chromosome is indicated by an arrow. Compare this photograph with that of chromosomes in normal human cells shown in Figure 3.1. (b) In chronic myeloid leukaemia, translocation between chromosomes 9 and 22 can result in the juxtaposition of *BCR* and *ABL* to create a BCR–ABL fusion protein whose ABL region is locked in its active form (c). Note that the translocated chromosomes are designated 9+ and 22− because they are longer and shorter, respectively, than the original chromosomes.

Like RAS, ABL is an intracellular signalling protein that initiates cell division when it is in its active form in response to the appropriate growth-inducing signalling molecules. When the region of chromosome 9 with the *ABL* gene is translocated to chromosome 22, it can be attached right next to another gene called *BCR* (Figure 3.7b). As a result, when the BCR protein is synthesised in the cancer cell, the mutated form consists of the 'fusion' of the two protein segments. The ABL portion of this new BCR–ABL fusion protein, like RAS in the previous example, is locked in its active form.

● What would be the probable outcome for cell division of a hyperactive mutated BCR–ABL fusion protein?

● The mutated BCR–ABL fusion protein constantly signals the cell to prepare to divide, regardless of whether the receptor is activated by signalling molecules outside the cell or not, promoting enhanced cell division.

3.5 How do mutations arise?

In the previous section, you have learnt that mutations are due to changes in the sequence of nucleotides (single or multiple base substitutions, deletions or insertions) and chromosomal changes; but how do these alterations in the DNA sequence occur? We will now look in detail at some of the mechanisms by which mutations come about in a cell. The most obvious cause of mutations is errors when copying the DNA during cell division and we shall look at it first.

3.5.1 DNA replication

Figure 3.8 outlines the process of **DNA replication** during the cell cycle. First, the DNA double helix 'unzips' exposing the bases on either strand. The exposed sequence of bases on each strand is then used as a template against which new strands of DNA are built aided by an enzyme called DNA polymerase. The exposed DNA bases pair with 'free' nucleotides, present abundantly in the nucleus, using exactly the same base-pairing rules as those described for the structure of DNA, i.e. C pairs with G, and G with C, T pairs with A, and A with T. At the same time, two new sugar–phosphate backbones are formed. The result is the production of two identical copies of double-stranded DNA molecules which are initially unwound, but later wind around each other to form the characteristic double helix structure. So in each new DNA molecule, one strand is 'original' and the other is 'new'. Before the 'parent' cell can divide, all of the genome in the cell has to replicate to produce two identical copies, one into each of the two daughter cells.

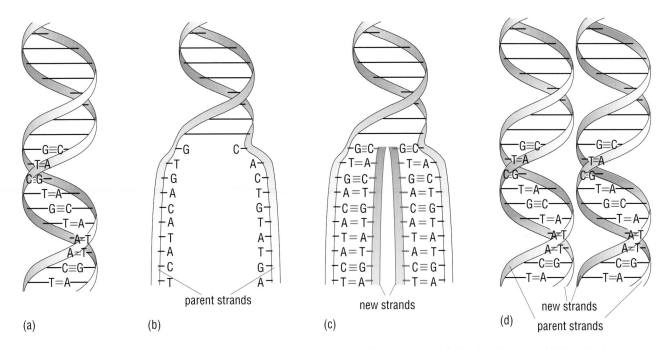

Figure 3.8 The process of DNA replication. (a) A portion of a DNA double helix showing 10 labelled complementary base pairs. (b) Part of the double helix unwinds revealing two single strands. (c) Part of each DNA strand has been replicated. The new strands are shown in colour. The process continues until the whole genome of the parent cell has been replicated. (d) The two copies of DNA wind into two daughter double helices, each with an original (parent) strand and a new strand.

3.5.2 Most mutations are repaired

DNA replication, however, is not without errors, i.e. the wrong bases may be added during DNA synthesis or a few nucleotides may be either deleted or inserted. Left to its own devices, DNA polymerase might incorrectly misplace, insert or delete as many as one base every 1×10^4 during DNA replication, i.e. there would be on average one error for every 10 000 nucleotides synthesised.

● During DNA replication, the G in the middle of the short sequence ATTGCTACC of a gene is read by DNA polymerase as C in one of the original strands.

  (a) What would be the sequence in the newly synthesised DNA strand?

  (b) What would this sequence be if it had not been misread?

● (a) TAAGGATGG; (b) TAACGATGG.

● When the cell divides, do you think that a sequence with a misread base will be transferred to both daughter cells?

● No, it would only be transferred to one of the daughter cells as the erroneous base has been placed while reading only one of the DNA strands. As the DNA in each daughter cell is formed by one 'original' strand and one 'new' strand, the genome of the daughter cell that receives the incorrect version will have a copy of the gene with the correct sequence and a copy of the gene with the incorrect sequence, while the genome of the other daughter cell will have both gene copies with the correct sequence.

As DNA polymerase has to replicate the whole genome, this would mean around 1×10^5 mutations in every single cell division (remember that the whole genome consists of 3×10^9 nucleotides). To counteract this, there are strict 'surveillance' processes in cells that can detect and correct most of the errors that arise during DNA replication (lowering the mutation rate to one mistake for every 1×10^9 nucleotides copied or, in other words, about three mutations per cell division). These processes are extremely complex but in simple terms they consist of enzymes that can identify a wrongly placed base in the growing DNA chain, remove it and replace it with the 'correct' base, so most errors are usually 'short-lived'. These specialised enzymes are termed **DNA repair proteins**.

In addition to correcting misplaced bases, some DNA repair enzymes can also 'eliminate' mutations at the level of chromosomes such as, for example, when a chromosome breaks into two. The integrity of the genome is usually monitored, and then repaired, even before DNA replication starts to occur. At times, however, if more than one chromosome break is present, the wrong fragments of chromosomes will be attached, as you learnt in Section 3.4.2 in the case of the 'Philadelphia' chromosome (Figure 3.7). At other times, DNA alterations are so huge that they cannot be repaired successfully. If this is the case, the normal response of a cell with gross DNA damage is to trigger the activation of apoptosis, i.e. programmed cell death (Section 2.9.4), leading to the controlled removal of the damaged cell.

● What would be a probable outcome of a mutation in a gene coding for a DNA repair enzyme that results in the inactivation of the enzyme?

● In a cell with an inactive DNA repair enzyme, the mutation rate during DNA replication would increase when the cell divides.

3.5.3 Mutations caused by environmental agents

Environmental agents can also produce mutations themselves or increase mutation rates during DNA replication. These agents are termed either **mutagens** (when scientists speak of their effects on DNA) or **carcinogens** (when clinicians speak of their effects on the body). Many chemical agents (e.g. compounds in tobacco) and some physical agents (e.g. radiation, including ultraviolet light from the Sun and X-rays) can be classified as mutagens, and hence exposure to them constitutes a major risk of DNA mutations. Infections can induce, either directly or indirectly, alterations in the structure of DNA, thus promoting the formation of tumours. Examples of such infections include those of viruses (e.g. papilloma virus and cancer of the cervix, the neck connecting the uterus to the vagina; hepatitis B and C viruses and liver cancer), bacteria (e.g. *Helicobacter pylori* and stomach cancer) and even parasites (schistosomes and bladder cancer).

We are following the usual convention in this course of giving species names in italic.

We will deal in detail with environmental factors predisposing an individual to cancer in Chapter 5. Here we should simply state that the mechanisms by which different environmental agents damage DNA are extremely varied, some even inducing DNA damage by more than one mechanism. Some mutagens bind nucleotides, or chemically transform them in some way, promoting DNA polymerase to 'misread' the sequence of bases and, in doing so, increasing mutation rates during DNA replication. This is the case of the chemical mutagen benzo[a]pyrene (Figure 3.9), one of the most well-known carcinogens in tobacco smoke, which binds to the nucleotide G in DNA, which is then misread by DNA polymerase as a T. Other mutagens such as ionising radiation directly induce breaks in the DNA double helix but also indirectly chemically transform bases in DNA. Another mechanism of DNA alterations is the infection of cells by some viruses which, by virtue of having their own viral genome, can induce the expression of viral proteins that promote cell growth and survival, and hence the formation of tumours.

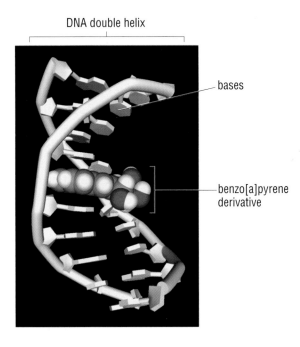

DNA double helix

bases

benzo[a]pyrene derivative

Figure 3.9   A molecular model of a derivative of benzo[a]pyrene binding to G in DNA. Benzo[a]pyrene is a carcinogen found in tobacco smoke.

3.5.4 Cancer-critical genes

Certain genes can acquire mutations that cause a tumour cell to survive or proliferate irrespective of normal regulatory events. These genes are collectively termed **cancer-critical genes** as they are directly involved in the formation of tumours. The protein products of many cancer-critical genes are involved in the growth- and/or survival-inducing mechanisms of the cell. These mutated genes are called **oncogenes**, and their non-mutated versions are called **proto-oncogenes**. Oncogenes either promote cell growth and division irrespective of signals or allow cells to survive in situations where apoptosis should have been triggered. In short, oncogenes promote cells to become self-sufficient in either proliferating or survival signals (or many times in both) (Sections 2.9.2 and 2.9.4). Oncogenes usually include genes that code for signalling molecules, receptors and intracellular signalling proteins whose mutation results in either a continuously activated protein or in higher levels of a protein.

● Can you think of two examples of oncogenes and their proto-oncogenes?

● A normal *RAS* is a proto-oncogene (Figure 3.6a), and its mutated gene that results in a hyperactive protein is an oncogene (Figure 3.6b). Similarly, *ABL* is a proto-oncogene (Figure 3.7c, left), and its gene mutated by chromosomal translocation, *BCR–ABL*, an oncogene (Figure 3.7c, right). You may have also thought of genes coding for signalling proteins that control cell proliferation such as *PDGF* or for their receptors such as *HER2*, mentioned in Section 2.9.2.

Certain genes are implicated in human cancer if they become inactivated, either by mutations or by the loss of the whole gene. These cancer-critical genes are called **tumour-suppressor genes** and their inactivation leads a cell to become insensitive to either growth-inhibitory or death-inducing signals (or both). The role of tumour-suppressor genes is to suppress cell division or to induce cell death. It is only when their function is absent that a cell becomes cancerous, i.e. cell division is no longer blocked or apoptosis is no longer triggered. Figure 3.10 summarises the contributions of oncogenes and mutated tumour-suppressor genes to cell division in a cancer cell (although not shown, a similar diagram could be constructed in the context of regulation of cell death).

Figure 3.10 Schematic diagram to show the role of oncogenes and tumour-suppressor genes in cell division. (a) Normal cell division is controlled by the protein products of proto-oncogenes and tumour-suppressor genes. (b) Uncontrolled growth is the result of mutations in both types of genes.

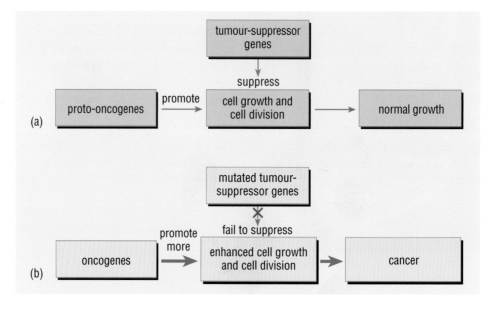

A notable example of a tumour-suppressor gene is the retinoblastoma gene (*Rb*) whose inactivation is associated with susceptibility to a tumour of the retina – a layer of tissue at the back of the eyeball that is sensitive to light. The Rb protein appears to be particularly important for restraining cell division during the development of the retina, but not so in the retina of adults. Hence, although still rare, the cancer known as retinoblastoma due to a loss in Rb function occurs mainly in children.

Another type of mutation in cancer-critical genes may even predispose the cell to further mutations, resulting in a state known as **genetic instability**.

● Can you suggest a group of cancer-critical genes that may predispose to genetic instability if mutated?

● Genes for DNA repair proteins. Therefore, DNA repair responses are impaired in tumour cells with this type of mutation.

Mutations in genes involved in DNA repair result in increased mutation rates and, sometimes, chromosomal aberrations in a cell. This makes it more likely that proto-oncogenes and tumour-suppressor genes will be altered. So mutations in DNA repair genes tend to increase the number of mutations a cell accumulates. This increased mutation rate accelerates the progression of tumours, as you will see below.

3.5.5 Several mutations are required to transform a normal cell into a cancer cell

Even though the DNA repair mechanisms of a cell are rather strict, errors may still pass undetected by repair enzymes during DNA replication – an event that occurs relative rarely considering the huge number of replicated DNA bases. It is important to realise that mutations, whether a result of cell division or of environmental agents, occur in all dividing cells and at any time. However, a single critical mutation is not enough to convert a cell into the completely unregulated proliferative state we know as cancer. Cancer results from the accumulation within cells of a small number of independent mutations that can take place over a long period of time. In fact many years may elapse between one mutation occurring and the next. Cancer starts with one mutation in a single cell which transmits it to all its progeny cells. Some generations of cell division later, a second mutation occurs in one of these cells; this mutation is then transferred to its progeny and so on (Figure 3.11). Only four cell generations are shown in the figure but in reality mutations accumulate randomly over a large number of cell generations. Mutations in at least five or six cancer-critical genes have to accumulate within a cell before it becomes cancerous.

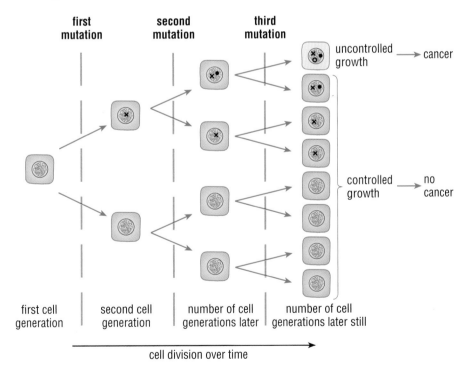

Figure 3.11   Over time a few mutations accumulate in the DNA of dividing cells, leading to the development of cancer.

When the first mutation occurs in a cancer-critical gene it may increase survival time or increase proliferation just enough to give more opportunity for a second critical mutation to occur in a cell within that expanded 'clone' of cells (although it may not be sufficient to turn the cell cancerous). In cell biology, a clone of cells is formed by a cell and all its progeny which contain the same genetic information. Each time a new mutation is acquired that changes a cellular property, a new clone of cells is generated.

A clone of cells harbouring advantageous mutations for proliferation will divide more rapidly and their cellular progeny will prevail over those cells that either have mutations that are deleterious and induce cell death or have no mutations (Figure 3.12). In this context, it appears as if a 'microevolutionary' process is going on in the formation of tumours, in which many cells die while others are better adapted to growth. As tumours become more advanced and especially as mutations that promote genetic instability are acquired, the cell population of a tumour becomes more diverse in the genetic information it carries; that is, within the same tumour there may coexist many cell 'clones' with different multiple mutations and with their own particular growth characteristics, but all originating from a single abnormal cell. Thus the population of cells in a tumour is said to be heterogeneous in their genetic content.

Figure 3.12 The evolution of a tumour. (a) A mutation in a single cell gives rise to increased cell proliferation. (b)–(d) Cells with additional mutations may acquire other properties favouring growth and their progeny become the dominant cell clone in the tumour (purple in (d)). (e)–(f) Further mutations may also lead to genetic instability, increasing mutation rate, which can either lead to growth advantage (red) or trigger cell death (black). Successive cycles of cell division and gene mutations lead to the formation of different cell clones with multiple different mutations (yellow and brown cells).

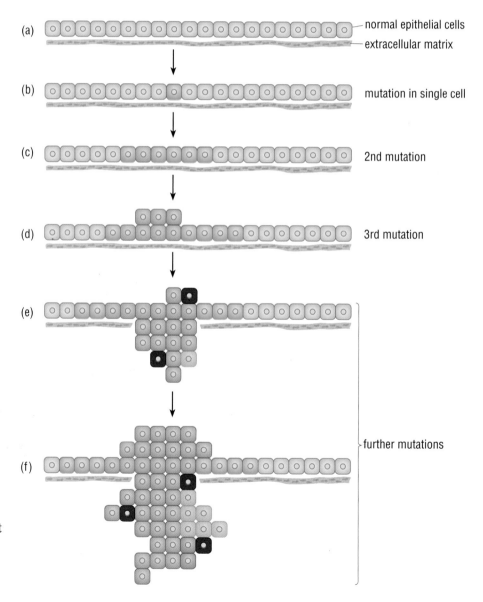

(a) normal epithelial cells / extracellular matrix

(b) mutation in single cell

(c) 2nd mutation

(d) 3rd mutation

(e) further mutations

(f)

3.6 Can you inherit cancer?

In most cells of the body the consequences of the mutation will be restricted to that particular cell and its progeny cells; these are called **somatic mutations**. However, mutations that occur in sperm- and egg-producing cells will be transmitted to the next generation; these are called **germline mutations**. Some of these mutations are new as they arise at the stage when the egg and/or the sperm are formed (in fact, most of us have received at least one of these new mutations from one or both of our parents). Some mutations may have happened generations before and be transmitted to all descendants of a particular individual. For example, you may have heard that some diseases such as haemophilia (a genetic disorder in which blood clotting is impaired) run in families. Likewise, a small proportion of cancers (less than 10%) are thought to be inherited. An example of a cancer that has two forms, **familial** (i.e. hereditary) and **sporadic** (i.e. spontaneously arising in an otherwise healthy individual), is retinoblastoma. In Section 3.5.4, you learnt that *Rb* is a tumour-suppressor gene, so to lose the expression of the protein product completely, both gene copies on each chromosome need to be inactivated (remember that for most genes there are two copies, one in each of the homologous chromosomes, each chromosome inherited from either the mother or the father). If an individual inherits a mutated copy of the *Rb* gene (as is the case in hereditary retinoblastoma), there is a very high probability that a second mutation that inactivates the 'healthy' copy of the *Rb* gene in the other chromosome may occur in at least one of the million or so cells that divide to form the retina. By contrast, the two 'healthy' copies of the *Rb* gene would need to be inactivated by mutations in the same cell in sporadic retinoblastoma. It is then not surprising that only 1 in about 100 000 children develop sporadic retinoblastoma, whereas most children with an inherited mutated *Rb* gene do so.

Although all humans usually have the same genome, each individual has his or her unique version of DNA and, hence, slightly different genes. Each possible version of a gene in the human genome is called a **variant**. Yet, even identical twins who share exactly the same genome may have distinguishing features (Figure 3.13). The reason is that the switching on and off of particular genes at a particular moment can be influenced by the environment. You can imagine that a person raised under adverse conditions might develop rather differently from an individual with the same genome raised in a healthy environment. This complex and continuous relationship between genes and environment may well determine our susceptibility to human disease, and in the context of this course, to cancer. A person may inherit a variant of a gene that predisposes that individual to cancer. Indeed, if an individual inherited a mutated gene like *Rb* the probability of developing cancer at an early age is close to 100%. Other gene variants such as those related to another type of inherited cancer called familial adenomatous polyposis also result in human colorectal carcinoma in almost all cases. In contrast, some gene variants that underlie familial cancers will only increase the risk of developing that form of cancer over the general population. This is the case of a familial cancer known as hereditary non-polyposis colorectal cancer or HNPCC for

Figure 3.13   A set of identical twins with slightly different facial features. (Source: Robert W. Ginn/Alamy)

short. Individuals who test positive in genetic tests for HNPCC inherit a copy of a mutated gene whose product is an abnormal DNA repair protein. However, these individuals show a 60% increased risk of developing colorectal cancer over the general population, and a regime including lifestyle changes and cancer screening procedures further reduces this risk.

Case study 3.1   Dave Bayler and his family

David (Dave) Bayler, an African-American of 42, has run a diner franchise in downtown St. Louis, Missouri, since his late twenties. He is a married father of four, a Democrat, a committed member of his Black-led Baptist church, and an almost fanatical supporter of the city's National League baseball team, the St. Louis Cardinals. However, his love of baseball is limited to watching it; he last played in high school. In fact, he is rather overweight – he loves burgers and grazes on them at his diner all day – and, although he is still in his early forties, he has recently noticed that climbing the steps at the stadium makes him out of breath.

At the moment, Dave is grieving the loss of his only and much younger sister, who died from endometrial cancer at the age of only 33. This is affecting him deeply not only because he loved and misses his sister, but because it has reminded him painfully of a much earlier loss: that of his mother, when he was a young teenager and his sister was in pre-school. She had also had cancer, colon cancer in her case, and her death left them to be brought up by an aunt and uncle. Dave has heard of cancer running in families, and knows that his own experiences match the pattern, although he hasn't thought – in fact he hasn't had the time – to ask his family doctor about it. With a diner to run, a large family to keep tabs on – his two youngest children are still in high school – and many Church and community commitments, Dave Bayler is a busy man. He has no time to think about keeping healthy, and has had no particular interest in doing so; he has dealt with the cancer in his family by putting it as far as possible out of his mind. If he has ever heard the 'five-a-day' rule about fruit and vegetables, he has immediately forgotten it; he may love burgers, but even these are snatched in spare minutes when the diner is quiet. His diet contains far too little fibre, vitamins and minerals to maintain good health. For most of his adult life, he has suffered from constipation, taking laxatives when necessary.

He has recently begun to notice that he is having his bowels open more often than he used to. He has tried to reassure himself that this can be explained by pressure of work and the stress of his sister's illness and death, but it is becoming harder to do so. When, quite soon after his sister's death, he begins to notice spots of blood in his stools, it is his wife who finally persuades him to make an appointment with the family physician.

Dave is right to be worried. Both he and his sister inherited a mutation in the *hMLH1* gene. This gene codes for a protein involved in DNA repair. Both siblings inherited a variant of this gene that does not lead to protein expression. In dividing cells whose other inherited copy of the gene is damaged (as can often happen in young adulthood or middle age), the DNA repair process is hindered. As a result, the probability of developing cancer increases. This mutation has been implicated in hereditary non-polyposis colorectal cancer (HNPCC) and 80% of males inheriting this particular gene variant will develop colon cancer. Cancer is also diagnosed at a younger age in people who have inherited this cancer-risk gene variant, and Dave is already approaching the peak age for diagnosis in people with his genetic background: 44.

3.7 Concluding remarks

Genetic differences brought about by mutations result in the enormous variation that exists in the human genome, so that no two people (apart from identical twins) alive today, or who have ever lived, have identical DNA sequences in their genome. This is called genetic variability. In a way, cancer may be considered as an undesirable by-product of the mechanisms that support genetic variability within a species, a feature that may have granted their success in adapting to the external environment.

In Chapter 2, you learnt that cancers are formed because tumour cells acquire cellular properties that make them divide uncontrollably. Here, you have learnt that tumour cells are able to do this because the structure of some of their proteins, and hence those proteins' properties, are altered, which is the direct consequence of alterations in their DNA, otherwise known as mutations. In the next chapter, you will examine how tumour cells can disrupt the coordinated cellular environment that forms a multicellular organism such a human.

3.8 Summary of Chapter 3

3.1   DNA is composed of two strands spiralled around each other to form a double helix molecule. Each strand consists of a string of nucleotides; each nucleotide is composed of phosphate, a sugar and a base.

3.2   Four bases, A, G, C and T, make up the core of the DNA double helix. These form complementary base pairs so that A and T on opposite strands always pair with each other and G and C on opposite strands always pair with each other.

3.3   A gene is a short section of DNA that contains the coded instructions for a specific protein. The information carried by DNA is in a simple coding language of just four bases which is transcribed into mRNA and then translated into the 20 amino acid code of proteins.

3.4   Mutations are changes in the DNA sequence of nucleotides. These may involve short sections of DNA (substitutions in one or a few nucleotides, insertions and/or deletions) or chromosomes (i.e. translocations). Mutations may result in changes in the sequence of amino acids of the encoded protein and, hence, in its biological function.

3.5   During replication, the DNA double helix unwinds, and each of the two parent strands forms a template on which a new strand is synthesised. DNA polymerase adds nucleotides to each separated strand according to the base-pairing rules. Two identical double helices are thereby produced, each consisting of a parent strand and a newly synthesised strand.

3.6 Most errors that arise during DNA replication are repaired by DNA repair proteins. Environmental agents can also produce mutations or increase mutation rates during DNA replication.

3.7 Cancer is a genetic disease of cells caused by mutations that result in uncontrolled cell growth and division. At least five or six mutations have to accumulate in a cell before it becomes cancerous.

3.8 Three types of genes are involved in the development of cancer (also called cancer-critical genes): oncogenes (mutated proto-oncogenes), which promote cell growth and division and/or cell survival; tumour-suppressor genes, which normally constrain cell division and/or induce cell death; and DNA repair genes.

3.9 A tumour is formed by a heterogeneous population of cell clones, each with its own set of mutations and particular growth characteristics.

3.10 An individual may inherit variants of genes that increase their susceptibility to a particular cancer. Cancer is caused by an interplay between many genes and environmental factors.

Questions for Chapter 3

Question 3.1 (Learning outcome 3.2)

In a fragment of double-stranded DNA, there are a total of 120 nucleotides, in which 40 of the bases are A. Calculate the total number of each of the following items in the DNA fragment: (a) complementary base pairs; (b) T bases; (c) G bases; (d) C bases.

Question 3.2 (Learning outcomes 3.2 and 3.4)

Figure 3.14 shows a part of a double-stranded DNA molecule during the process of replication. Each square represents a base.

(a) Identify the missing bases in the figure and write the correct letter (A, C, G or T) in each of the blank squares.

(b) At what stage of the cell cycle would the DNA in Figure 3.14 be undergoing replication?

Question 3.3 (Learning outcomes 3.1, 3.3 and 3.4)

Match one of the following terms with each of the definitions (a)–(d): gene mutation; chromosome mutation; mutagen.

(a) A tumour cell in which one of the homologous pair of chromosome 12 is half the length of the other.

(b) The change of one base within a gene to a different base.

(c) A chemical that induces mutations in cells.

(d) The insertion of a nucleotide within a gene.

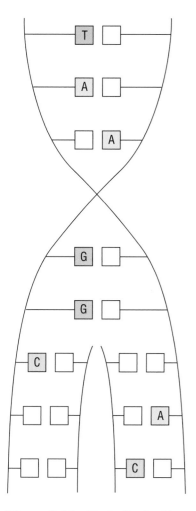

Figure 3.14 Part of a double-stranded DNA molecule during replication.

Question 3.4 (Learning outcomes 3.5 and 3.6)

(a) Draw a diagram similar to that shown in Figure 3.10 summarising the contributions of oncogenes and mutated tumour-suppressor genes to cell death in a cancer cell.

(b) How many clones of cells and how many cells in each clone have been depicted in a simplified way in Figure 3.11?

Question 3.5 (Learning outcomes 3.5, 3.6 and 3.7)

Explain why a person who has an inherited predisposition to defective DNA repair is more prone to cancer.

Further reading

If you would like to read further about this topic, please refer to the following publications.

Alberts, B., Johnson, A., Lewis, J., Raff, M., Roberts, K. and Walter, P. (2000) Chapter 23: Cancer, in *Molecular Biology of the Cell* (4th edn), New York and London, Garland Science.

Merlo, L.M.F., Pepper, J.W., Reid, B.J. and Maley, C.C. (2006) 'Cancer as an evolutionary and ecological process', *Nature Reviews Cancer*, vol. 6, pp. 924–35.

CHAPTER 4

THE HUMAN BODY AND CANCERS

Learning outcomes

After studying this chapter and its associated activity, you should be able to:

4.1 Define and use in context, or recognise definitions and applications of, each of the terms printed in **bold** in the text.

4.2 Explain in basic terms the human physiology relevant to understanding cancer as a disease.

4.3 Outline the basic nomenclature of different types of cancers.

4.4 Explain the principles behind the growth and spread of tumours, in particular angiogenesis, tissue invasion and metastasis.

4.5 Explain in basic terms the possible relationship between cancers and the immune system.

4.6 Give examples of general signs and symptoms of cancers and their biological basis.

4.7 Describe the concept of homeostasis and how it may be disrupted by cancers.

4.1 Introduction

In 1948 the WHO defined health as 'a state of complete physical, mental and social well-being and not merely the absence of disease or infirmity'. More recently (in 1995), this statement was modified to include the ability to lead a 'socially and economically productive life'. In this chapter, you will learn how cells collaborate with each other in order to maintain the health of a person and how, from a physical point of view, the collection of diseases known as cancer affects this fine balance, thus disrupting the health of individuals. Later on in the course, you will focus on how patients are affected socially and psychologically at the time of diagnosis and during and after treatment, setting some individuals further apart from the definition of health given above, and others on their path to recovering their state of health. First, however, a biological perspective is needed in order to study how cancers affect the human body, so that you may be able to gauge all the consequences that these diseases may have for the individuals concerned and for their relatives, friends and carers.

4.2 Benign and malignant tumours

It is worth stressing at the start of this chapter that not all cell proliferative events in the human body are harmful to health. To start with, cell proliferation may be part of a normal response of the human body such as, for instance, when we catch a cold and we notice lumps in our neck due to enlarged glands (more correctly called lymph nodes) in which some leukocytes of the immune

Lymph nodes are described further in Section 4.2.2.

system are proliferating to fight infection. In other instances, an increase in cell numbers may be abnormal but somehow restricted. For example, many of us have moles or warts on the surface of the skin, or a *polyp* – a fleshy growth of cells in the epithelial lining of the colon or rectum. These are examples of irregular cell proliferation that is localised to the tissue of origin or, in other words, cell proliferation that, although anomalous, is not completely out of control.

● Why do cells stop dividing within a tissue or organ?

● Signals from adhesion molecules in neighbouring cells and the extracellular matrix communicate to cells to stop dividing. If a cell does not receive this type of signal, the cell commits 'suicide' by apoptosis (Sections 2.9.3 and 2.9.4).

As you read in Section 1.1, a tumour that is not harmful to health is termed benign whereas a tumour that results in cancer is called malignant (Figure 4.1). In general, the nomenclature of benign tumours follows a logical pattern, similar to that described for malignant tumours (Section 2.8.2). The names of benign tumours are derived from the name of the tissue plus the ending *-oma*. So, an adenoma is a benign tumour of epithelial cells, whereas an adenocarcinoma is malignant. Similarly, a chondroma is a benign tumour of cartilage cells, whereas a chondrosarcoma is malignant. However, to make matters somewhat confusing, recall from Chapter 2 that some malignant tumours such as melanoma and lymphoma do not follow these rules. Box 4.1 explains cancer nomenclature in more detail.

There are three properties that differentiate benign and malignant tumours:

1   Malignant tumours grow in an aggressive way, i.e. malignant tumour cells are insensitive to the growth-inhibitory signals sent by the surrounding tissue. As a result, they do not stop dividing or do not die by apoptosis (or, more often, both) in response to these signals, in contrast to cells in benign tumours.

2   In malignant tumours, cells that would normally have all the characteristics of a particular cell type (a gut epithelial cell, for example) lose their specialised structure and functions and become *undifferentiated*. In contrast, cells in benign tumours are more like their cell type of origin.

3   Benign tumours tend to be localised, usually contained within a capsule of connective tissue, whereas malignant tumours tend to spread by invading the surrounding tissue and cells may even escape the 'original' tumour and metastasise to form new tumours in distant organs.

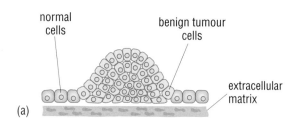

normal cells

benign tumour cells

extracellular matrix

(a)

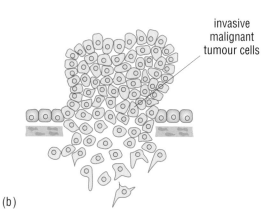

invasive malignant tumour cells

(b)

Figure 4.1   (a) A benign tumour shows controlled growth, usually within a capsule of connective tissue, and its cells resemble those they derive from. (b) A malignant tumour grows aggressively, invading surrounding tissue, and its cells become undifferentiated.

Box 4.1 Some cancer nomenclature

The naming convention for cancers uses prefixes, suffixes and combined terms that provide information about their type and origin. Names of the majority of malignant tumours usually end in either *-carcinoma* (epithelial cell cancers) or *-sarcoma* (connective or supportive tissue cancers) (see Section 2.8.2). Common prefixes used in naming cancers are listed in Table 4.1 together with their meaning and examples of the corresponding cancer names.

Table 4.1 Naming malignant tumours.

Prefix	Meaning of the prefix	Example of cancer name
adeno-	gland	adenocarcinoma
chondro-	cartilage	chondrosarcoma
erythro-	red blood cell	erythroblastoma
haemo- or haema-	blood or blood-forming tissue	haemangiosarcoma
hepato-	liver	hepatocarcinoma
lipo-	fat	liposarcoma
lympho- or lympha-	may refer to the lymphatic system or to a type of white blood cell called a lymphocyte	lymphoblastoma, lymphangioma
melano-	skin pigment cell	melanoma
myelo-	bone marrow	myelosarcoma
myo-	muscle	myoblastoma
osteo-	bone	osteosarcoma
neuro-	nervous tissue	neuroblastoma

As can be seen from Table 4.1, other information about a cancer type can be included in the name. Common elements that can form part of the name are cyto = cell; blasto = immature cell; and angio = vessel. For example, neuroblastoma could be defined as 'cancer of immature cells in nervous tissue', and haemangiosarcoma as 'cancer of the connective tissue forming the blood vessels'.

Note that some cancer types are accompanied by the name of the doctor who first described them such as Hodgkin's lymphoma and Kaposi's sarcoma.

4.3 Tumour cells require a blood supply to grow into larger tumours

Most cells in multicellular organisms face the problem that they are not close enough to the outside environment to obtain all the nutrients they need, or to expel their waste, simply across the cell membrane. Oxygen and nutrients can theoretically disseminate in the fluid that surrounds cells, but this is a very slow process, and above a distance of 1 mm is inefficient (a millimetre or mm is an example of a scientific unit; see Box 4.2).

The most important functions of the **cardiovascular system** are to collect and transport oxygen (from the lungs in the respiratory system) and nutrients (absorbed by the digestive system following the breakdown of food) to all cells in the body. The cardiovascular system also collects carbon dioxide (the cell's main metabolic by-product) and other waste to be released into the outside environment by other organs, e.g. the lungs. At this point you may be attempting to recall what a 'system' means in biology, a term that was introduced in Table 2.1. Organs usually work together with other organs to achieve a common goal. So the cardiovascular system is formed by the blood, the heart and blood vessels which together transport oxygen and nutrients to the whole organism. Another example of an organ system is the respiratory system, which comprises the lungs, trachea and other organs to allow respiration (the exchange of oxygen and carbon dioxide). Such a collection of organs is referred to as a **biological system** (or organ system).

The blood consists of a fluid called **plasma** in which red cells, also known as erythrocytes, are suspended (along with other cells as you will see in Section 4.5). Red cells contain a protein called haemoglobin that binds oxygen and carbon dioxide. In this way, haemoglobin transports oxygen into organs (and hence to their constituent cells) and carries carbon dioxide out of organs, exchanging the two in the process (at the organ level, gas exchange between tissue and blood is in the opposite direction to the gas exchange in the lungs, where carbon dioxide is released into the air and oxygen taken up by the blood).

The heart is a muscular organ that pumps blood through a type of blood vessel, the arteries. The arteries branch repeatedly, culminating in an extensive network of fine vessels, called capillaries, which penetrate almost all parts of the body. Most of the exchange of oxygen and nutrients between circulating blood and cells in tissues and organs occurs through the capillaries. Blood is then collected from the capillaries into veins, which return it to the heart from all organs. The heart then pumps blood out to the lungs where it becomes oxygenated (takes up oxygen); the oxygenated blood then returns to the heart to be distributed again to all organs. Figure 4.2 summarises the main features of the human blood circulatory or cardiovascular system.

Normal cells within tissues are rarely further than 100 μm away from capillaries, so they can easily access the oxygen and nutrients essential for life. If cells were positioned further away, they would eventually die because the low levels of oxygen (termed **hypoxia**) and nutrients would compromise their metabolism.

Box 4.2 Scientific units

The mention of distances within tissues and organs gives us an opportunity to make a short detour to show you how scientists communicate numerical information about, for example, how big a tumour is, how far the Sun is from the Earth, or how much of a particular chemical there is in a given amount of water. In Chapter 2, you learnt a way of dealing with very large and very small numbers by using the powers of ten notation, for example, the number of molecules of water in a raindrop or the number of cells in the human body. But how does one communicate measurements of size, or weight or distance or time? In order to express such values accurately and unambiguously, something else is required: a standardised set of units. **SI units** (which stands for the French *Système Internationale*) is the term given to those units of measurement that scientists all over the world have agreed to use. For example, the second (abbreviated to s) is the standard unit of time, the kilogram (abbreviated to kg) is the standard unit for the mass of an object, and the metre (abbreviated to m) is the standard unit for the size of objects or distance between objects. These standard units are fine for expressing measurements over a certain range, but become unwieldy when values are very large or very small. One solution is to use power of ten notation (Box 2.2) but, within a smaller range, one can also use other units based on the standard units described above. As an example, the units for describing objects and distances larger and smaller than one metre are shown in Table 4.2. The third column in Table 4.2 shows how clumsy and long-winded communication would be if, for size and distance, the metre was the only unit available. Typically the diameter of human cells is between 0.000 01 and 0.0001 m (although some nerve cells are much larger). It is very much easier to say that cells in the human body are usually between 10 µm and 100 µm in diameter.

Table 4.2 SI units based on the metre (m). The right-hand column has been filled in power of ten notation (Box 2.2).

Name of unit	Symbol	Value in metres expressed in words, as a fraction and as a decimal number	as a power of ten
kilometre	km	one thousand metres (1000 m)	1×10^3
metre	m	one metre (1 m)	$1 \times 10^{0*}$
centimetre	cm	one-hundredth of a metre ($\frac{1}{100}$ m or 0.01 m)	1×10^{-2}
millimetre	mm	one thousandth of a metre ($\frac{1}{1000}$ m or 0.001 m)	1×10^{-3}
micrometre	µm	one-millionth of a metre ($\frac{1}{1000\,000}$ m or 0.000 001 m)	1×10^{-6}
nanometre	nm	one-thousand-millionth of a metre ($\frac{1}{1000\,000\,000}$ m or 0.000 000 001 m)	1×10^{-9}
picometre	pm	one-million-millionth of a metre ($\frac{1}{1000\,000\,000\,000}$ m or 0.000 000 000 001 m)	1×10^{-12}

*Note that 10^0 is the number 1 expressed in the power of ten notation.

Figure 4.2 The main features of the human cardiovascular system. (You don't need to memorise the names of the particular vessels.)

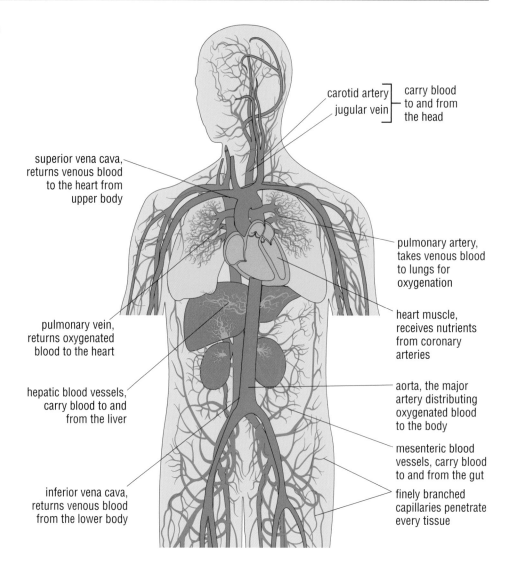

carotid artery
jugular vein
} carry blood to and from the head

superior vena cava, returns venous blood to the heart from upper body

pulmonary artery, takes venous blood to lungs for oxygenation

pulmonary vein, returns oxygenated blood to the heart

heart muscle, receives nutrients from coronary arteries

hepatic blood vessels, carry blood to and from the liver

aorta, the major artery distributing oxygenated blood to the body

mesenteric blood vessels, carry blood to and from the gut

inferior vena cava, returns venous blood from the lower body

finely branched capillaries penetrate every tissue

This is also the case for tumour cells. In fact, most tumours are not very large initially (at most 1–2 mm or the size of the metal ball at the end of a ballpoint pen) as their growth is restricted by the limiting step of accessing oxygen and nutrients. If the tumour were to grow larger, the region within the core of the mass would become packed with dead cells. This is certainly the case unless tumour cells acquire a property (as a result of random mutations) that allows them to progress to large tumours. The biological feature that allows tumour growth is called **angiogenesis**, which consists of the formation of new blood vessels from the pre-existing vessels that surround the tumour (Figure 4.3).

● Can you think of an example of a cancer in which neoplastic cells are not dependent on angiogenesis to grow?

● Neoplastic cells that do not form solid tumours, but instead circulate in the blood, e.g. leukaemia (Box 2.1).

During the growth of a tumour, some of its cells may acquire a mutation that allows them to secrete a specific class of growth factors in large amounts. These growth factors, which are called angiogenic growth factors, have two functions. They induce the proliferation of endothelial cells, the cells that form the blood vessels, and they also attract the endothelial cells. As a result, endothelial cells divide towards the site where the angiogenic growth factors have been released, in the process forming new capillaries that surround and penetrate the solid tumour. The most well-studied growth factor that acts in this manner is called vascular endothelial growth factor or VEGF for short, a protein that is overproduced (i.e. synthesised at abnormally high levels) by many tumour cells. The fresh supply of oxygen and nutrients provided by the new growth of blood vessels allows the solid tumour to expand to a larger size. Note that in this case the endothelial cells, although actively dividing and forming part of the tumour, are not tumour cells as they have not acquired mutations and they respond normally to the presence of growth factors by proliferating.

● How could a solid tumour growing larger affect the function of the cells in the organ or tissue in which it resides?

● In two main ways. First, the increased blood supply towards the solid tumour could deprive the tissue or organ, where it is located, of essential oxygen and nutrients and it could also increase its accumulation of metabolic by-products, which may become toxic to normal cells. Second, a large tumour could exert physical pressure against neighbouring cells altering their function and even damaging them, or against the capillary network of the tissue and/or organ, which may end up by blocking the blood circulation that supplies normal cells.

Eventually, and as the solid tumour grows larger, the lack of oxygen and nutrients, the accumulation of waste and the physical pressure could increase to such an extent that results in the organ that contains the tumour malfunctioning, and even in organ failure. Indeed, scientists consider angiogenesis to be so important in the progression of tumours towards malignancy that a vast amount of research is being focused on finding drugs that selectively inhibit the proliferation of endothelial cells and, subsequently, the formation of new blood vessels in solid tumours.

4.4 How do tumour cells spread?

The most deadly aspect of cancers is their ability to spread. In Chapters 2 and 3, you learnt that tumour cells accumulate mutations randomly, some of them favouring progression towards

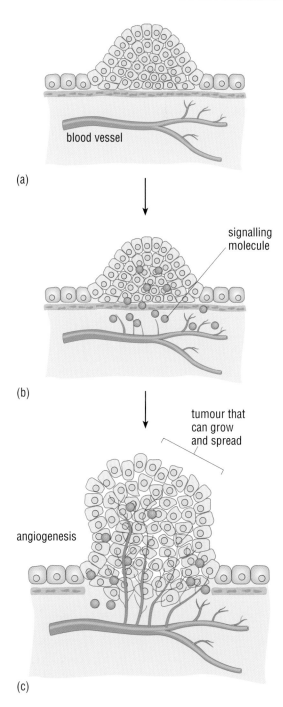

Figure 4.3 Angiogenesis allows the progression of cancer. (a) A small tumour is restricted in growth by lack of oxygen and nutrients. (b) Tumour cells secrete angiogenic growth factors that cause sprouting of existing blood vessels towards the tumour. (c) The newly formed blood vessels surround and penetrate the solid tumour which can then grow to a larger size.

malignancy. Amongst these, there are mutations that inhibit the normal cell adhesion properties of tumour cells (e.g. epithelial cells that lose the expression of E-cadherin, Section 2.9.3). Tumour cells with these mutations do not stick together and may invade the nearby tissue. They do this by mechanisms that require the breakdown of the extracellular matrix, where cells are embedded within a tissue. One of these mechanisms is the overproduction of a type of enzyme called proteases. As their name indicates, proteases digest proteins. When released outside the cell, these enzymes destroy the proteins of the extracellular matrix, thereby opening up a path for the tumour cells to spread in the tissue surrounding the tumour. Sooner or later, tumour cells that spread out of their tumour of origin may invade nearby tissues and/or organs. There are four routes by which tumour cells may metastasise to other tissues or organs. The first one is to spread to nearby organs or tissues, the second one is to spread via body cavities and the last two are via the blood circulation and the lymphatic system. These last two routes will be discussed in more detail in the next two sections.

4.4.1 Metastasis via the blood circulation

Frequently, some spreading tumour cells will reach a blood vessel (either within the tumour itself or in a nearby tissue) and may even cross the lining of endothelial cells that forms the blood vessel, thereby accessing the blood circulation (Figure 4.4). If a circulating tumour cell survives the foreign environment provided by the blood, it may end up adhering to the wall of a small vessel in a distant organ and, subsequently, invade a new tissue and proliferate to form another tumour. In essence, this is the process called metastasis (Section 2.9.3). As you read in Section 1.1, the tumour in the tissue of origin is termed the primary tumour, whereas tumours originated by metastatic cells in other tissues are called secondary tumours. The secondary tumours are still labelled by the tissue of origin. So clinicians refer to, for example, hepatocarcinoma in the lungs if the primary tumour was located in the liver, and not to lung cancer.

● Would a hepatocarcinoma metastasised to one lung affect its function? Explain your reasons why.

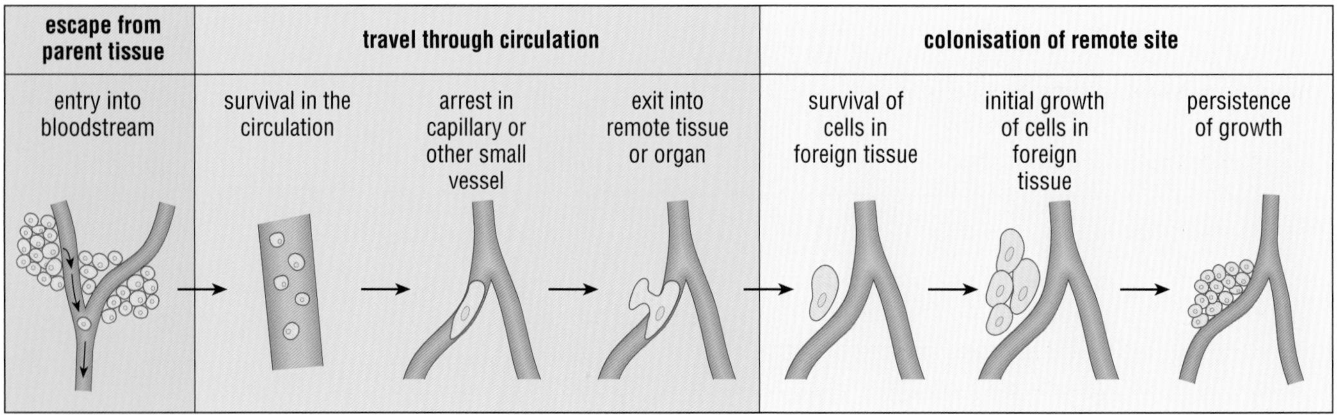

escape from parent tissue	travel through circulation			colonisation of remote site		
entry into bloodstream	survival in the circulation	arrest in capillary or other small vessel	exit into remote tissue or organ	survival of cells in foreign tissue	initial growth of cells in foreign tissue	persistence of growth

Figure 4.4   The process of metastasis.

● Yes if the metastasised hepatocarcinoma grows sufficiently large to obstruct blood circulation in the lung by, for example, exerting mechanical pressure on the nearby tissue or by affecting the surface area of the lung, thus disrupting the exchange of gases. The end result of liver cancer might be malfunction of that lung and, subsequently, respiratory symptoms, e.g. shortness of breath.

Thus, in similar ways to the primary tumour in the tissue of origin, secondary tumours may affect the function of the new tissue and/or organ they grow in.

● What would be an essential feature for a secondary tumour to grow large enough to affect the function of the new tissue and/or organ it has invaded?

● The formation of new blood vessels or angiogenesis. However, as the primary tumour grew large enough to be able to metastasise, tumour cells that have metastasised in other organs are very likely to already have angiogenic properties.

4.4.2 Metastasis via the lymphatic system

The other biological system that has to be considered in the context of tumour metastasis is the **lymphatic system** (Figure 4.5). The lymphatic system consists of specialised lymphoid organs, lymphatic vessels and the lymph fluid. During the passage of blood through organs and tissues, fluid leaks out of blood capillaries, into the spaces between cells. This fluid that bathes cells is called the **interstitial fluid**. It then drains into the lymphatic capillaries (a network of fine lymphatic vessels), where it is called the **lymph**. The lymphatic vessels collect into masses of lymphoid tissue called the **lymph nodes** located in very specific sites around the body, and eventually return the lymph to the bloodstream via a duct connecting the lymphatic and cardiovascular systems in the neck. Unlike the cardiovascular system, this one-way transport system has no pump. Lymph movement through the lymphatic vessels relies on the squeezing and pumping action of skeletal muscles (the muscles that provide body movement). The lymphatic system is important because it collects and returns the interstitial fluid with all its contents to the blood. Without this drainage, all organs would swell and ultimately burst. Large tumours may also block lymphatic vessels leading to swelling around the tumour area as a result of lymph accumulating. This condition is called **lymphoedema**. Finally, the lymphatic system also forms part of the body defences against invading organisms by means of the immune system (Section 4.5).

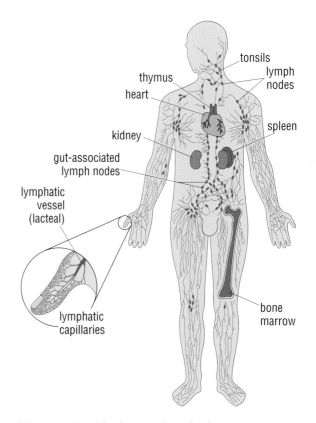

Tumour cells also induce the formation of a network of lymphatic vessels which enter the solid tumour in a similar fashion to that explained for angiogenesis – in a process called *lymphangiogenesis*, a name you need not remember. Tumour cells that escape into the lymphatic vessels usually accumulate in the regional lymph nodes localised nearest to the tumour where the lymph from the surrounding tissue is collected. For example,

Figure 4.5   The human lymphatic system.

melanoma cells originating in a malignant mole located in the thigh will form metastases in the first lymph node they encounter in the groin. Another example is human breast carcinoma, which tends to metastasise to the lymph nodes located under the armpit. From there, tumour cells either invade the fat tissue surrounding the lymph nodes or continue migrating through the lymphatic system, from lymph node to lymph node. Whatever path metastasis via the lymphatic system may take, it eventually results in the tumour cells reaching the blood circulation and, subsequently, the formation of secondary tumours in distant organs.

Case study 4.1 Terri in 2008

It is over 45 years after we first met Terri Moloney, and she feels that she has been very lucky in life. She has been able to combine a very successful career as a lawyer with marriage and bringing up two children, both of whom have achieved some success in their chosen careers, and she adores her three small grandchildren. At the age of 67, she is beginning to take things easier, although still working reduced hours; she takes an active part in the life of her local community, has many friends, and has recently splashed out on a season ticket for the Sydney Opera House. Her main regret is the ending of her marriage after almost 20 years; she is, however, still in touch with her ex-husband, who recently retired from practice as an architect and is living in Melbourne, over 500 km away.

Terri has a large mole on her left leg above the knee. A few months ago, while getting ready for the opera, she thought the mole looked different: bigger, and more irregular around the edges. She has now noticed that it has begun to itch, and to bleed very slightly. Apart from the itching, she still feels fine, but she also notices a lump in the left side of her groin, resembling the enlarged lymph glands she gets in the neck when she has a cold. Finally, these symptoms are enough to send her to her doctor, who refers her to hospital for further tests.

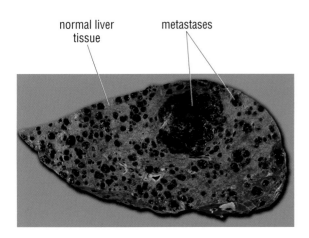

normal liver tissue   metastases

Figure 4.6 Pigmented melanoma cells metastasised to the liver. (Source: MEDIMAGE/ Science Photo Library)

4.4.3 Where and why do tumour cells metastasise?

Metastasis mainly occurs in advanced cancer disease. In addition to lymph nodes, the most likely organs where tumour cells metastasise are the lungs and the liver (Figure 4.6). We have to look into the anatomy of the cardiovascular system in more detail in order to explain why this is so (Figure 4.2). The circulation of blood in capillaries is much slower than in veins or arteries or in the heart. So a tumour cell entering the circulation is more likely to become 'trapped' in the capillary network of the first organ it encounters from its point of origin. Recall that the heart receives the blood from all organs and then pumps it into the lungs and it is in the capillary network in the lungs where gas exchange occurs, i.e. carbon dioxide is released and oxygen absorbed. The liver collects blood via the veins exiting the gut which passes through the liver's capillary network before reaching the heart. Therefore, the capillary network of the lungs would be the first location where blood flow slows down for circulating tumour cells originating in tumours anywhere in the body (apart from the gut) allowing the process of metastasis, whereas for circulating tumour cells originating in tumours of the gut, this would be the capillary network in the liver. In essence, the large volumes of venous blood delivered to organs such as the liver and the lungs determine the high incidence of metastasis in these organs.

Anatomy may play an important role in many metastases (e.g. metastasis to regional lymph nodes or to the liver due to the high venous circulation), but it does not always explain the preferred location of metastasis in many cancers. Other organs such as the brain and the bones also show high incidence of metastasis. The mechanisms by which certain cancers preferentially metastasise to specific locations are not completely understood and have been the subject of much debate amongst scientists. More than a century ago, it was recognised that the tissue where the primary tumour originates influences the location of the secondary tumour. This is because the tissue that is to be metastasised must provide a favourable environment for the tumour cell to invade it and proliferate. For example, prostate and breast carcinomas usually metastasise in the bones. It is thought that this may relate to the ability of breast and prostate carcinoma cells to express (see Section 3.3) certain receptors to which growth factors released by bone cells attach, so inducing tumour cell division and survival.

The short answer to the question of why tumour cells metastasise is that scientists still do not know. The genetic alterations that lead to metastasis in a particular organ are yet to be unravelled. What is clear is that metastasis is a very inefficient process. For example, it has been shown in blood samples taken before surgery for primary human renal (kidney) carcinoma that over 1×10^7 tumour cells are released into the circulation every day. Obviously then, the vast majority of tumour cells that enter the bloodstream never manage to colonise another tissue. Because of the heterogeneity of different clones of tumour cells (Section 3.5.5), only a subset of tumour cells that reach the blood and lymphatic vessels must have the necessary mutations to allow them to thrive in other tissues. It is possible that the cells that do are more self-sufficient in growth and survival signals. During the lifetime of this course, it is likely that this area of cancer research will become much clearer.

4.4.4 Staging of cancers

In order to make a sensible prognosis, it is extremely useful for clinicians to evaluate the findings about a cancer patient using a system that classifies the stage of tumour progression; in other words, to categorise the extent to which the tumour has spread, i.e. its size, how invasive it is, etc. The process of doing examinations and tests to classify a particular cancer into a group of similar cases is called **staging**. Staging provides a valuable tool not only for diagnosis (Chapter 6) but also for choice of treatment (Chapters 7 to 10). The parameters used to stage a cancer may involve:

- an evaluation of the structure of the tumour following either a biopsy (a sample of the affected tissue) or surgery, which involves a medical expert

Remember, prognosis is a medical term that indicates the doctor's view of how a specific disease will progress for a particular patient (Chapter 1).

called a pathologist examining the tumour cells under the microscope. This process is called grading, which determines the differentiated and proliferative state of tumour cells. You will learn more about this in Section 6.6.

- a clinical evaluation, which includes physical examination and imaging techniques to determine the size of the tumour and where it has spread.

There are many cancer staging systems in use. For example, there are two conventional staging systems for colorectal carcinoma, the Dukes and the Astler–Coller, which label the cancer stage, according to severity, as either A, B, C or as A, B, C, D, respectively. In addition, the Astler–Coller staging system has several subcategories such as B1, B2, etc. As you may imagine, this is not a very precise way of staging different types of cancers. In order to achieve consensus on different cancer types, the International Union Against Cancer developed another system which is currently used for many solid tumours. This is the **TNM staging system**, which relates to concepts explained in Sections 4.3 and 4.4. In the TNM system, cancers are classified according to:

- the size of tumours at the primary site and whether they have invaded nearby tissue (T)
- whether they have invaded lymph nodes (N) and
- whether they have metastasised to other organs (M).

Each letter is followed by a number, usually between 0 and 4, which indicates the severity of each stage (or an X if the parameter was not assessed).

Although TNM is the most commonly used staging system, the same number may still have different implications for each particular type of cancer. This is best illustrated with an example by looking at what T2 represents in prostate and colorectal carcinoma staging. T2 indicates that the colorectal tumour has grown to a size such that it penetrates into the muscle layer of the bowel wall but, by contrast, in the prostate cancer it merely means that it is confined to the prostate (as the prostate has two different lobes, there is a further T2a and T2b classification according to whether it involves one or both lobes). Another difference in the staging of prostate and colorectal carcinomas is the numbers used to determine N. For example, N2 indicates that colon carcinoma cells have invaded four or more lymph nodes that are further than 3 cm away from the solid tumour whereas no N2 category exists for prostate carcinoma. For prostate carcinoma staging, only N0 and N1 are used, the latter indicating that tumour cells have been detected in the regional lymph nodes.

Once a tumour's T, N, and M categories have been determined, usually after surgery (Chapter 8), this information is combined in a process called stage grouping. For stage grouping, the Roman numeral overall system uses, as its name indicates, the numerals I, II, III, and IV (plus the 0) to describe the progression of cancer. Stages are divided into the following:

- slightly abnormally dividing cells (Stage 0)
- tumour cells localised to the tissue of origin (Stage I)

- tumour cells invasive to nearby tissues and/or lymph nodes (Stages II and III) and

- tumour cells metastasised in distant organs (Stage IV).

Table 4.3 shows the TNM system after grouping by the Roman numeral system of colorectal carcinoma in comparison with the two classical systems. As you can see, the Dukes and Astler–Coller staging systems often combine different Roman numeral stage groupings and are not as precise.

Table 4.3 Colorectal carcinoma staging systems. (You do not need to memorise the individual groups for each staging system or the names of the two conventional staging systems; these have been included as examples of the diversity of cancer staging systems.)

Roman numeral (TNM)	Dukes	Astler–Coller
0 (T0, N0, M0)	–	–
I (T1, N0, M0 or T2, N0, M0)	A	A, B1
IIA (T3, N0, M0)	B	B2
IIB (T4, N0, M0)	B	B3
IIIA (T1, N1, M0 or T2, N1, M0)	C	C1
IIIB (T3, N1, M0 or T4, N1, M0)	C	C2, C3
IIIC (any T, N2, M0)	C	C1, C2, C3
IV (any T, any N, M1)	–	D

4.5 Cancers and the immune system

The **immune system** is a complex collection of coordinated mechanisms by which the organism can defend itself against infectious agents that cause disease (e.g. viruses, bacteria and parasites). Protection of our bodies from attack by external agents is mediated by a variety of cell types. They all belong to a 'single' family called *leukocytes* (from the Greek, meaning 'white cells'), of which **lymphocytes** are the most common. Some of them can be found circulating in blood vessels going in and out of tissues as part of a surveillance mechanism against infection and damage; others form part of the lymphatic tissue, notably of the lymph nodes, where they screen the lymph collected from tissues for potentially harmful agents.

Once leukocytes come across an agent that they do not recognise as forming part of the organism (or, in other words, of the 'self'), they launch a counter-attack. This involves the production of **antibodies**, proteins that bind the foreign agent and precipitate their destruction, and the activation of some lymphocytes that kill virus-infected cells and damaged cells.

The antibody binds to a specific region on the foreign agent. This region is called the antigen.

One important feature of the immune system is that it recognises foreign agents that invaded the organism in the past, the so-called immunological memory, so that a more robust and efficient response can be organised if it comes across the same agent again. Many of the actions of the immune system described above are mediated by a type of signalling molecule called **cytokines**, which may act locally in the damaged or infected tissue, causing inflammation, or be released into the bloodstream.

For many years, it was considered that, as tumour cells derive from normal cells within one's own body, the immune system would not recognise tumour cells as 'foreign' (with the exceptions of cancers induced by infection of cells with viruses in which tumour cells express viral 'foreign' proteins). However, most solid tumours contain large numbers of lymphocytes, suggesting that the cellular immune system recognises malignant cells as foreign and attacks them. As a result, it has been suggested that tumour cells, in order to grow larger, must somehow mutate to escape the surveillance of the immune system. This has provided the rationale for a type of cancer therapy called immunotherapy. (This will be discussed further in Chapter 10.) The aim of immunotherapy is to activate the immune system either by antibodies or cytokines, or to improve recognition of tumour cells as foreign (i.e. by using vaccines) with the hope that lymphocytes will destroy tumour cells and restrict tumour growth.

4.6 Symptoms of cancers

In studying this course, you may have guessed that cancers, due to their heterogeneity in type, location, size, invasiveness, etc., may give rise to a myriad of different symptoms in the affected individual, many shared by unrelated diseases such as cardiovascular disorders or chronic infections. Indeed, the list of symptoms that a patient may present is far longer than the number of different cancer types and a detailed explanation of each one goes beyond the scope of this course.

However, it is important to make the distinction between **symptoms**, a range of physical and psychological manifestations that the patient experiences subjectively, and **signs**, which are measurable evidence of a disease detected by doctors, nurses or even patients themselves. So feeling fatigued or sick or losing your appetite may be a symptom of cancer (and of many other diseases), whereas finding blood in your stool or having a reduced lung capacity constitutes a sign of the digestive and respiratory systems, respectively, not functioning properly. Here, we will concentrate on symptoms (and some signs) that a person may present in the early stages of cancer, prompting them to seek medical advice. Other symptoms and signs commonly experienced by individuals with cancer at one point or another during the progression of the disease are also described here if they are due to the cancer itself. By contrast, symptoms and side effects resulting directly from treatment will be discussed later on in the course. (Note that this distinction is not completely clear-cut and some symptoms that are caused by the cancer itself may also result from medical intervention.)

Many cancer organisations throughout the world have launched campaigns to educate the general public about signs and symptoms of cancer, since early detection improves the prognosis of a person with cancer (Figure 4.7). Information usually reflects the prevalence of different cancers within the local population. In countries with a high proportion of individuals of European descent, brochures may include warnings about the early signs of skin melanoma (e.g. changes in the appearance of skin moles), whereas information campaigns in other countries with high incidence of prostate cancer (highly prevalent in males of African descent) may explain in more detail early signs of this condition.

Cancer – know the warning signs

look after number one

When cancers are found early they are nearly always easier to treat and cure.

Facts about cancer

- More than one in three people in the UK will develop cancer during their lifetime.

- Cancer can develop at any age, but it mainly affects older people. Most cases occur in people aged 60 or over.

- More people in this country survive cancer now than ever before, thanks to earlier detection and better treatments.

- Knowing what to look out for gives you a better chance of finding the disease early.

- It is important to know your body so that you notice any changes, and see a doctor if you do.

- There are over 200 different types of cancer that may cause many different symptoms.

Turn over this page to find a list of the major cancer warning signs. This is not a complete list, but experts agree that these are some of the important changes to look out for.

reduce the risk

CANCER RESEARCH UK

www.reducetherisk.org.uk

What should I look out for?

See your doctor as soon as possible if you have any of the following changes. Usually they are not caused by cancer, but it is better to play safe.

- A new or unusual lump or swelling anywhere on your body
- A sore that will not heal, anywhere on your body or in your mouth
- A change in the shape, size or colour of a mole
- Blood in your urine or bowel motions
- A cough, croaky voice or difficulty swallowing that lasts longer than 4 weeks
- A change to looser or more frequent bowel motions lasting longer than 4 to 6 weeks
- Difficulty passing urine
- Unexplained weight loss
- Bleeding from the vagina after the menopause or between periods
- Unexplained pain or ache that lasts longer than 4 weeks

Further information

For more about cancer visit our patient information website www.cancerhelp.org.uk

For more about the early signs of cancer and the healthy choices that could reduce your risk go to www.cancerresearchuk.org/health

If you need health information or advice at any time of the day or night, call NHS Direct on **0845 4647**.

If you want to talk in confidence about cancer, call our information nurses. Direct line **020 7061 8355** or freephone **0800 CANCER**, that is **0800 226237**.

Order copies of this and other cancer awareness leaflets at www.cancerresearchuk.org/leaflets

Reg. charity no.1089464 rtr200 2005

Figure 4.7   An information leaflet from Cancer Research UK.

Nevertheless, there are some general symptoms and signs common to many cancers. These can be divided into *local*, affecting the organ where the tumour grows or surrounding tissues, and *systemic*, affecting the body as a whole (rather than one specific organ). Note that, in advanced cancer, local symptoms may arise not only as a result of growth of the primary tumour, but also due to the tumour metastasising in distant organs, i.e. forming a secondary tumour.

4.6.1 Local signs and symptoms

The most frequent local sign is the presence of an abnormal solid lump or mass due to tumour cell growth (e.g. breast or testicular cancer, or enlarged lymph nodes with metastases). However, this is not always the case; for example, in hepatocarcinoma, where tumour cells spread all over the liver causing the whole organ to swell, and in leukaemia, where tumour cells circulate in the blood. The tumour may increase in size, thereby altering the function of the local tissue and/or organ where it develops, resulting in symptoms related to the role of the biological system of which it forms part (Table 4.4). You are not expected to memorise the information in this table; rather, you should use it as a reference for the remainder of the course when we refer to particular examples of cancers, as you may be interested to know what function of the human body may be affected by a particular cancer depending on the biological system in which it has either developed or metastasised.

Table 4.4 The biological systems in the human body.

Biological system	General function	Organs
Digestive system	Digests and processes food	Salivary glands, oesophagus, stomach, intestines (small and large), rectum and anus Associated organs: liver (metabolism, bile production and detoxification), gall bladder (stores and secretes bile, which aids in digestion of fats) and pancreas (secretes digestive enzymes and hormones)
Cardiovascular system	Delivery of oxygen and nutrients to the rest of the body	Heart, blood vessels and blood
Respiratory system	Exchange of oxygen and carbon dioxide with the air (breathing)	Pharynx, larynx, trachea, bronchi, lungs and diaphragm
Lymphatic and immune systems	Transport of lymph and defence against disease-causing agents	Lymph, lymphatic vessels, lymph nodes, leukocytes, tonsils, adenoids, thymus and spleen
Nervous system	Collecting, transferring and processing information	Brain, spinal cord, peripheral nerves and sensory organs
Endocrine system	Release of signalling molecules into the blood (hormones) that regulate metabolism, growth and tissue functions	Pituitary gland, pineal gland, thyroid, parathyroid and adrenal glands
Reproductive system	Reproduction	Ovaries, Fallopian tubes, uterus, vagina, mammary glands, testes, vas deferens, seminal vesicles, prostate glands and penis
Urinary system	Fluid and electrolyte (salt) balance, excretion of urine	Kidneys, ureters, bladder and urethra
Muscular system	Movement of the whole body and also within the body	Skeletal and smooth muscle
Integumentary system	Protective barrier	Skin, hair and nails
Skeletal system	Structural support and protection	Bones, cartilage, ligaments and tendons

As a tumour grows larger in size, it may start tearing the blood vessels that go in and out of an organ, causing internal bleeding, or it may compress nearby structures such as bones, nerves and other organs. The most common outcome of this is pain (Figure 4.8), which is mediated by the **nervous system**. The nervous system consists of specialised cells, called nerve cells or **neurons**, that are adapted to pass information one to another in the form of electrical impulses and chemical signals. The transmission of information by the nervous system is very fast and the response to the processed information may be very rapid indeed (think about how long it takes you to withdraw your finger when you prick it with a needle, even before you feel the pain!).

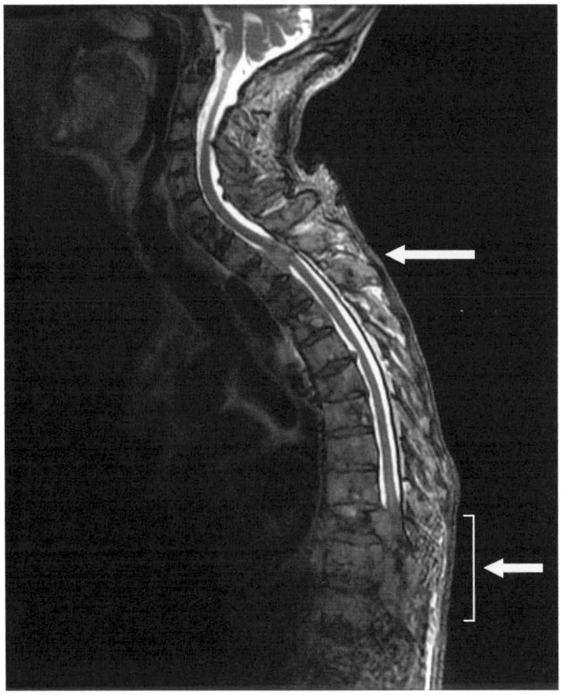

An important function of the nervous system is to receive information about the outside world from sense organs, such as the eyes, the ears, the nose and the skin, and to control the movement of the body through its environment. Although we may be less aware of it, the nervous system also continuously receives information and controls the function of our internal organs; a more obvious example of this type of internal control is when some sort of tissue damage occurs; the nerve endings of neurons in that organ become activated and transmit this information to the brain (the central organ of the nervous system) which processes it as pain. Pain is usually experienced in advanced cancer, when the tumour has grown large enough to activate the nerve endings of surrounding tissues, but in some cases, such as osteosarcoma (cancer of the bones: Table 4.1) it can also be an early sign.

4.6.2 Systemic signs and symptoms

Systemic signs and symptoms which include fatigue, appetite and weight loss, skin changes and sickness, may be caused by pressure on nearby organs (Figure 4.9) or by substances produced by tumour cells. A good example of substances released by tumours is cytokines which are

Figure 4.8   Magnetic resonance imaging (MRI) scan showing a 75-year-old man with secondary tumours in his spine metastasised from colon carcinoma (arrowed). The secondary tumour growth induced the collapse of the vertebrae resulting in the abnormal curvature of the back and pressure on the spinal cord. In this case the patient was rendered wheelchair-bound as the condition makes it very painful to stand upright. (Source: University Hospitals Coventry and Warwickshire NHS Trust)

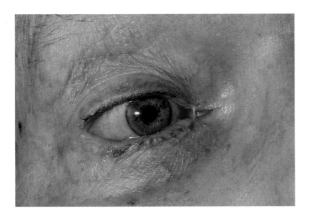

Figure 4.9   Jaundiced eye of a 60-year-old man caused by pancreatic cancer. A tumour at the head of the pancreas has blocked the bile duct, resulting in a build-up of bile. The yellow-brown bile pigment bilirubin accumulates in body tissues, causing yellow discoloration of the skin and eyes. Jaundice is not a disease in itself, but is a sign of many disorders of the liver and biliary system. The biliary system consists of the organs and ducts (bile ducts, gall bladder, and associated structures) that are involved in the production and transportation of bile (Table 4.4). (Source: Dr P. Marazzi/Science Photo Library)

released by some tumours in large amounts into the bloodstream (e.g. ovarian cancer). In addition to their actions on the immune system which may result in flu-like symptoms, cytokines can induce the rapid breakdown of fats and protein in the diet, contributing to the weight loss and muscle wasting observed in many patients with advanced cancer (also known as **cachexia**).

Cytokines, amongst their many actions, can also either induce or inhibit the production of **hormones**, depending on the cytokine and on the hormone involved. Hormones are signalling molecules synthesised by a number of glands that make up the **endocrine system**. Hormones pass into the bloodstream and act on target cells in distant tissues and/or organs.

● From your understanding of the basic properties of a cell, how do you expect a hormone to be able to 'select' the correct target cells with which it interacts?

● By interacting with specific receptors on the target cells (Section 2.9.1). Cells that do not have the correct receptor cannot interact with that particular hormone.

The endocrine system comprises a number of diverse groups of cells scattered throughout the body (some of them, such as the pineal gland, are located in the brain; see Table 4.4). Hormones are involved in regulating growth and development, sleep/wake cycles and even responses to stressful situations. The transmission of information via hormones in the bloodstream is somewhat slower than in the nervous system and hormonal responses may be more long-lasting. An example of a hormone is oestrogen, synthesised by the ovaries from puberty, which binds to the oestrogen receptor of cells in certain body tissues, including the breast, giving the signal to these cells to grow and multiply. Many breast tumour cells are still sensitive to the proliferating action of oestrogen and some therapies are targeted at disrupting this relationship (e.g. tamoxifen). As you may imagine by the multiple actions that hormones have, hormonal imbalances induced either directly by cancer of endocrine glands (e.g. adrenal glands, testes and ovaries), or indirectly by the release of cytokines and other substances, produce a multitude of symptoms (e.g. sleep disturbances).

4.6.3 Local and systemic signs and symptoms are complex in origin

Many signs and symptoms experienced by patients cannot be attributed to a particular cancer type, as their causes may be extremely complex and indicative of malfunctioning in different organs (which may also be due to diseases other than cancer). For example, breathlessness, a local symptom, may certainly result from alterations in lung function. Indeed, lung cancer very often manifests itself as breathlessness, either as a result of tumour size (which reduces the capacity for gas exchange), or because of fluid accumulation in the lungs, or due to obstruction of blood vessels in and out of the lungs. However, ovarian cancer frequently induces the accumulation of fluid in the abdomen; this fluid, called ascites, presses up against the diaphragm (a membrane separating the lung cavity from the abdomen), also causing the symptom of breathlessness. Although these two may still be considered local effects, breathlessness can also be caused by systemic factors. For example, myeloma is a tumour in the bone marrow, where red blood cells (and other blood-circulating cells, i.e. leucocytes) are produced (Figure 4.10). If tumour cells displace normal cells in the bone marrow, myeloma – just like any other bone marrow tumours – can lead to a decrease in the number of red cells in the blood. This is termed **anaemia**. As red cells transport oxygen and carbon dioxide, myeloma-induced anaemia leads to low levels of oxygen and high levels of carbon dioxide in the blood, a process that can make an individual feel as if breathing is hindered.

Myeloma is another type of cancer, like melanoma, that doesn't follow the naming convention given in Box 4.1 and is considered to be malignant in most instances.

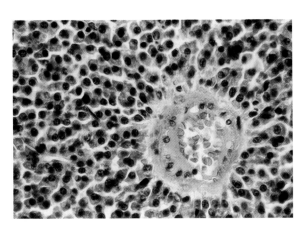

Figure 4.10 Light micrograph of a bone marrow cancer, myeloma. Tumour cells (purple, darker staining) have replaced most of the healthy tissue, leaving a patch of dying normal cells (pink). Myeloma is a cancer of plasma cells (antibody-producing cells found in bone marrow). As well as damaging bones, myeloma can cause anaemia and reduce the ability of the body to fight infection. (Source: CNRI/Science Photo Library)

Case study 4.2 Naheed Jones

Naheed emigrated from Iran in her youth and settled in the UK in the late seventies after she married Duncan Jones, a British university lecturer. She is now a 55-year-old mother of three and works as a research assistant at the same university as her husband. A few months ago she started getting vague abdominal pain on the right side of her abdomen. She describes this as a dull ache that gradually worsened into a gnawing pain that was present all the time. As the pains got worse, she also noticed that her bowel habit had changed. She was getting intermittent loose stool followed by bouts of constipation. Naheed was also generally feeling quite run down and her appetite was not what it used to be. After 2 months of things steadily getting worse, Naheed's husband finally managed to persuade her to see the family doctor. The examination at the surgery did not reveal anything unusual but some blood tests done by the doctor showed that she was anaemic (has a reduced level of red blood cells). The symptoms shown by Naheed prompted the doctor to refer her to a gastroenterologist, a medical doctor specialised in the stomach and bowel.

Systemic symptoms may also be indirectly due to local effects. For instance, fever can be directly caused by neoplastic cells in cancers affecting the immune system such as lymphoma or leukaemia. However, the blockage of the bowel or bladder locally by a tumour may favour local bacterial infections which indirectly activate the immune system, inducing fever in the process.

Case study 4.3   Trupti Shah's first symptoms

It has been five years since the birth of Trupti. Recently, Mr and Mrs Shah have become increasingly worried about their youngest daughter. Little Trupti has just completed her first term at the local infant school. A few weeks into the term, she began to complain that she felt unwell. From being a lively little girl, always getting into mischief and trying endlessly to keep up with her older brothers and sister, she has become lethargic and clingy, often complaining of pains in her arms and legs. At first, her parents were not particularly worried. Starting school is a big step for a child, and her brothers and sister had also found their first term exhausting. But in the last week, Mrs Shah found a rash of tiny purple dots over Trupti's shins. Trupti has also started to bleed frequently from her nose and bruise for no apparent reason. On Friday evening, a few days before Christmas, Trupti develops a very high temperature, over 40 °C. Trupti's parents are now extremely worried. They decide to leave their three other children with Mrs Shah's sister, a few minutes away from the Shah's, and rush Trupti to hospital.

4.7 Maintaining the whole: body homeostasis

Why is it that cancers, especially if they have invaded or metastasised to other tissues, may be deadly diseases? The answer is that organisms can only survive if the many processes going on in the body operate within certain narrow limits. Maintaining the internal environment may involve, for example, keeping the concentration of nutrients and waste products within certain levels, or maintaining the most favourable temperature for chemical reactions to occur optimally, or keeping blood pressure within certain limits optimal for adequate blood flow in and out of tissues. This phenomenon of self-regulation is called **homeostasis**, which may be defined as the maintenance of a stable internal environment close to the optimum conditions for maintaining life. Homeostasis of a living organism is regulated by the coordinated activity of the nervous and endocrine systems, together with the processes already described that regulate the internal environment of cells, and even by the activity of the immune system which keeps the body free from detrimental agents.

Precise regulation of all organs within a multicellular organism is essential to life. Complete failure of an organ as a result of disease may lead to multiple organ failure and death, as the various functions of each and every biological system in the human body are interrelated with the others. This may well be the case in advanced stages of cancer. For example, kidney failure due to a renal tumour (whether primary or secondary) will result in fluid and salt imbalance within the body (Table 4.4), which may lead to liquid filling up the lungs. As a result, the respiratory system, and also the cardiovascular system that pumps blood through the lungs, will have to function well over their normal capacity in order to maintain oxygen levels in the blood; if this is not sufficient, cells in other organs may start suffering from hypoxia and lack of nutrients, which ultimately may result in cell death and failure of many organs. Given the range of external conditions that complex organisms such as humans usually subject themselves to over the whole of a lifetime, from conception to death, it is breathtaking to realise that homeostasis, and hence life, is usually maintained within such narrow limits, even in the presence of disease.

Case study 4.4 Julie Simpson

Julie Simpson is 23 and lives in central London where she works as a personal assistant to a senior City executive. She rents a flat in Canary Wharf with her partner, Jane. She is a typical City girl, a natural extrovert who throws herself whole-heartedly into everything she does, whether it is work, partying, the club scene, or keeping fit; however busy her schedule, she manages to fit a work-out in the gym into almost every day. She would admit, if she had to, that she sometimes drinks rather more than is good for her during her nights out, but she has never smoked and she has always steered clear of recreational drugs.

Today, Julie is pushing herself to her limits on the treadmill. She thinks that she might like to have a go at her first half-marathon during the next year but knows she is not quite up to it yet. As she increases the slope she is running up, she increases the amount of mechanical work that her body is doing. Many of the chemical reactions taking place in her body also speed up, and all this extra work – both mechanical and chemical – generates heat. Humans, like all mammals, need to maintain their temperature within a small range (close to 37 °C). As Julie exercises, she perspires. Water evaporation from the surface of her body removes the excess heat and helps lower her body temperature. Had she been running through the streets on a hot day, instead of in an air-conditioned gym, she would have perspired much more and may also have felt uncomfortable.

One evening after a strenuous workout, while massaging her neck, Jane notices that Julie seems to have a lump in her neck. Julie herself has noticed nothing as the lump is not painful or even uncomfortable. For some weeks she tries, and mostly succeeds, to put the lump out of her mind. For one thing, she doesn't have time to be ill: a colleague in her company has gone on maternity leave, and she needs to work extra hours helping her temporary replacement get up to speed. But the lump seems to be growing, and, finally, Jane persuades Julie to make an appointment with her family doctor.

Activity 4.1 Cancer symptoms

Allow about 60 minutes in total for this activity

Now do Activity 4.1, where you will use the internet to learn about some symptoms of cancer.

4.8 Concluding remarks

In this chapter, you have learnt how the random accumulation of mutations that occur by chance in tumour cells may ultimately result in the range of diseases we know as cancers and how cancers can affect the delicate balance of different biological systems, resulting in ill health. However, as stated previously, the pathways leading to cancer are extremely complex. In contrast to other diseases such as infections or some inherited genetic disorders where disease can be attributed to a single causative agent, cancers are considered to be multifactorial; that is, many factors contribute to their onset. Indeed, all dividing cells in an organism have the potential to become cancerous as a result of interactions between genes and the environment. The different factors contributing to the development of cancers will be the topic of discussion of the next chapter.

4.9 Summary of Chapter 4

4.1   Tumours may be benign, if they are not harmful to health, or malignant. Cells in malignant tumours grow aggressively, become undifferentiated and invade other tissues.

4.2   Tumours require the formation of a network of new blood vessels in order to grow into larger tumours. This process is mediated by angiogenic growth factors released by tumour cells.

4.3   Tumour cells that have acquired specific mutations involving cell adhesion molecules and proteases spread to nearby tissue.

4.4   Tumour cells metastasise to other parts of the body via the blood circulation and the lymphatic system, forming new tumours termed secondary tumours.

4.5   Clinicians classify cancers into groups of similar cases, a process called staging, to facilitate diagnosis and choice of treatment. The most commonly used systems are the TNM staging system and the Roman numeral grouping system.

4.6   The relationship between cancers and the immune system is complex and as yet not well understood but has provided a rationale for a type of cancer therapy called immunotherapy.

4.7   The symptoms and signs of cancers are extremely diverse. Some are local, affecting the tissue or organ where the tumour grows, whereas others are systemic, affecting the whole organism.

4.8   Homeostasis is the equilibrium by which the internal environment of the body is regulated and maintained. Homeostasis is often disrupted in advanced stages of cancers.

Questions for Chapter 4

Question 4.1 (Learning outcomes 4.1, 4.2 and 4.5)

Complete each of the phrases (a)–(h) with one of the answers selected from 1–8.

(a) Arteries...

(b) Lymphocytes...

(c) Veins...

(d) Hormones...

(e) Antibodies...

(f) Lymph nodes...

(g) The heart...

(h) Hypoxia...

1... refers to low levels of oxygen in a tissue.

2... are cells of the immune system that may be found in the blood and in lymph nodes.

3... are a type of blood vessel that carry oxygenated blood to all organs.

4... are a type of blood vessel that collect blood from organs and return it to the heart.

5... pumps venous blood to the lungs and receives oxygenated blood from the lungs. Oxygenated blood is then pumped to all organs of the body.

6... are masses of lymphoid tissue where the lymph is drained.

7... are molecules that circulate in the bloodstream and act on distant tissues.

8... are proteins that mediate part of the immune response against 'foreign' agents.

Question 4.2 (Learning outcome 4.3)

Describe in general terms the type and/or tissue of origin of the following cancers or benign tumours:

(a) hepatocarcinoma

(b) lung squamous cell carcinoma

(c) erythroblastoma

(d) prostate adenocarcinoma

(e) lipoma.

Question 4.3 (Learning outcome 4.4)

Describe in your own words why anti-angiogenic drugs may be useful to treat colon carcinoma but not leukaemia.

Question 4.4 (Learning outcomes 4.6 and 4.7)

Adrenal adenoma is a benign tumour of the adrenal glands. The adrenal glands secrete, amongst others, a hormone called aldosterone which regulates blood pressure. Explain how such a tumour may disrupt homeostasis in the human body.

Further reading

If you would like to read further about this topic, please refer to the following publications.

Chambers, A.F., Groom, A.C. and MacDonald, I.C. (2002) 'Dissemination and growth of cancer cells in metastatic sites', *Nature Reviews Cancer*, vol. 2, pp. 563–72.

Friedl, P. (2003) 'Tumour-cell invasion and migration: diversity and escape mechanisms', *Nature Reviews Cancer*, vol. 3, pp. 362–74.

Spivak, J.L. (2005) 'The anaemia of cancer: death by a thousand cuts', *Nature Reviews Cancer*, vol. 5, pp. 543–55.

Stacker, S.A., Achen, M.G., Jussila, L., Baldwin, M.E. and Alitalo, K. 'Lymphangiogenesis and cancer metastasis', *Nature Reviews Cancer*, vol. 2, pp. 573–83.

Tisdale, M.J. (2002) 'Cachexia in cancer patients', *Nature Reviews Cancer*, vol. 2, pp. 862–71.

de Visser, K.E., Eichten, A. and Coussens, L.M. (2006) 'Paradoxical roles of the immune system during cancer development', *Nature Reviews Cancer*, vol. 6, pp. 24–37.

RISK FACTORS FOR CANCERS

Learning outcomes

After studying this chapter and its associated activity, you should be able to:

5.1 Define and use in context, or recognise definitions and applications of, each of the terms printed in **bold** in the text.

5.2 Explain how some of the risk factors for cancer were identified.

5.3 Outline some of the important features of the incidence and age distribution of different cancers.

5.4 Explain issues related to the various cancer risk factors, such as genetic, environmental and lifestyle risk factors or exposure to radiation and carcinogens.

5.5 Describe ways in which cancer risks can be reduced.

5.1 Introduction

We have seen in the previous chapters how cancers may arise from mutations in DNA and what worldwide implications this may have. However, there are a number of factors that may actually increase the probability of such mutations happening and thus, potentially, lead to cancer. There is, thus, one word that is often linked to cancer and that is 'risk'. We frequently hear or see news stories that include phrases like 'working in industry X has been found to increase the risk of developing bladder cancer by 40%' or 'a new study has shown that eating blackberries once a day will reduce your risk of breast cancer by Y%'. What do we understand by the word 'risk'? The situation can become a bit more complicated when risk is described as being either 'absolute' or 'relative' – what do these terms mean? In the case of cancers the situation is further complicated by the very long time – many decades – that it takes for cancers to develop. In general, we find it easier to deal with risk when the time between an event and its consequences is very short. This is for two main reasons: firstly, the link between cause and effect is obvious (if you touch a hot kettle you will burn your hand); and secondly, the management of the risk is similarly obvious (avoid the pain of a burn by not touching the kettle). A consequence of the long delay between exposure to risk and appearance of cancer is that the link (usually referred to as the **causal link**) between likely cancer risk factors and the diseases is very difficult to establish.

It used to be thought that cancer was a chance event – you just happened to be unlucky if you developed cancer. This chapter will introduce you to the idea of cancer risk factors – things that can influence the risk of developing cancers. It does not require a great leap of imagination to see that, if there are factors that *increase* our risk of getting cancers, then there might just as well be things that *decrease* such risk, and this turns out to be exactly what happens. Looking deeper into this, we need to understand the difference between factors that are linked or *associated* with increases or decreases in cancer risk and those that actually are responsible for or *cause* the increase or decrease. This distinction is particularly significant if you are interested in changing cancer risk. In an academic study, it might be interesting to observe that living in South-Eastern Asia is *associated* with a high risk of developing liver cancer, particularly for males (see Figure 1.3). If you are a WHO official, with responsibility for reducing the global burden of liver cancer, it is even more interesting to know *why* living in South-Eastern Asia increases the risk of liver cancer, and this specific example is described in this chapter. The identification of factors that influence the risk of cancers is something that has benefited immensely from laboratory experiments. Firstly, it has been possible to reproduce the same cancers in experimental animals as those that occur in humans, often using a mixture of chemicals or even pure chemicals. Secondly, not only do these experiments help to confirm the causal link between risk factors and cancers, but they also allow studies on the way in which the risk factors actually affect the cancer process. This understanding of what are called the mechanisms of cancer can lead to the identification of ways in which cancer risk could be reduced. These aspects will also be discussed in this chapter.

5.2 What is a risk factor for cancers?

Intuitively, we feel that we understand the difference between 'safe' and 'risky' situations or behaviours. For example, it seems common sense to say that walking is safer than parachuting. This is because the possibility of something going wrong and leading to serious harm seems more obvious with parachuting than with walking – once again, we can also clearly see where things might go wrong. However, suppose you were a parachutist who had previously made several hundred jumps quite safely – the prospect of jumping out of the plane has little risk because you have made careful preparations so that everything is OK for this jump. In contrast, if you were trying to walk across a busy motorway because your car had broken down in the fast lane, you would very quickly appreciate that unless you were very careful there would be a high chance of serious injury. However, just suppose that there are things that could have a major influence on the outcome of your choices, for which you have little or no control: freak weather conditions, for example, if you are a parachutist, or unpredictable lorry drivers and icy roads if you are on a motorway. You can therefore conclude that there are two important aspects to risk, and they are:

- **personal risk** – you can do something about these risk factors (carefully pack your parachute or decide to stay with your car)

- **environmental risk** – these are factors outside your control (a sudden gust of wind could collapse the parachute or a lorry driver could hit a patch of icy road and crash into your stationary car).

These two types of risk are just as relevant for cancer as they are for walking and parachuting; that is, there are things that *you* can do that have a direct impact on *your* personal risk of getting cancer but there are equally things in the environment, over which you have little or no control, that will also influence the risk of you developing cancer. It is worthwhile making the point at this stage that the word 'environment' refers here to everything that is external to your body; in short, everything that is out there in the wide world that could have an influence on your health. Note that apart from these two there is also a *genetic* risk of developing cancer which is neither a personal risk nor an environmental risk (this is discussed further in Section 5.4).

Before going further into the study of cancer risk factors, it is important to appreciate how the notion that cancer is caused by 'something' arose. Over 100 years ago, it was noticed that some groups of people seemed to develop certain cancers much more frequently than others. Notable examples include the observations by the surgeon Sir Percivall Pott in 1775 that boys who climbed chimneys to remove soot developed cancer of the scrotum (Box 5.1), and the work of Ludwig Rehn in Germany in 1895, who noted that aniline dye workers would frequently be diagnosed with bladder cancer. Both of these cancers were otherwise extremely rare diseases and in both studies it was concluded that there was a link or an *association* between working in a particular industry and an increased risk of particular cancers.

● Why wouldn't Pott and Rehn immediately conclude that cleaning chimneys and working in an aniline dye factory *caused* the two types of cancer?

● Because the two types of cancer do occasionally occur in people who have *never* worked in either of the two occupations.

The strength of the association between certain industrial exposures and rare cancers was sufficiently convincing for public health authorities to introduce legislation to reduce exposures. For example, an Act of Parliament requiring weekly baths and regular changes of clothes in chimney sweeps was passed in 1788. Note here that the practice of sending young boys up chimneys wasn't banned outright, but, nonetheless, the legislation was presumably based on some notion that the accumulation of soot on the affected areas of the skin was somehow linked to the eventual occurrence of the disease.

Box 5.1 Percivall Pott – chimney sweeps and cancer

In 1775 Sir Percivall Pott (Figure 5.1), a surgeon at St Bartholomew's Hospital, London, published his classic account of an occupational cancer in chimney sweeps:

… there is a different disease peculiar to a certain set of people which has not … been publicly noticed. I mean the chimney sweep's cancer.

It is a disease which makes its first appearance on the inferior part of the scrotum, where it produces a painful, ragged, ill-looking sore. The trade call it the soot wart.

(from *The Chirurgical Works* of Percivall Pott, first published 1819 and reproduced in Dronsfield and Ellis, 2006)

Pott's astute observation made this one of the first reports of a link between exposure to an external agent and a cancer.

Figure 5.1 Percivall Pott. (Source: Science Photo Library)

An animal model is the use of an animal as an experimental model system for a human disease. This can be to test a particular agent for either causing the disease in a healthy animal or for curing it in a diseased one.

Even in cases where an otherwise rare cancer occurs in a group of workers, it is still very difficult to identify what it is about the job that increases the risk of cancer. It wasn't until the early years of the 20th century that it was shown that experimental animals exposed to soot developed cancer. In 1915, two Japanese researchers, K. Yamagawa and K. Ichikawa, reported that repeated application of coal tar, a component of soot, to ears of rabbits caused skin cancer, thus providing a basic animal model for the earlier occupational observations of Pott. By the 1930s, the chemical in soot that was responsible for causing the cancer had been isolated.

In this section you have seen that cancers can be caused by exposures to certain chemicals. As you will see later in the chapter, this phenomenon is not restricted to chemicals, as exposure to different kinds of radiation can also cause cancer. We will now turn our attention to the problem of identifying and quantifying cancer risks in the general population.

5.3 Identifying and quantifying risk factors for cancers

For the past 100 years, data have been collected on the incidence and mortality of cancers each year in the UK and many other countries. These data can be analysed to give clues as to the causes of cancer. You have already heard that it can take decades for cancers to develop. The underlying biology that explains why cancers take so long to appear has been covered in Chapters 2 and 3. It turns out that 'time' is also a general risk factor for cancer; that is, the longer you live, the greater your risk of developing cancer. This can be seen very clearly in Figure 5.2, where the risk of dying from cancer in both men and women in the UK increases significantly past the age of 40 and rises inexorably with each decade thereafter. Why should age be a risk factor for cancers? One hypothesis is that deleterious mutations gradually accumulate in DNA of cells until a stage is reached where the risk of a cancer developing from cells with many mutated genes accelerates.

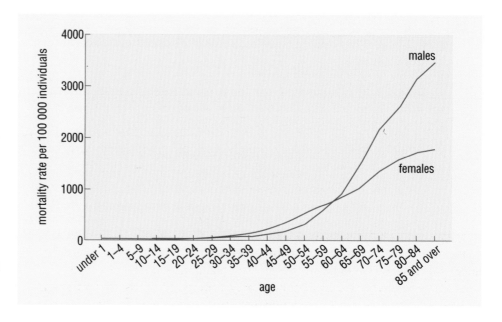

Figure 5.2 Age-specific mortality from all cancers (excluding non-melanoma skin cancer) in England and Wales in 1997. (Data from Quinn et al., 2001)

● What can you conclude from Figure 5.2 about the different age-related cancer risks for men and women?

● Above the age of 60 years men are progressively at greater risk of dying of cancer.

You might also conclude from the data in Figure 5.2 that men are at *intrinsically* greater risk of dying from cancer than women. To see if this might be true you need to look at where in the body the cancers are occurring in both men and women. Figure 5.3 shows the deaths in men and women from all cancers in the UK and you can see that the pattern is somewhat different (Cancer Research UK, 2008). Lung cancer is the leading cause of cancer death in men in the UK, well ahead of the second highest cause of death in males, prostate cancer. By contrast, the major causes of cancer deaths in women in the UK are related to lung and breast cancers, with roughly equal numbers of deaths. Note that globally, the leading causes of cancer deaths in women are breast and ovarian cancers (see also data for 2002 in Figure 1.2). The picture then is somewhat more complicated than at first sight.

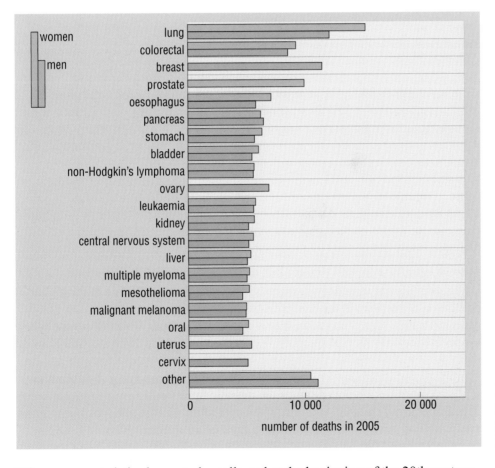

Figure 5.3   Cancer deaths in men and women in the UK in 2005. (Data from Cancer Research UK)

When cancer statistics began to be collected at the beginning of the 20th century, lung cancer was a comparatively rare disease. In fact, around 1900 stomach cancer was the major disease in men in the UK but its incidence and mortality have progressively declined since then. This phenomenon has been called, somewhat ironically, 'the greatest unplanned triumph of cancer epidemiology' (Figure 5.4) because it was something that was observed without knowing why it happened. In fact, it is only recently that the underlying risk factors associated with stomach cancer has been understood (see Section 5.5.3).

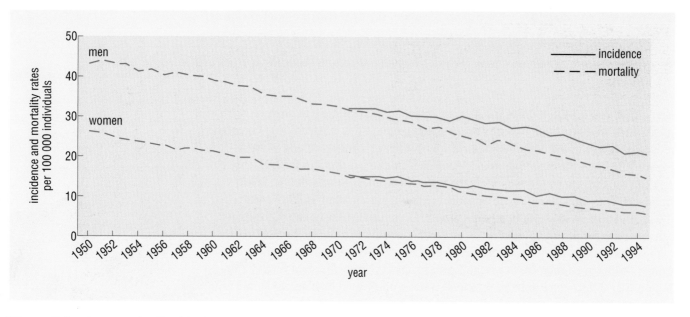

Figure 5.4   Age-standardised incidence of, and mortality from, stomach cancer by sex, England and Wales, 1950–1994. (Incidence was only recorded from about 1970.) (Data from Quinn et al., 2001)

Although tobacco had been used for centuries, principally in the form of pipe tobacco and snuff, it was only from about 1900 that it became widely used and socially acceptable through the use of cigarettes (Figure 5.5). For many people, it was difficult to imagine that such a pervasive and pleasurable habit could be associated with disease. However, during the 1930s and 1940s physicians began to become concerned about the link between tobacco smoking and lung cancer. During the Nazi regime in Germany tobacco smoking was discouraged on the basis of its negative effects on health and its link with cancer in particular. However, in the immediate post-war years, the significance of these results was understandably diminished by their association with the inhuman face of Nazism.

In 1950 Ernst Wynder and Evarts Graham, in the USA, asked people with lung cancer whether they smoked or not and discovered that there was a much higher proportion of smokers in the cancer cases than those in hospital with other non-cancer diseases. This is an example of a **case-control study** in which people with cancer are matched with people with non-cancerous diseases who are similar in as many ways as possible, such as age and occupation. The aim of such a study is to identify some factors that are correlated with the incidence of cancer, in the hope of identifying the cause or causes of the disease. Such studies are **retrospective** in nature, in that the investigators start with cases of the disease and look backwards in time to find the causes. There can be a number of problems with such studies including the fact that people may inaccurately recollect what they did many years before. In the case of cancer this can be a real problem as the disease tends to develop slowly, taking years or decades to be detected. In fact, Wynder and Graham found that smoking tobacco took about 20 years to have its maximal effect on the risk of lung cancer. However, despite the apparently very clear evidence from this study that there was a link between tobacco smoking and lung cancer, there was considerable scepticism about the conclusions.

Figure 5.5 Some of the well-known personalities who were quite happy to be seen smoking in public. (a) Harold Wilson, British Prime Minister in the late 1960s and early 1970s and champion of the Open University. Some of them even endorsed cigarette advertisements: for example, (b) Ronald Regan, a Hollywood actor who became the President of the USA in the 1980s, and (c) Rock Hudson, a well-known Hollywood actor in the 1950s and 1960s. (Sources: (a) Rex Features; (b) and (c) Advertising Archives)

One way around some of the problems of retrospective studies is to conduct **prospective studies** in which large numbers of healthy individuals are recruited in a study and are then followed for many years. At the stage of recruitment, a questionnaire is completed which details as much information about people and their habits as the investigators think will help them to identify the risk factor(s). As cases of cancer arise, the group (usually termed a **cohort**) is matched

Cohort is a Latin term originally meaning the tenth part of a legion of Roman soldiers.

with a control group who share as many habits and features in common. These are members of the cohort who have not developed the disease. Consistent differences between cases and controls will indicate possible risk factors. In general, this prospective approach is considered much more robust than the retrospective case-control method.

In 1951, British epidemiologist Richard Doll sent a questionnaire on tobacco use to 34 439 British medical doctors and followed them up at regular intervals thereafter. By 1954, this prospective study had already confirmed the excess of lung cancers among smokers that had been seen in the retrospective studies. However, as the years passed, the British doctors study revealed the more wide-ranging effect of tobacco smoking not only on cancers but also on health generally (Doll et al., 2004). For example, in terms of general mortality, long-term smokers lived on average ten years less than non-smokers. Furthermore, other rarer cancers such as mouth, larynx (voice box), oesophagus (food pipe), liver, pancreas, stomach, kidney, bladder and cervix, as well as some types of leukaemia, were found to occur at higher levels in smokers than in non-smokers.

The large amount of data collected by Doll and colleagues on tobacco smoking and cancer risk has been used to quantify the risks for cancer. In the cohort study of British doctors the **relative risk** of developing lung cancer was found to be about 40 times greater for a lifetime smoker than for a lifetime non-smoker. In making this comparison, the two groups were matched for as many factors as possible such as age, weight, occupation (in this case, doctors) and location of residence. This kind of approach maximises the possibility of identifying the size of the risk due to smoking. It is important to note that lung cancer is not unknown in non-smokers, but that the risk is very much greater in smokers.

In general, men began smoking about 20 years before women took up the habit to a similar extent. One consequence of this is that the worldwide rate of lung cancer deaths in women is still rising and is yet to peak. Deaths from lung cancer in women will soon exceed those due to breast cancer, which is the major cancer in women globally (see also Figure 1.3). However, it is interesting to note that the mortality from lung cancer in older men in the UK began to fall during the 1980s, because the number of male smokers had already started to decline in the 1960s (Figure 5.6). If you now look again at Figure 5.6 you can see that it corresponds to a snapshot in time of cancer risk. Whilst it looks as if men are somehow more susceptible to dying from lung cancer, the real reason is that men have been exposed to a strong risk factor – tobacco smoke – for longer than women. Because men have now stopped smoking in larger numbers, their risk of dying from lung cancer is also falling dramatically. In contrast, many women have taken up smoking in the past few decades and it is now possible to confidently predict that there will be a lung cancer 'epidemic' in women over the next 20 years. The start of this can already be seen in the lower curve in Figure 5.6. As Richard Peto, a long-time colleague of Sir Richard Doll, has said: 'the people who will develop lung cancer in 20 years time are smoking now'. It is worth noting that the reduction in lung cancer mortality has had little, if anything, to do with improvements in cancer treatment or detection, in fact, lung cancer is usually detected at a late stage in the disease and it is notoriously difficult to treat. Rather it is due to the simple fact that men are giving up smoking. We will return to this subject later in the chapter when we look at strategies for cancer prevention.

So, what is it about smoking tobacco that *causes* the increased risk? The study of tobacco smoking and lung cancer is an area that has attracted much controversy. In the early days, it was suggested that whilst there was a correlation between smoking tobacco and lung cancer, the link was not causal. For example, it was suggested that smokers were at higher risk of developing lung cancer because some factor that predisposed them to start smoking also predisposed them to lung cancer. It is almost impossible to resolve such an issue using the tools of epidemiology alone. As an example of the distinction between something that correlates with cancer risk and a true causal risk factor we can look at what has been described as a 'yellow finger' hypothesis for lung cancer. It has been observed that men with yellow fingers get lung cancer. Do yellow fingers cause lung cancer? If they did, one obvious conclusion might be to remove the coloration by careful washing of the hands and thus lower the risk of lung cancer. No, yellow fingers are of course caused by smoking cigarettes. The fact that smoking cigarettes is a very strong risk factor for both lung cancer and yellow fingers means that the two outcomes are highly correlated, but it does not mean that yellow fingers cause lung cancer. This simple example serves to highlight the importance of distinguishing between factors that simply *correlate* with cancers and those that are truly *causal*.

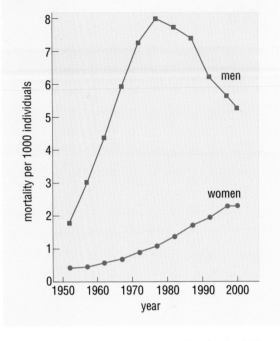

Figure 5.6 Lung cancer mortality in the UK per 1000 individuals aged 75–79. (Data from Peto et al., 2006)

As with the case of soot and skin cancer that you read about in Section 5.2, it was only when laboratory studies of tobacco smoke and lung cancer could be carried out that the understanding of the underlying risk factors in tobacco smoke became progressively clearer. One of the reasons why people smoke tobacco is that nicotine, a nitrogen-containing chemical that is naturally present in tobacco, is addictive. There are many carcinogens in tobacco smoke; you came across benzo[a]pyrene in Section 3.5.3. Another example is *N*-nitrosonornicotine. Experimental studies have shown that this derivative of nicotine, which is formed during the curing of tobacco leaves, is capable of causing the same kind of lung tumours in animals that are observed in tobacco smokers (IARC, 2007). The chemistry of this is not something you need to consider here.

The soot and tobacco smoke stories described above allow us to come to an important conclusion: cancer can be *caused* by exposure to certain chemicals that are called carcinogens (see Section 3.5.3). The epidemiological studies in humans hinted at the possibility of cancers being caused by something and the laboratory studies allowed the identification of specific agents that were responsible. In the next section you will look at factors that link genetics to cancer risk and the extent to which genetic risk factors contribute to the risk of developing cancers.

Case study 5.1   Anneke de Groot's addiction to nicotine

Retired maths teacher Anneke de Groot, 62, lives with her husband of 35 years in a quiet, prosperous suburb of Amsterdam, in the Netherlands. Although she was a popular and successful teacher for many years, she has always felt her family to be the centre of her life. She is very close to her two daughters, who live nearby, and dotes on her three small grandchildren. A much younger son is studying for a PhD in the USA.

Anneke has always tried to live healthily. Like many Dutch people, she cycles whenever she can; she is a good cook, and the family eats a healthy diet rich in fruit and vegetables. She enjoys a glass of wine with her meals but has never been a heavy drinker. However, she does have one unhealthy habit, which she is quite ashamed of: she has been a regular smoker since her mid-teens. Forty-five years ago, smoking was very fashionable and very much less was known about the serious health risks attached to the habit. Anneke is an intelligent woman, and knows only too well that she is addicted to nicotine. She has tried to give up several times, using nicotine replacement therapy, and once joined a support group, but although she was sometimes able to stop for a time she always re-started, triggered by stressful events such as an extended battle of wills with a particularly troublesome pupil or a daughter's difficult first pregnancy. She has, however, managed to cut down from 30 cigarettes a day to 20 and now 10, helped by increasingly strict laws against smoking in public places, and she has never smoked close to her grandchildren.

5.4 Genetics and cancer risk

As you have seen in Chapter 2, cancers are effectively colonies of cells that have escaped the control mechanisms of normal cells that limit growth and remove abnormal cells. The genes of cancer cells usually contain many more mutations than those of normal cells (see also Section 3.5.5). But where do these mutations come from? It turns out that the chemical and biochemical properties of DNA are such that mutations can arise spontaneously, albeit normally at a very low rate. In fact, such a low rate of spontaneous mutation is almost certainly essential for the process of evolution, because adaptation to changing environments requires an ability to change (literally, mutate) and these changes are underpinned by mutations in DNA. If, however, the rate of mutations increases beyond a certain level, then an undesirable, but almost inevitable, side effect is an increased rate of cancers (Greaves, 2000). We know this because there are some examples of inherited mutated genes that lead to greatly increased rates of random mutations which are then accompanied by an increased risk of cancers. One such example is that of Lynch syndrome (Box 5.2).

Although DNA can spontaneously become damaged (being a very large molecule, DNA is somewhat 'fragile') it is also susceptible to chemical 'attack'. In fact, some of the mutagens that we have already mentioned, such as those in soot and tobacco smoke, appear to act by very specifically 'attacking' DNA in such a way that, unless the resulting damage is quickly repaired, mutations will

Box 5.2 An inherited cancer risk – Lynch syndrome

Lynch syndrome is a rare inherited condition that increases the risk of colon cancer and other cancers. Lynch syndrome is also known as hereditary non-polyposis colorectal cancer (HNPCC). A number of inherited syndromes can increase the risk of colon cancer, but Lynch syndrome is the most common. An estimated 2–3% of colon cancers, i.e. two to three out of every 100 colon cancers, are thought to be caused by Lynch syndrome. The mutated genes inherited in Lynch syndrome are responsible for specific DNA repair proteins. As cells grow and divide, they replicate their DNA and it's not uncommon for some minor mistakes to occur (see Section 3.5.2). Recall that normal cells have mechanisms to recognise mistakes and repair them. But people who inherit one of the gene variants associated with Lynch syndrome lack the ability to repair these replication errors.

The key point about the genetic mutation associated with Lynch syndrome is that *every* cell in the body of an affected person carries the inherited genetic mutation (a germline mutation) which vastly increases the chance of acquiring spontaneous genetic mutations (somatic mutations, i.e. mutations that occur in single cells after cell division; Section 3.6) accumulating within cells, leading to them becoming cancerous. Families that have Lynch syndrome usually have more cases of colon cancer than would typically be expected. Lynch syndrome also causes colon cancer to occur at an earlier age (i.e. 30–40 years of age) than that typical of the general population.

ensue (see Section 3.5.2). Hence, alterations in DNA repair protein levels and/or activity, in combination with exposure to chemicals that damage DNA, act as an important 'driver' of cancer risks.

There has been great interest in developing tests for genetic susceptibility to cancer risks. Such tests are based on the fact that, all else being equal, a difference in cancer risk between two individuals will depend on differences in the functioning of various genes. In recent years, tests for breast cancer susceptibility genes have attracted great interest (Box 5.3).

Despite the intense interest in genetic testing for cancer, it appears that genetic factors are the overwhelming risk factors in only about 5–10% of all cancers. Put another way, more than 9 out of 10 cancers occur in individuals for which there is no prior family history of cancer (in this sense, family history means cancers occurring in close – first-degree – family members or that cancers occur at a particularly young age). The vast majority of cancers are called 'sporadic'; that is, they appear to arise randomly in the population.

No prior family history does not rule out an individual's genetic predisposition for cancer. For example, in a case where the family is too small for the cancer risk to be identified.

At this point, you need to take stock because something paradoxical seems to be happening. On the one hand, you have seen that cancers are essentially genetic diseases in the sense that variants in genes are a characteristic feature – a 'hallmark' – of cancers. On the other hand, genetic risk factors seem to account for only a small proportion (no more than 10%) of all cancers. The explanation for this apparent paradox can be seen by recounting the story of the overflowing bath, as told by Dennis Burkitt, the doctor who discovered

Box 5.3 Genetic testing for breast cancer genes

It is thought that there are probably several gene variants (Section 3.6) that can increase the risk of developing breast cancer. Tests are available for two of them, *BRCA1* and *BRCA2*. The risk of getting breast cancer in your lifetime if you carry either of these breast cancer gene variants (Section 3.6) could be as much as 85%. Up to half of all women (50%) who carry a variant of the breast cancer gene will have developed breast cancer by the time they are 50 years old. Thus, carrying one of these variant genes means that you are more likely to get breast cancer than someone who does not carry the gene variant. But it is not a certainty. Gene variants associated with a trait (i.e. a higher incidence of a type of cancer, but it can also relate to incidence of any other disease or even to a physical characteristic, i.e. eye colour) may or may not show up in all individuals that carry that gene variant. The proportion of individuals with a particular gene variant that do show the associated trait is called **penetrance**. That is, a highly penetrant cancer risk gene variant will result in a high proportion of individuals that possess that gene variant developing the disease. The breast cancer-risk variant of *BRCA1* is highly penetrant. This means that up to 85 out of every 100 of the people who carry it will develop breast cancer. However, this also means that not all individuals who carry it (~15%) will develop breast cancer. This is because the activity of a particular gene (i.e. the extent to which a particular gene product is expressed) in an individual is not only affected by that gene's variant itself but also by other genes (and their particular variants) present in the individual, and certainly by any other risk factors to which the individual is exposed, such as lifestyle or environmental exposure to other carcinogens. Indeed, most breast cancers appear to happen by chance. Only about five out of every hundred (5%) are related to a known inherited breast cancer-risk gene variant. The older you or your relatives are when diagnosed, the less likely it is that an inherited gene variant is the direct cause.

both the cause and the cure for a cancer that now bears his name – Burkitt's lymphoma. The story goes like this: in your bathroom the bath is overflowing and water is all over the floor. You are concerned that water will damage the downstairs ceiling so you begin to mop up the water with sponges. All the time that you are doing this, water is still coming out of the taps. But still you keep on mopping up the water and searching for sponges that will do the job more efficiently. To the outside observer, the solution is obvious – turn off the taps! The point of this story is that DNA repair enzymes exist to repair ('mop up') deleterious DNA damage, but it is the environment ('the taps') that continually provide exposure to agents, such as soot and tobacco smoke, that generate the damage. Unless we are very careful, it is tempting to focus too much on genetic variability ('I should use a better sponge') rather than reducing the impact of overriding risk factors ('I should turn the taps off'). The key conclusion that comes out of this discussion is that the risk of most cancers is 'driven' by a combination of factors – genetic ('sponges') and environmental ('taps'). In terms of understanding what might be the relative contribution of each factor to cancer risks, a lot of information has come out of studies of the *p53* gene and its associated protein product (see Box 5.4).

Box 5.4 *p53* – 'guardian of the genome'

The p53 protein (p, protein; 53 signifies the size of the protein) is a tumour suppressor encoded by a gene whose disruption is associated with approximately half of all human cancers. The p53 protein acts as a checkpoint in the cell cycle: the protein checks for the errors at the stage of DNA replication: if they are repaired the cell cycle can continue; if not, p53 initiates apoptosis (see Section 2.9.4). The central role of p53 in determining whether cells can divide or not has led to it being described as the 'guardian of the genome'. Since cancer is the unchecked proliferation of cells, the role of p53 is therefore critical. Despite this key role, the p53 molecule can be inactivated in several ways that result in impaired function. In some families such as those, for example, with Li–Fraumeni syndrome, *p53* germline mutations are inherited and family members have a high incidence of cancer. However, in the majority of cancers, the molecule is inactivated by somatic mutations caused by environmental factors. Analysis of the types and distribution of mutations in the *p53* genes isolated from tumours can give clues to the identity of the external agents.

Familial cancers associated with a particular cancer-risk gene variant such as *BRCA1* or *p53* are indeed very rare. However, it is not clear whether individuals may have combinations of variants of several genes that, although individually may not predispose to cancer, together would increase the risk of developing a particular type of cancer. Much research is currently being carried out on identifying probable combinations of genetic variants of proto-oncogenes, tumour suppressor genes and genes that encode DNA repair proteins that might predispose an individual or a family to increased risk of cancers.

5.5 Some environmental risk factors for cancers

5.5.1 Radiation

The term 'radiation' is used very generally and actually means any form of energy that travels outwards from a source. This could be light from a table lamp, microwaves, infrared radiation (heat) from a fire, sound, or a stream of high-energy particles from a radioactive source. However, in terms of causing cancer, it is the higher-energy radiation that needs to be considered. In this chapter, we shall explain how two types of radiation can cause cancers; these are ultraviolet radiation and what is known as ionising radiation (see Box 5.5 overleaf); the latter includes X-rays, gamma rays and the high-energy particles emitted by radioactive sources.

Ultraviolet rays, **X-rays** and **gamma rays** are all forms of **electromagnetic radiation** – an important form of energy that can be described as either a wave or as a flow of photons or 'packets' of energy. Although physicists use both models to explain electromagnetic radiation, we shall only use the photon model of electromagnetic radiation in this book.

You may not be familiar with the term 'electromagnetic radiation', but a look at Figure 5.7, which shows the **spectrum**, or range of energies, of electromagnetic radiation should convince you that you are familiar with several forms of it.

Figure 5.7 The electromagnetic spectrum. The energy of the photons is given in units of electronvolts, eV, a very small unit commonly used by physicists.
($1 \text{ eV} = 1.6 \times 10^{-19}$ joules)

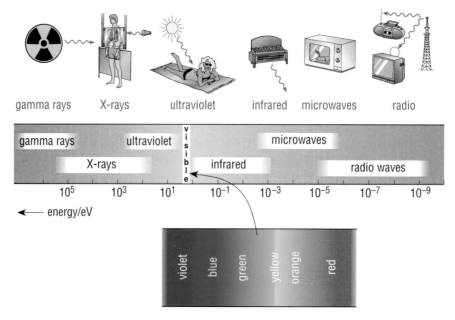

● Look at Figure 5.7. Which forms of electromagnetic radiation do you use in everyday life? And where do they fall in the spectrum?

● Visible light is the most obvious, but you also use several other parts of the electromagnetic spectrum. Starting from the low-energy end of the spectrum:

* radio waves – for listening to local and national radio stations and for television transmission
* microwave – for ovens and mobile phones
* infrared for heat lamps, TV remote controls and for 'night imaging', formerly only used by the police and the military, but now available on the latest digital cameras
* ultraviolet radiation – for air disinfection and pest control in the catering industry, and for checking 'hidden' signatures; also received from the sun and sunlamps
* X-rays– used for imaging (Section 6.5) and for cancer treatment (Chapter 9).

In terms of causing cancer it is, as stated above, ultraviolet rays, X-rays and gamma rays that are of interest. As you can see from Figure 5.7, ultraviolet rays have a higher photon energy than visible light. Damage caused by ultraviolet photons is linked to skin cancers.

X-rays and gamma rays, which have even higher energies, are more penetrating and are forms of ionising radiation (see below). They can cause cancers anywhere in the body.

Ultraviolet radiation

Ultraviolet (UV) light from sunlight or sunlamps is divided into three bands: UVA, UVB, and UVC. UVB is the most effective carcinogen and is absorbed by bases in the DNA, causing characteristic patterns of DNA damage. UVA damages

DNA through generation of reactive molecules containing oxygen. UVC in sunlight is absorbed by ozone in the atmosphere and does not reach the surface of the Earth, although damage ('holes') in the ozone layer can result in increasing amounts of UV radiation reaching the planet and so increase the risk for cancer. UV radiation causes both malignant melanoma and non-melanoma skin cancer, as exposure to UV light leads to damage of the DNA in epidermal cells. In normal skin cells, this damage is repaired by a set of DNA repair enzymes. In some individuals, however, one or more of these enzymes is defective, resulting in an increased risk of developing skin cancer.

Ionising radiation

The term ionising radiation refers to the fact that very energetic radiation is capable of removing electrons from atoms and molecules to form ions (Box 5.5).

You will see in Chapter 6 how ionising radiation can be used to image cancers and in Chapter 9 how it can be used in radiotherapy to treat cancer.

Box 5.5 Elements, atoms, molecules and ions

You read in Section 2.3 that all matter, whether it is in a living organism like a tree or a person, or in non-living material such as the rocks and the atmosphere, is composed of chemical elements.

● From what you read in Chapter 2, can you recall the three most abundant elements in living things?

● The most abundant elements are carbon, oxygen and hydrogen.

Each element is built up from very small particles known as atoms and these in turn are composed of three fundamental particles.

Within an atom there are equal numbers of positively charged and negatively charged particles. The negatively charged particles are called **electrons** and the positively charged particles are called **protons**. The charge on a proton and on an electron is equal and opposite. Because the numbers of protons and electrons in an atom are the same, an atom is electrically neutral; that is, it has no net electrical charge. The third type of particle is the **neutron**, which has the same mass as a proton but carries no charge. One element is distinguished from another only by the number of protons (and thus electrons) that each atom contains. For example, hydrogen, the simplest atom contains one proton and one electron only. In contrast, the most common form of sodium possesses 11 protons and 11 electrons (and 12 neutrons).

Protons and electrons have equal and opposite charge, but their masses are very different – a proton is approximately 2000 times as heavy as an electron. The neutrons and protons are to be found in the very small and very dense core of the atom, known as the **nucleus**, while the negatively charged electrons circulate around the nucleus, taking up most of the space.

We shall return to the details of the nucleus in Section 6.5; the main point that is of interest here is the fact that, under certain circumstances, an atom can gain or lose one or more of the electrons which are circulating around the nucleus.

● What will happen if an atom loses an electron?

● It will become positively charged because it has lost a negatively charged electron; the positive charge in the atom's nucleus now exceeds the negative charges of the electrons.

Similarly, if the atom gains an electron, it will become negatively charged.

This process of electron loss or gain is referred to as **ionisation** and the charged particles formed, are known as **ions** (pronounced 'eye-ons'). One way in which this ionisation can occur is by interaction with high energy photons of electromagnetic radiation. Such radiation is often known as **ionising radiation**.

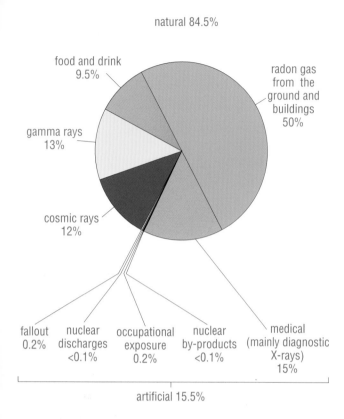

natural 84.5%

food and drink
9.5%

gamma rays
13%

cosmic rays
12%

radon gas
from the
ground and
buildings
50%

fallout
0.2%

nuclear
discharges
<0.1%

occupational
exposure
0.2%

nuclear
by-products
<0.1%

medical
(mainly diagnostic
X-rays)
15%

artificial 15.5%

Figure 5.8 A pie chart showing the proportions of background ionising radiation received by the population of the UK from different sources. Note that radon is a radioactive gas from rocks and is potentially harmful when it is breathed in. Cosmic radiation is the ionising radiation from the sun and outer space; fortunately much of it is filtered out by the atmosphere but this means that the amount received increases with increasing height above the Earth's surface. (Source: adapted from Health Protection Agency, 2005)

These reactive molecules are sometimes described as 'free radicals' or 'reactive oxygen species' (see Section 5.5.3).

Ionisation can be caused either by high-energy electromagnetic radiation or by high-energy particles emitted by radioactive substances. X-rays and gamma rays are, like ultraviolet radiation, forms of electromagnetic radiation; the high-energy particles emitted by radioactive substances are usually either fast-moving electrons or heavier alpha particles (see Section 6.5). All of these are classified as ionising radiation and all of us are exposed to ionising radiation all the time. The pie chart in Figure 5.8 shows the proportions of the radiation we receive from different sources. This radiation is known as background radiation and most of it is unavoidable.

● What percentage of the radiation received by someone living in the UK could be described as 'unavoidable'?

● The 50% from radon gas, the 13% from gamma radiation, the 12% from cosmic rays and the 9.5% from food and drink are all hard to avoid. So are most of the very small amounts from nuclear discharges, nuclear products, etc. So some 85% of the radiation received in the UK is unavoidable. Only the medical radiation can be avoided and that only by a very healthy person!

The amount of radiation received will vary from country to country because of different rock types; in some countries the amount of radiation received from the rock (radon gas and gamma rays) is very much greater because the geology is different. The amount received will also vary from person to person depending on exactly where they live, how much medical radiation they receive, and how much air travel they do (because the amount of cosmic radiation received increases with height).

There are various interactions that can take place between the ionising radiation hitting the body and the molecules in tissues but the end result of all such interactions is a fast-moving electron. This then undergoes several reactions to form a reactive molecule containing oxygen and hydrogen. This reactive molecule in turn can cause damage to the cell DNA leading to either a single-strand break or a double-strand break (Figure 5.9). As you learnt in Section 3.5, DNA breaks can be repaired, and most of them are, otherwise they can lead to mutations that can result in a cancer.

As mentioned above, damage by UV light mainly results in cancers of the skin. With the higher-energy, more penetrating radiation, the cancers can be formed anywhere in the body.

Radiobiology, which is the study of the effects of radiation on cells, is a large and fascinating subject but unfortunately it is not possible to delve deeper into that subject here. All we can do is to say that the evidence suggests that the probability of developing radiation-induced cancer is proportional to the amount of radiation received, the type of tissue and the type of radiation. Note that, as with other risk factors already discussed in this chapter, it is never possible to say exactly who will develop cancer as a result of exposure to radiation, only to say that the probability of developing cancer increases with the amount of radiation received.

For someone who receives the normal UK background amount of radiation, the risk of developing a radiation-induced cancer is about one in 10 000 – a very small risk indeed in comparison to the risk of developing a cancer from some other cause.

● Astronauts are exposed to much larger amounts of radiation because they are not protected from cosmic radiation by the atmosphere. If an astronaut receives 20 times the amount of UK background radiation, what is their risk of developing a radiation-induced cancer?

● Their risk will be 20 times larger, i.e. 20 in 10 000, which is equivalent to $1 \text{ in } \dfrac{10\,000}{20}$, i.e. 1 in 500.

So you can see from these figures that the risk of getting a radiation-induced cancer is only significant for people who have received a large dose of radiation. One might include amongst these astronauts, airline pilots and crew, patients who have received a large number of diagnostic X-rays or a treatment involving ionising radiation and people who have been the victims of a nuclear accident. However, you should bear in mind that there are some problems with estimating the risks due to radiation in that most of the data that has been collected relates to people who have been exposed to a large amount of radiation, as, for example, in a nuclear accident. There is much discussion as to whether it is possible to use the same figures for very small amounts of radiation. There is even some evidence to suggest that small amounts of gamma or X-radiation reduce the risk!

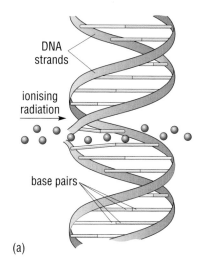

(a)

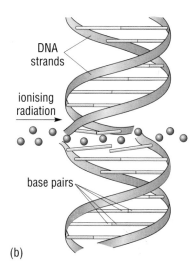

(b)

Figure 5.9 Damage to the DNA structure can lead to either (a) single- or (b) double-strand breaks.

Activity 5.1   Cancer risk in the news

Allow about 30 minutes in total for this activity.

In this activity you will look at a short report in the news concerning cancer risks.

5.5.2 Tobacco use

You have already heard how smoking tobacco causes cancer. You will now look at the scale of the cancer 'epidemic' linked to tobacco use. Tobacco causes an estimated 20% of all cancer deaths, with an estimated worldwide total of 1.2 million in 2002. Smokers have an increased risk of a number of different cancers (as noted in Section 5.3). Worldwide, around 80% of lung cancer cases in men and 50% in women are caused by tobacco smoking. In 2002, out of all new cases of cancer in low-income countries, over 20% (i.e. 1 in 5) in men and almost 4% in women were attributable to tobacco. Average daily cigarette consumption in Chinese men, for example, has risen steadily from one in 1952 to 11 in 1996.

Based on the experience in Europe and the USA, where widespread cigarette smoking began 50 years earlier, it has been predicted that tobacco will kill about 100 million of the 0.3 billion Chinese males who were aged 0–29 in 1998 with half these deaths occurring in middle age and half in old age. Recent Chinese data show that 15% (or 15 million) of these deaths will be due to lung cancer (Liu et al., 1998). In high-income countries, one-third of all new cancer cases in men and just over 12.5% (i.e. 1 in 8) in women were attributed to tobacco smoking.

5.5.3 Infectious agents

Towards the end of the 19th century, when Louis Pasteur and Robert Koch discovered infectious agents as the cause of human diseases, cancer was also considered a candidate infectious disease. Initial experiments performed in the 1870s with tumour tissue transferred from one animal to another demonstrated the general principle of limitless growth intrinsic to tumours. However, these findings did not offer proof that an infectious agent existed that caused cancer. Later, in 1910, Peyton Rous from the Rockefeller Institute in New York was the first to show that cancer could have an infectious origin. Rous' findings initially suggested that a virus-like agent was the cause of cancer. Later on, the link between certain viruses and cancer became well established and a number of viruses have been found that are clearly related with cancer. Viruses have the ability to integrate their genetic material into the host cell's DNA, and this process can often result in DNA damage and mutations that result in cancer initiation.

In addition to viruses, bacteria have also been found to be related to cancer. Bacterial as well as some viral infections can cause chronic inflammation, which is accompanied by the formation of reactive molecules, such as reactive oxygen species (ROS) and reactive nitrogen species (RNOS) which can also lead to DNA damage and carcinogenesis. Another important mechanism for the development of cancer after an infection is associated with severe and long-term immunosuppression by viruses, such as human immunodeficiency virus (HIV) which is clearly related with Kaposi's sarcoma. In this case, the immunosuppression caused by HIV leads to increased susceptability to infection by other viruses that are linked with the development of rare cancers like a type of the human herpes virus and Kaposi's sarcoma.

Some examples of infectious agents, viruses or bacteria, associated with cancer include: hepatitis viruses and liver cancer, human papilloma virus (HPV) and cervical carcinoma, human T-cell leukaemia virus (HTLV) and leukaemia in adults, and the bacterium *Helicobacter pylori* (*H. pylori*) and gastric adenocarcinoma (see Box 5.6).

Infection is a major cause of cancer worldwide. Approximately 1 in 4 cancers (i.e. 25%) in low-income countries are estimated to be attributable to infection. In 2002, this represented some 1.9 million cancers or close to 1 in 5 of all cancers worldwide (WCRF/AICR, 2007).

Box 5.6 Stomach cancer caused by a bacterium

The bacterium *Helicobacter pylori* (Figure 5.10) has adapted to live in a rather unusual ecological niche – the highly acidic environment of the human stomach. *H. pylori* infects the lining (mucosa) of the stomach which results in a persistent inflammation that predisposes not only to ulcer in the stomach (peptic ulcer), but also to stomach cancer (gastric adenocarcinoma). This cancer has decreased in incidence in many countries during the last half-century but still ranks as number two in the world in terms of cancer deaths.

Inflammation in the stomach mucosa is also a risk factor for another type of cancer in the stomach, MALT (mucosa-associated lymphoid tissue) lymphoma. Since such lymphomas may regress when *H. pylori* is eradicated by antibiotics, the bacterium must play an important role in perpetuating this tumour. It is somewhat unusual for a tumour to be treated with antibiotics, but in this case it is highly effective!

The 2005 Nobel Prize for Physiology and Medicine was awarded to Australians Barry Marshall and Robin Warren for their discovery of the role of *H. pylori* in gastritis and peptic ulcer disease.

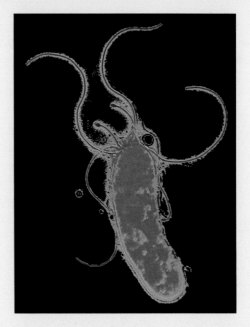

Figure 5.10 The bacterium *Helicobacter pylori*. (Source: P. Hawtin, University of Southampton/Science Photo Library)

Fighting infections can be a very effective way of reducing cancer incidence worldwide. Thus, in the case of bacterial infections like *H. pylori*, a simple case of treating with antibiotics may be sufficient to produce a significant reduction in stomach cancers, which used to be very prevalent (see also Figure 5.3). Similarly, screening programmes (see Section 6.7) for the presence of HPV have strongly reduced the number of cervical cancers in the high-income countries. However, the incidence of cervical cancer is much higher in women who do not have access to such screening programmes. The recent development of a vaccine against HPV for women of pre-sexual age may provide an opportunity to further reduce the incidence of cervical cancer worldwide.

Case study 5.2   Lin Ming's blood transfusion

Lin Ming is 41 years old and has been working for an electrical wire factory in Jiangsu, China, for over 20 years. Because he lives quite a distance from the factory, he used to ride his motorcycle to get to work. About 15 years ago, Lin was involved in a serious traffic accident when he was run over by a car while riding home from work. His left leg was crushed and the femoral artery ruptured, so he lost a lot of blood by the time the medical emergency team arrived and applied a tourniquet to his thigh. In hospital, he immediately received a transfusion of several pints of blood that matched his blood group. When his condition had stabilised, Lin consented to an emergency operation to save his badly injured left leg. It took several weeks before Lin was dismissed from hospital. Although his leg never completely recovered its full function, Lin was still able to do his skilled job in the factory but he had to use the bus to get about.

Ten years after the accident, he and his work colleagues are asked if they would like to donate blood during a national campaign to increase blood stocks in hospitals. Lin is very proud to be able to provide blood so that sick people could have a chance to be treated, like he had been a few years back. Unfortunately, Lin's blood is found to be positive for hepatitis C virus (HCV) (since 1995, Anti-HCV is a routine laboratory test for blood donors in China). He is told that HCV had been discovered in 1989 and that some blood used in transfusions in the late eighties and early nineties may have been contaminated with HCV. He is not particularly worried by this news because he has never shown any symptoms associated with liver disease. In fact, Lin has always thought of himself as a very healthy person.

5.5.4 Industrial chemicals and exposures

In terms of the overall cancer incidence, industrial chemicals do not appear to contribute greatly to the risks of developing cancers. However, as you have already seen with chimneys sweeps and dye workers, the unique occupational exposures have given early clues to the causes of cancers.

In the early 1950s two Medical Research Council pathologists, John Barnes and Peter Magee, were asked to investigate cases of liver disease in workers exposed to a solvent in the synthetic textile industry. The solvent was a pale yellow oily substance that had been known for 100 years and was called dimethylnitrosamine (DMN). Barnes and Magee decided to investigate the problem by trying to reproduce the effects in experimental animals. When they administered low doses of DMN to animals to simulate the occupational exposure, they discovered that not only could they reproduce the liver toxicity seen in workers but that prolonged exposure gave rise to liver cancers. This was yet another example where exposure to a simple chemical could induce a specific type of cancer. However, the particular significance of this study was that DMN turned out to be the first of many N-nitroso chemicals that can induce a whole range of specific cancers, some of which turn out to be relevant for common cancers. Not least of these is the nicotine derivative, N-nitrosonornicotine, found in tobacco smoke that we encountered earlier.

5.5.5 Carcinogens in food

Food may be contaminated with natural or synthetic carcinogenic agents. Moulds and the toxins produced by some moulds are known to be carcinogenic. Aflatoxin B, for example, is an established cause of liver cancer.

The aflatoxins are a group of chemicals produced by fungal metabolism that are found in foodstuffs such as grains and peanuts contaminated with *Aspergillus* moulds. The fungal contamination occurs when the susceptible foodstuffs (maize and groundnuts) are stored in warm and humid climates. There has been concern for a long time that human exposure to aflatoxins is a major risk factor for liver cancer, but the epidemiology has been confounded by the risks of the same disease due to hepatitis infections. A large prospective cohort study in South-East Asia was carried out to identify and quantify the contribution of the various risk factors for liver cancer. Between 1986 and 1989, 18 244 men (aged 45–64 years) were recruited into a cohort which was followed up with respect to the occurrence of liver cancer. At recruitment into the study, each subject was interviewed, using a questionnaire, for details of dietary and other past exposures. Samples of blood and urine were also collected and stored for future analysis. Over the following years, 55 cases of liver cancer and 267 matched controls were collected and analysed as a case-control study. The stored urine samples were also analysed for the presence of aflatoxin metabolites. The blood samples were used to determine if individuals had past infections with hepatitis. It turned out that those people who had traces of aflatoxin in their urine, as well as evidence of having had hepatitis, were at the highest risk of cancer.

In recent years there has been quite a lot of publicity about the links between red meat and colorectal cancer. The situation in this case is quite different from the liver cancer story described above. As summarised in a major report on diet and cancer published in 2007 (WCRF/AICR, 2007), 16 cohort and 71 case-control studies investigated red meat. Nearly all the cohort studies showed an increased risk of developing colorectal cancer with a higher intake of red meat. A statistical analysis of the combined cohort studies showed a 15% increased risk of colorectal cancer per 50 grams per day of red meat consumed.

The size of this risk appears small, but it is an example where this small risk actually ends up as a large number of cases. Whilst it is not possible to say how many of the 15 000 deaths annually from bowel cancer in the UK are due to red meat, the evidence suggests that it is a major risk factor for this cancer (WCRF/AICR, 2007).

In the next section, you will see another way in which a strong environmental influence on cancer risk factors has been seen. This time the evidence has come from the study of quite large populations living in, and moving between, different parts of the world rather than small and rather exceptional occupational groups.

5.6 Lifestyle, environment and cancers

The incidence of many cancers around the world varies greatly from country to country and from region to region. One possible explanation of this could be that variations in the genetic make-up of different populations would lead to differing susceptibilities to cancer. Another explanation could be that variations

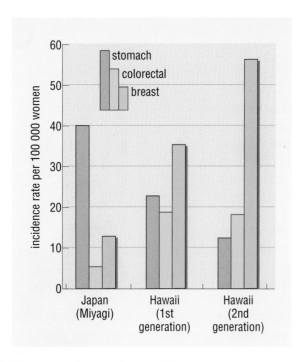

Figure 5.11 Incidence of three types of cancer in Japanese women and their families after they emigrated to Hawaii. The women are grouped by generation in Hawaii and Japan, 1968–1977. (Data from WCRF/AICR, 1997)

in exposure to **environmental carcinogens**, or differences in lifestyle due to the range of cultural profiles around the world, might lead to differences in cancer risk. Studies of migrant populations offer the possibility to examine the contributions of these alternative explanations. The genetic profile of individuals within a migrant population will not change within one generation, or within several generations for that matter. In contrast, exposures to environmental carcinogens will change immediately upon arrival in a new country and lifestyle changes will follow as assimilation of migrants into a new culture occurs. Thus, cancer risks driven predominantly by genetic factors would show little if any change in migrant populations, whereas those influenced by environmental or lifestyle factors would reflect the changes in the profile of exposures.

A classic example of changes in cancer risk for different cancers is found in Japanese migrants to Hawaii (Figure 5.11).

● What can you deduce from Figure 5.11?

● Japanese women living in Japan have a high risk of stomach cancer and an almost three times lower risk of breast cancer. The first generation of Japanese migrants in Hawaii showed a halving of their stomach cancer risk and an almost trebling of their breast cancer risk. By the second generation, the Japanese-Hawaiians had a stomach cancer risk one-third that of women in Japan but a breast cancer risk that was more than four times higher. A similar pattern has been seen in a number of other studies, with incoming migrants 'adopting' the profile of cancer risks of the indigenous populations.

Thus, the available evidence suggests that most cancer risks fit the environmental/ lifestyle model of causation rather than the genetic model. Migrant studies provide compelling evidence that cancer risk is principally determined by environmental factors, including diet. Patterns of cancer among migrant groups, as they move from country to country, often change faster than those within any country.

There is also another phenomenon that has a major influence on cancer risk in relation to lifestyle, and that is when major changes occur within societies; these can sometimes be as dramatic as those experienced by migrant populations.

Body fatness and organ mass and composition, commonly assessed by body size measurements, are key factors influencing health and well-being throughout the life course. The main concern of nutrition science, since its beginnings and until the mid-20th century, has been to protect populations against the consequences of malnutrition in the 'classic' sense of the word. That is undernutrition, which increases vulnerability to infectious diseases, especially in infancy and childhood, and results in people who are small and weak, unable to be productive, and with low life expectancy. This remains a central public health priority for middle- and low-income countries.

In the final two decades of the 20th century and into the 21st century, however, a different and imperative public health nutrition concern has emerged: weight gain, overweight, and particularly obesity. At first, it was generally assumed that societies whose babies are big, whose children grow fast, and whose adults are heavy and tall, were healthy. Compared to societies with inadequate nutrition and poor public health provision, such populations are indeed physically stronger, more productive, have longer lives, and are generally healthier. However, since the 1980s, a series of reports based on a rapidly increasing body of evidence have concluded that populations of high-income countries, and now also populations of many middle- and low-income countries, are becoming overweight to an extent that is bad for health. These countries are almost exclusively those experiencing social, economic, and nutritional transition. The nutritional transition is characterised by a shift from 'traditional' diets that are low in fat and high in fibre to high-energy 'Western' diets that are high in fat and low in fibre. It is now generally accepted that obesity, as well as being overweight though not obese, increases the risk of a number of major chronic diseases including type 2 diabetes, coronary heart disease and some forms of cancer including cancers of the liver and digestive, urinary and reproductive systems (Calle et al., 2003). The mechanisms by which obesity may result in cancer are not known and currently much debated by scientists. One possible mechanism is the hormonal and cytokine imbalances observed in obese individuals.

5.7 Cancer prevention

You have looked in this chapter at the various ways in which factors affect cancer risk. What can you learn from this about preventing cancer? Perhaps one of the most obvious conclusions is that the incidence of some cancers can be reduced by simply avoiding certain exposures. You saw that early on some occupational exposures to carcinogens could be reduced in order to avoid rare and fatal cancers. However, the impact of these interventions on the burden of cancers is actually very small. Nonetheless, these occupational examples provide confidence in the view that cancer, more generally, could be reduced by removing various exposures. One of the important results that came out of the British doctors study (Section 5.3) was that stopping smoking led to a reduction of the risk of lung cancer, even in long-time smokers. It is salutary to note that at the beginning of the study in 1950 more than 80% of British male doctors smoked. After several decades of study, but not necessarily as a consequence, the situation had reversed and more than 80% were non-smokers. Other than the fact that smoking is addictive (the addictive nature of nicotine, the key stimulant in tobacco, explains why smokers find it hard to stop) and that tobacco excise duties contribute mightily to public finances all over the world, there is no real reason why the enormous death toll due to tobacco could not be addressed by simple avoidance of its use.

Another such simple example is related to the exposure to UV radiation, or more specifically related directly to the exposure to direct sunlight. Avoiding direct exposure to sunlight, such as sunbathing, or by using high UV filter sun protection lotions when exposed to direct sunlight, could significantly reduce the incidence of skin cancer.

As our knowledge increases about the various risk factors for cancer, it has become apparent that avoidance of carcinogenic exposures is only one aspect of reducing cancer risk. Figure 5.12 shows how cancer risk can be reduced at various stages in the development of the disease.

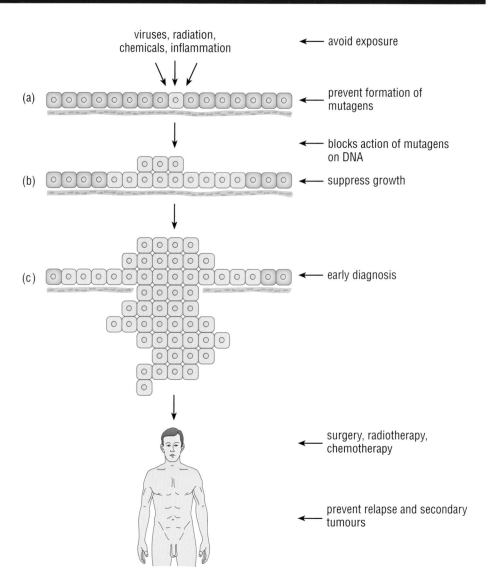

Figure 5.12 A general scheme showing how cancer could be prevented at various stages of the disease.

● What advantages are there in intervening as early as possible?

● In the very early stages of cancer, the steps are reversible. However, once a sufficient number of cells have accumulated with many of the genetic changes required for cancer to develop, it becomes progressively more difficult to prevent a cancer developing.

Focusing on finding specific causes of cancer can be extremely useful, especially where a virus might be responsible, as in the case of HPV and cervical cancer where screening and vaccination can be very effective. However, it may be that efficient public health interventions could be made by tackling seemingly indirect causes of cancer. As noted above, the emerging epidemic of obesity is likely to have a major effect on cancer risk in the years to come. If a measure such as body mass index (BMI) could be used as means to encourage individuals to lose weight, then this would be accompanied by a reduction in cancer risk.

Body mass index (BMI) is defined by your weight in kilograms divided by your height in metres and the result divided again by your height in metres. BMI is an indicator of how healthy a person's weight is.

5.8 Concluding remarks

Cancers are characterised by having accumulated mutations in genes. While there are rare genetic syndromes that predispose individuals to very high risks of cancers, the vast majority of cancers arise in people for whom environmental factors are the overriding driver of their cancer risk. The identification of some of these factors has been relatively straightforward in some cases; for example, the link between tobacco smoking and lung cancer is now almost beyond doubt. In other areas, such as diet, the personal risks are very low, despite the cumulative effects appearing as quite large numbers of cancer cases in the overall population. Thus, in the long term, avoiding or minimising environmental risk factors is likely to have the largest effect on cancer risk.

5.9 Summary of Chapter 5

5.1   There are various risk factors that can affect the chances of getting cancer, some of which we can directly influence, personal risk factors, whilst others we cannot, environmental and genetic risk factors.

5.2   Various epidemiological studies have been used to identify risk factors related to cancer. These can be retrospective, where scientists analyse what has already occurred from what data they can collate, or prospective, where experiments are planned in controlled ways and monitored over many years to see what the outcome will be.

5.3   In case-control studies, people who got cancer are matched with healthy individuals of similar age/lifestyle, etc. and the differences between the two are analysed to find out what may have been the factor that contributed in the cancer incidence.

5.4   A number of risk factors can influence the development of cancer, including genetic, environmental and lifestyle factors, infection, inflammation, exposure to radiation or certain chemicals or changes in diet.

5.5   Although cancer cannot directly be inherited, inherited genetic mutations can significantly increase the risk of developing cancer. Yet, only a small percentage of cancers actually arise from inherited cancer-risk gene variants.

5.6   Radiation is an established risk factor for cancer and can cause cancer either directly or indirectly. UV radiation, can be absorbed by and damage directly the DNA of skin cells, whereas ionising radiation can interact with molecules in tissues of the body to generate free radicals that can also damage DNA. Unchecked DNA damage can lead to mutations and cancer.

5.7   One of the main lifestyle factors associated with cancer is tobacco smoking, which can account for 20% or all cancer deaths and about 80% of lung cancer cases in men and 50% in women worldwide.

5.8   Infections are now clearly linked with risk of cancer, often due to the fact that they result in chronic inflammation and the formation of reactive molecules that can damage DNA. Known viruses directly associated with cancer include HPV and HTLV (and indirectly, HIV), and bacterial infections include *Helicobacter pylori*.

5.9 Exposure to certain chemicals that can cause cancer, i.e. carcinogens, can be either environmental, work or diet related, as ascertained by observation in humans and experiments in animal models. Such examples include chemicals in soot, certain dyes, toxins from moulds (such as aflatoxins) and diet related to cancer.

5.10 Ideas to prevent cancer are related to both the avoidance of exposure to such risk factors as those identified above, as well as to increasing education in order to modify general public attitudes and improve lifestyles.

Questions for Chapter 5

Question 5.1 (Learning outcome 5.1)

Explain what a *case-control study* and a *prospective study* are.

Question 5.2 (Learning outcomes 5.2 and 5.3)

'Cancer is a disease of old age'. Give one historical example that shows that this statement is not always true.

Question 5.3 (Learning outcome 5.2)

How do animal experiments help us to identify causes of cancer?

Question 5.4 (Learning outcome 5.4)

In what sense are not all genes equal when it comes to cancer risk factors?

Question 5.5 (Learning outcome 5.4)

There are often reports in the media of protests against the building of nuclear power plants. Looking at Figure 5.8, what you can say about the increased risk of developing cancer due to the presence of nuclear power stations?

Question 5.6 (Learning outcomes 5.4 and 5.5)

What two major pieces of information have been gained from studies of cancer in migrant populations?

Question 5.7 (Learning outcome 5.5)

What is the major difference between approaches to managing possible cancer risks related to pesticides and those related to diet?

References

Calle, E.E., Rodriguez, C., Walker-Thurmond, K. and Thun, M.J. (2003) 'Overweight, obesity, and mortality from cancer in a prospectively studied cohort of US adults', *The New England Journal of Medicine*, vol. 348, pp. 1625–38.

Cancer Research UK (2008) [online], available at http://www.cancerresearchuk.org.uk (Accessed June 2008).

Doll, R., Peto, R., Boreham, J. and Sutherland, I. (2004) 'Mortality in relation to smoking: 50 years' observations on male British doctors', *British Medical Journal*, vol. 328, pp. 1519–28.

Dronsfield, A. and Ellis, P. (2006) 'Percivall Pott, chimney sweeps and cancer', *Education in Chemistry*, March issue.

Greaves, M. (2000) *Cancer: The Evolutionary Legacy*, Oxford, Oxford University Press.

Health Protection Agency (2205) *Health Protection in the 21st Century*. Available at http://www.hpa.org.uk (Accessed July 2008).

International Agency for Research on Cancer (2007) *Smokeless Tobacco and Some Tobacco-specific N-Nitrosamines*, IARC Monographs on the Evaluation of Carcinogenic Risks to Humans, vol. 89, Lyon, France, IARC.

Liu, B.Q., Peto, R., Chen, Z.M., Boreham, J., Wu, Y.P, Li, J.Y., Campbell, T.C. and Chen, J.S. (1998) 'Emerging tobacco hazards in China: 1. Retrospective proportional mortality study of one million deaths', *British Medical Journal*, vol. 317, pp. 1411–22.

Peto, R., Lopez, A.D., Boreham, J. and Thun, M. (2006) 'Mortality from smoking in developed countries 1950–2000' (2nd edn) [online] International Union Against Cancer http://www.deathsfromsmoking.net (Accessed May 2008).

Quinn, M., Babb, P., Brock, A., Kirby, L. and Jones, J. (2001) [online], *National Statistics. Cancer Trends in England and Wales 1950–1999*. Studies on Medical and Population Subjects No. 66. London, The Stationery Office. Available at http://www.statistics.gov.uk/downloads/theme_health/cancertrends_5099.pdf (Assessed June 2008).

World Cancer Research Fund/American Institute for Cancer Research (1997) *Food, Nutrition and Cancer and the Prevention of Cancer: A Global Perspective*. WCRF/AICR, London and Washington DC, USA. [online] http://www.wcrf.org (Accessed June 2008).

World Cancer Research Fund/American Institute for Cancer Research (2007) *Food, Nutrition, Physical Activity, and the Prevention of Cancer: A Global Perspective*, WCRF/AICR, Washington DC, USA, AICR.

Wynder, E.L. and Graham, E.A. (1950) 'Tobacco smoking as a possible etiologic factor in bronchiogenic carcinoma. A study of six hundred and eighty four proved cases', *Journal of the American Medical Association*, vol. 143, pp. 329–36.

Yamagawa, K. and Ichikawa, K. (1915) 'Experimentielle Studie über die Pathogenese der. Epithelialgeschwülste [Experimental studies on the pathogenesis of skin growths]' *Mitteilungen Med Fakultat Kaiserl. University of Tokyo*, vol. 15, pp. 295–344.

DIAGNOSIS AND SCREENING

Learning outcomes

After studying this chapter and its associated activities, you should be able to:

6.1 Define and use in context, or recognise definitions and applications of, each of the terms printed in **bold** in the text.

6.2 Outline the types of tests that might be used to diagnose cancer.

6.3 Describe examples of physical examinations and laboratory tests for people with suspected cancer.

6.4 Explain the principles behind the major imaging techniques and understand what they can and cannot show.

6.5 Give examples of the use of the major imaging techniques in the diagnosis, staging and management of cancer.

6.6 Describe the use of biopsies and their pathological evaluation to diagnose cancer.

6.7 Outline the advantages and disadvantages of screening for cancer and name some common tests that can be used.

6.1 Introduction

The diagnosis of cancer is not usually straightforward. Cancer may be detected because a person goes to the doctor with symptoms, or it may be detected with specific diagnostic cancer tests in an individual who is asymptomatic, following screening of target populations. We shall return to cancer screening at the end of this chapter; for the moment, we shall consider the person with a range of symptoms who presents at the local clinic or surgery. These are likely to be disparate and complex symptoms, ranging from local to systemic (as you learnt in Section 4.6), and which are common to a myriad of other chronic and acute conditions unrelated to cancer. In essence, the cancer diagnostic process involves two main steps (described in Section 6.2): first, detecting an abnormal growth in a tissue or organ and, second, determining whether the cells forming this abnormal growth are malignant and, if so, to what extent they may have spread. Physical examination and laboratory tests will be discussed in Sections 6.3 and 6.4, respectively, and X-ray techniques will be discussed in Section 6.5, along with some other imaging methods currently available. Other diagnostic tests are likely to include the analysis of samples of the abnormal tissue (Section 6.6). Finally, Section 6.7 will look at the advantages and disadvantages of using some diagnostic tools for cancer screening.

6.2 An overview of the diagnostic process

The first stage of diagnosis for any condition involves a primary healthcare professional (see Box 6.1) who will interview the person (and also the parents in the case of a child) to obtain first-hand information about the range of symptoms and signs that the patient is experiencing. They will then carry out a variety of tests before considering whether to refer the patient to a specialist. The diagnostic tests performed will depend on the specific symptoms present, which point the healthcare professional towards possible initial diagnoses, but they invariably involve a physical examination. Initial tests may also include routine health checks such as measurement of blood pressure, and more specific tests such as a urine test or a blood test. Sometimes the person will be sent to the nearest hospital for more specialised tests which cannot be carried out at the surgery/clinic, for example a chest X-ray. Note that for many of the procedures discussed in this chapter the patient's consent is required. For simple procedures such as taking a blood sample, putting out your arm is considered to be implied consent. However, for more invasive diagnostic procedures, and for therapeutic procedures, a more formal process has to be followed. This will be discussed in Chapter 7.

> ### Box 6.1 Primary, secondary and tertiary health care
>
> Health services all over the world describe what they provide in terms of three 'levels' of care. The levels of care are often represented as a pyramid with the largest sector (primary health care) at the bottom and the smallest sector (tertiary health care) at the top.
>
> Primary health care refers to all the services provided locally in the community in health centres, pharmacies, small clinics and in the workplace or in schools. Primary health care is delivered by family doctors, community nurses and midwives, health visitors, pharmacists and (in the rural villages of most low- and middle-income countries) community health workers with limited training.
>
> Secondary health care is the level of medical care that occurs in district hospitals. Secondary health care provides a wide range of services requiring a greater degree of specialisation from the health professionals and more advanced equipment and drugs than is possible at the primary level.
>
> Tertiary health care refers to the most specialised services. For example, relatively few specialist cancer hospitals exist even in the UK. Although the majority of cancer surgery is performed in district general hospitals (the secondary level), patients requiring certain technically difficult operations such as head and neck surgery would be referred to a tertiary level hospital where the necessary skills and equipment exist.

Depending on the results of these tests, the patient is likely to be referred to a specialist if cancer emerges as a probable diagnosis. In fact, primary healthcare staff usually have access to recommendations given by their medical professional bodies or by governmental agencies on how to proceed with patients with a suspected type of cancer. As an example, the referral guideline for patients with suspected lung cancer given by the UK National Institute for Health and Clinical Excellence (NICE) is shown in Figure 6.1.

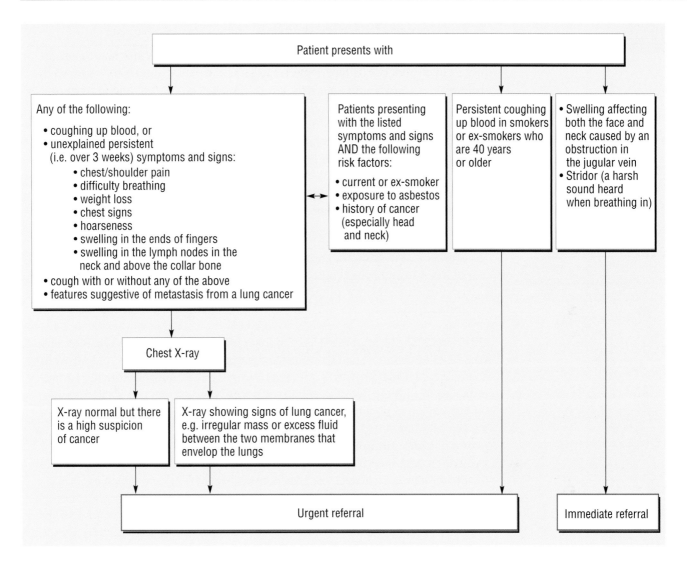

Figure 6.1 UK NICE guidelines for referring patients with suspected lung cancer. (Source: NICE, 2008, p. 105)

The patient's symptoms and other results of initial tests will determine how urgently the patient needs to be seen by a specialist. For instance, an immediate referral means that the patient needs to be seen by a specialist within hours, whereas an urgent referral may take days or even weeks, depending on the geographical area where the patient lives. Note that in many countries the diagnostic process, and indeed medical care, may be generally restricted to this initial stage and only individuals who can afford further medical treatment may be referred to a specialist. In the specialist clinic, more tests will be carried out to detect the location of a tumour and, if a cancer diagnosis is confirmed, the spread of the malignancy. These diagnostic tests may involve imaging techniques and the examination of samples of the abnormal tissue under the microscope. Once the results of all the clinical tests and examinations are obtained, if the results are negative the person is reassured and discharged. However, if a diagnosis of cancer is confirmed, a team of healthcare professionals (called the multidisciplinary team) decides what the best treatment is for the patient. (The multidisciplinary team is discussed in Chapter 7.)

6.3 Physical examination

After talking to the patients about their signs and symptoms and their medical history, the primary healthcare professional will usually continue by performing a clinical examination to identify signs of disease and, in the context of cancer, of an abnormal growth or lump. Some types of abnormal growth are easy to detect simply by visual inspection; for example, a simple examination of the skin will indicate whether irregular moles suggestive of melanoma are present, but visual inspection can also provide information about the general health of the patient.

● Can you suggest an example of a sign easily detected by visual inspection that may provide information about the general functioning of an internal organ?

● Irregular skin or eye colour, for example jaundice, which involves yellowing of the skin and eyes (Figure 4.9, Section 4.6.2), may indicate accumulation of bilirubin, which is suggestive of malfunction of organs involved in bile production.

Other external procedures are used to assess the size and shape of the internal structures of the body, and therefore to determine whether there is organ swelling and/or an abnormal growth. These may include **palpation** (pushing the surface of the body with the flat of the hand) or **percussion** (tapping with the fingers on the surface of the body to assess the organs beneath by the sound emitted or the sensation imparted to the fingers) (Figure 6.2). Another technique the doctor may use is **auscultation**; that is, listening to the sounds inside the body. This is carried out with the help of a stethoscope (a device which usually hangs around the doctor's or nurse's neck for easy access (Figure 6.2)) and which can be used to assess the general functioning of specific biological systems such as the cardiovascular, respiratory and gastrointestinal systems.

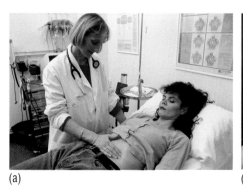 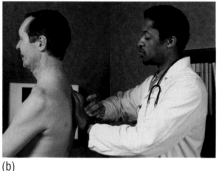
(a)   (b)

Figure 6.2 The diagnostic techniques of (a) palpation and (b) percussion provide the primary healthcare professional with information about underlying internal structures. (Sources: (a) BSIP Laurent/Trunyo/Science Photo Library; (b) CC Studio/Science Photo Library)

These relatively straightforward external procedures may alert the examiner to the presence of an abnormal growth, characteristic of some types of cancer such as breast or testicular carcinoma, or to enlarged lymph nodes, which may be indicative of leukaemia, lymphoma or even metastases from a primary tumour. An internal examination may also be helpful in the case of patients whose symptoms involve biological systems that are readily accessible. Indeed, some internal procedures may be easily performed in the primary health centre by a healthcare professional; these might include using a pair of latex gloves to try to feel the presence of an abnormal lump with the fingers or using basic medical equipment to observe the hollow cavity of an easily accessible organ (e.g. a speculum, an instrument for dilating the opening of a body cavity for medical examination). Examples of these techniques include:

- digital rectal examination used for the detection of colorectal and prostate cancers in which the doctor inserts a lubricated, gloved finger into the rectum and feels for anything that is not normal

- pelvic examination used for the detection of cancer of the cervix (Figure 6.3).

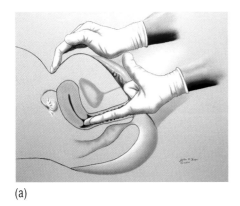
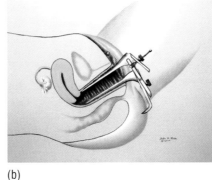

(a)   (b)   (c)

Figure 6.3   (a) An illustration of a pelvic examination being performed by a healthcare professional. (b) A pelvic examination with a speculum. (c) A cervical polyp (bright red and round at centre) seen through a cervical speculum. (Sources: (a) (b) John Foster/Science Photo Library; (c) Dr P. Marazzi/Science Photo Library)

Other observational methods used to detect the presence of tumours (and indeed many other diseases) use highly sophisticated specialised equipment that allows visualisation of some internal hollow organs by introducing an **endoscope**, a thin flexible lighted tube with a camera, through a body orifice. This diagnostic technique is generally known as an **endoscopy** (the word endoscopy comes from the Greek words *endo* meaning 'inside' and *skopeein* meaning 'to examine'). Depending on the organ that is being examined, endoscopies may take specific medical names. So doctors speak of a colonoscopy when the colon is being examined and of a bronchoscopy if it is the lungs that are being investigated (the bronchi are the tubes that connect the lungs to the trachea or windpipe). Endoscopes contain fibre optic cables that carry the image back to the surgeon's viewing lens or to a computer where it is processed and displayed on a screen (Figure 6.4). Endoscopes also contain small surgical instruments which may be manipulated by remote control. As a result, endoscopes are valuable not only in diagnosis but also to remove small polyps (Section 4.2), to collect cells for evaluation of disease malignancy (Section 6.6), or to perform surgery (Chapter 8).

- In both Figure 6.3c and 6.4b, the abnormal growth appears a brighter red or pink than the surrounding tissue. Explain a likely reason for this phenomenon.

- Tumour tissue is usually packed with blood vessels to allow them to grow to a larger size (Section 4.3). The high blood content in tumours makes them usually appear brighter red or pink than the surrounding tissue.

Figure 6.4 (a) Doctors performing an endoscopy, in this case a gastroscopy, of a patient's stomach. The endoscope has been inserted through the patient's mouth and fed down through her throat. The image obtained by the endoscope is on a computer screen at the upper left of the photo. (b) Endoscope view (during a colonoscopy) of an adenocarcinoma (bright pink, upper centre) on the inside wall of the colon. (Sources: (a) Deep Light Productions/ Science Photo Library; (b) David M. Martin, MD/ Science Photo Library)

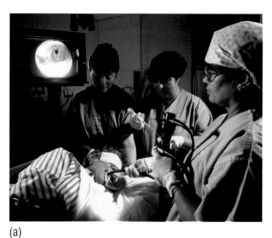
(a)

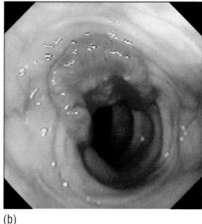
(b)

Case study 6.1   Dave Bayler's initial tests

The Bayler family's physician knows the family well, and has treated the children for everything from childhood infections to sports injuries in high school, but he has difficulty remembering the last time Dave visited him on his own behalf. After an initial consultation, in which he palpates his abdomen, examines his rectum and takes a detailed family history, he is seriously worried. Although most men in early middle age presenting with blood in the stools will be diagnosed with the common, if embarrassing, complaint of piles, Dave's case looks very different. With two first-degree relatives (a parent and a sibling) having developed cancer before early middle age, he is in the highest cancer risk category; his other main symptom, a long-lasting change to looser stools with no obvious explanation, is often found in patients with colon cancer; and the initial examination revealed what seemed to be an unusual growth in the lower part of the colon. The physician refers Dave for further investigations as a hospital outpatient; the letter is marked 'Urgent'.

Less than two weeks later, Dave is lying on his side on a hospital bed, while a charming young nurse passes a flexible tube up his rectum and into his colon. He finds this test – a colonoscopy – to be uncomfortable, rather than painful. In fact, he is chiefly feeling hungry; for several days before the test, he has been on a very restrictive diet designed to empty his bowels completely. He has also been given a sedative. The colonoscopy tube carries a tiny light and camera that throws images of the inside of

Dave's bowel onto a screen. He can see these images, which he finds rather disconcerting. Using the endoscope, the doctor scrapes up a sample of cells from the 'growth' for a biopsy. After the test, Dave's wife picks him up and drives him home. He is feeling rather sleepy (as well as worrying about the results) and is very grateful that his wife and eldest son can take care of the diner for the rest of the day.

6.4 Laboratory tests

The most common laboratory tests are *a complete blood count* to measure the important components of the blood, and urine tests in which, for example, levels of albumin, a protein found in plasma, are determined to test kidney function. (Proteins such as albumin do not usually leak from plasma into the urine; high levels of albumin in urine indicate that the kidney is not filtering the plasma appropriately.)

A complete blood count comprises the measurement of the levels of red cells (Section 4.3), leukocytes (Section 4.5), and platelets (the blood cells responsible for coagulation, i.e. the formation of blood clots) in the patient's blood. In the context of cancer, the levels of haemoglobin are useful to determine whether the patient has iron-deficiency anaemia, a common occurrence in bowel cancers (and indeed many other conditions). Recall from Section 4.3 that haemoglobin is the protein in red blood cells responsible for transporting oxygen and carbon dioxide in the blood. Since iron is required to form the haemoglobin protein, low levels of haemoglobin may indicate either a decreased absorption of iron from the diet through the gut or the occurrence of bleeding in, for example, the colon as a result of a tumour. In this context, a more specific test that indicates colon malfunction and, in particular, bleeding, characteristic of colon carcinomas, is known as the faecal occult blood (FOB) test, which detects the presence of haemoglobin in faeces. (The FOB test detects hidden, hence the name 'occult', blood in the stool which may come from anywhere along the digestive tract and which is not present if the digestive system is healthy.)

However, these tests are limited in the information that they can provide, since they usually refer to the general health of the patient or are indicative of the normal or otherwise functioning of an organ but not specifically of the onset of cancer. If the whole picture of symptoms and initial tests is consistent with cancer, then further specific tests may be advisable. These include various diagnostic imaging techniques (Section 6.5) and tissue biopsies (Section 6.6) but also, more recently, **tumour markers** have emerged as potential diagnostic tools. The term 'tumour marker' refers to the levels of a substance that can be measured in blood, urine or body tissues. In order to be able to discriminate between healthy individuals and patients with cancer, the measured levels of the tumour marker should be abnormally high in patients with cancer compared to the levels in a healthy individual.

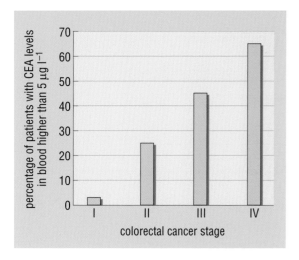

Figure 6.5 The percentage of patients with colorectal cancer with CEA blood levels higher than 5 μg l^{-1} according to cancer stage. (See Section 4.4.4 for an explanation of the staging process.) (Source: Duffy, 2001)

The list of tumour markers available to doctors is growing rapidly due to extensive research in this area (Table 6.1). Here we will do no more than describe the use of one of the first tumour markers to be identified, carcinoembryonic antigen (CEA). CEA is a protein that functions as an adhesion molecule (Section 2.9.3) and is normally present in fetal blood but not in that of adults. CEA is also present at high levels in the blood of patients with colorectal cancer. Patients with late-stage colorectal cancers tend to have higher CEA levels in their blood than those with early-stage cancer or those in the general population (Figure 6.5). A high CEA level in the blood of a patient may therefore alert the physician to a possible colorectal cancer. However, the use of tumour markers such as CEA as diagnostic tools has been controversial mainly due to two observations:

- Many patients with a particular type of cancer do not show elevated blood levels of the tumour marker, i.e. the tests are not sensitive enough to detect all patients with cancer.

- Levels of tumour markers can be elevated in a variety of other conditions, either other types of cancer or diseases unrelated to cancer. In these cases, these cancer diagnostic tests can give 'false' positives (Section 6.7). Note, for example, that smokers have generally higher CEA blood levels than non-smokers and that patients with liver disease or gastric, pancreatic, lung and breast carcinomas also present elevated CEA blood levels.

Table 6.1 Some tumour markers shown to be prognostic in malignancy. (You do not need to memorise the details of this table.) (Source: Duffy, 2007)

Cancer	Tumour marker(s)
breast	oestrogen receptor*, HER2*
prostate	PSA
colorectal	CEA
ovarian	CA 125
lung	CYFRA 21–1
non-seminomatous germline cell tumour (a type of testicular cancer)	AFP, HCG, LDH
trophoblastic neoplasms (a type of cancer associated with pregnancy in which a tumour grows instead of a fetus)	HCG
neuroblastoma (a type of tumour associated with tissue of the nervous system)	*N-myc* gene amplification*

*These tumour markers are measured in tumour tissue rather than in the blood.

Consequently, tumour markers are at present most often used in patients already diagnosed with cancer for prognostic purposes, rather than as diagnostic tools. For example, CEA can be used to monitor the progression of the disease in patients with colorectal cancer within the same cancer stage. Many studies have shown that patients with pre-surgery levels of CEA in blood above 5 µg per litre have a worse outcome than those with lower levels (see Box 4.2 for an explanation of scientific units, and Box 6.2 for concentration). In addition, tumour markers may be useful either to predict or to confirm the therapeutic efficacy of a particular treatment. To do this, doctors usually take samples to determine the level of a tumour marker before treatment (i.e. the baseline level) and compare it to the levels sampled following treatment. A post-treatment

Box 6.2 Concentrations

Concentration is a way of expressing the amount of a substance in a known volume of liquid. For example, if you dissolved 5 grams of sugar in a litre of water the concentration of the resulting solution would be 5 grams sugar per litre of water. If you were to pour half this solution (i.e. 500 ml) into a beaker the concentration would still be 5 grams per litre even though you had half the volume.

1 litre = 1000 millilitres (ml).

● How much sugar would there be in 500 ml of this solution in the beaker?

● The concentration is 5 grams per litre, so that is 5 g per 1000 ml. The beaker contains 500 ml of this solution and therefore it contains 2.5 g of sugar.

● If you were to add further 500 ml water to the beaker containing 500 ml of the 5 grams sugar per litre solution, how much sugar would there be in the new solution? What would the concentration of sugar be in the new solution?

● Adding 500 ml water does not modify the amount of sugar contained in the beaker which remains constant. Therefore in 1000 ml of the new solution there will still be 2.5 g of sugar. However, the concentration of sugar in the new solution will be changed to 2.5 g per 1000 ml or, in other words, 2.5 grams per litre.

As with very small numbers, scientific units can also be expressed as negative powers (Box 2.2). So, just as $\frac{1}{10}$ can be written as 1×10^{-1}, grams per litre can also be expressed as g/l (or $\frac{g}{l}$), which is the same as $g \times l^{-1}$, which is abbreviated as $g\ l^{-1}$.

● You read above that CEA is present in the blood at a level of 5 µg l^{-1}. What is this value expressed in words?

● 5 µg l^{-1} is five micrograms of CEA per litre of blood.

decrease in the levels of the tumour marker would indicate a partial or complete removal of the tumour. Similarly, if the levels of the tumour marker are low following treatment, a later increase might indicate that the cancer has recurred.

Even though there are inherent problems with tumour markers as diagnostic tools, some organ-specific markers have been proposed for cancer screening purposes. This is the case of **prostate-specific antigen (PSA)**, a protein whose levels in blood are measured to detect prostate cancer. However, the possible benefits of this type of screening in target populations (e.g. men over the age of 50) in reducing cancer mortality still remain unclear (Section 6.7).

6.5 Imaging tests

6.5.1 Imaging and cancer

Imaging plays an important role in almost all aspects of modern medicine and is very widely used in the diagnosis and treatment of people with cancer. Many books and journal papers have been written on different imaging techniques (or modalities) and on their use in cancer; in a course of this nature it is only possible to explain the basic principles of the most widely employed imaging techniques and to give you some examples of their use in relation to cancer. First of all, have a go at the question below – your answers to this will depend on your previous studies and your experience as either a patient or perhaps as a healthcare professional.

● List all the imaging techniques you have come across that might be used in a modern hospital.

● You may have thought of X-rays (including computed tomography (CT) scans), ultrasound, magnetic resonance imaging (MRI) and radionuclide imaging.

Sections 6.5.2–6.5.7 will show how these different techniques work and give examples of where they can be used.

Before looking at the individual imaging techniques, consider what roles imaging can play in cancer treatment. Obviously it can play an important role in diagnosis, but it can be used in several other ways as well. In this chapter, we shall show examples of imaging techniques being used for:

• *Diagnosis*: Imaging can be used to show the presence of tumours; it can also be used to show the absence of tumours. In other words it can be used to 'diagnose in' or 'diagnose out'.

• *Staging*: The TNM staging system was described in Section 4.4.4. Imaging is important not only in determining the presence, position and size of the primary tumour (T), but also in looking for affected lymph nodes (N) and the presence of metastases (M). The staging of a patient is crucial as it has a very large effect on the management of that patient's disease. Imaging can also be useful in looking for what is described as 'co-pathology' – any other diseases that may be present in the patient and which may affect the management of the cancer.

- *Monitoring of treatment*: When treatment is being given, repeated imaging can help to answer questions about its efficacy. It can be used to answer questions such as: 'Has the primary tumour shrunk?' 'Have new metastases appeared?' and it can also check for side effects of radiotherapy or chemotherapy.

- *Radiotherapy treatment planning*: Radiotherapy plays a very important role in the treatment of cancer. As you will see in Chapter 9, all radiotherapy treatments have to be very carefully planned so as to give a large enough dose of radiation to tumour tissue to kill it, and as low a dose as possible to normal tissue to avoid complications. This can only be done with the help of accurate imaging techniques, so imaging is essential to treatment planning.

6.5.2 X-ray imaging

The discovery of X-rays in 1895 can really be said to have been the beginning of medical imaging; prior to that time the only means that doctors had of finding out what was inside a patient was either to feel, or to pick up a scalpel and open up the patient! X-rays were discovered almost accidentally by Wilhelm Conrad Roentgen. Once he had established that he had some new kind of ray, he carried out various investigations. He found that the rays travelled through wood quite well, but not through metal, and, almost by chance, found that they could be used to produce images of the bones inside people. (The first X-ray was of the hand of his wife.)

The discovery was greeted with great excitement in the scientific community. X-ray imaging spread rapidly and for about 50 years was the only method of medical imaging in use. Today X-rays are still widely used as a cheap, quick and easy method of making an initial assessment – many students of this course will probably have had an X-ray for a suspected broken bone. However, they are now supplemented by a range of other imaging techniques.

Roentgen used the name 'X-rays' because X denotes an unknown. Today they are known in German-speaking countries as Roentgenstrahlung (Roentgen rays).

While it is not the intention of this course to study the detailed physics of X-rays, it is helpful for you to understand how the image is formed and how X-rays can best be used.

Look at Figure 6.6. This image – known as a planar X-ray because it is a planar (two-dimensional; 2D) projection of a three-dimensional patient – is taken with the patient standing close to a detector screen and a beam of X-rays is passed through the chest from back to front. It is easy to identify the major features – the ribs, the sternum, the heart, etc. But you may be asking yourself some questions:

- Why is there an image?

- Why is it possible to distinguish between different types of tissue?

To understand the basis of X-ray imaging you need to know more about the nature of X-rays and the way in which X-rays behave when they interact with matter. You will recall from

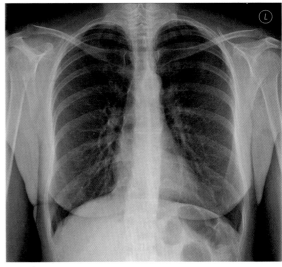

Figure 6.6 A normal chest X-ray. (Source: University Hospitals Coventry and Warwickshire NHS Trust)

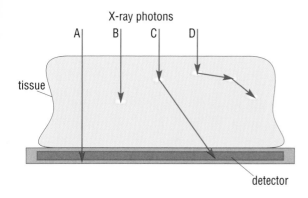

X-ray photons

A B C D

tissue

detector

Figure 6.7   Diagram showing the possible different paths of X-ray photons through tissue.

Section 5.5.1 that X-rays are a form of electromagnetic radiation – a form of energy that can be described as either a wave or as a flow of photons or 'packets' of energy. X-rays are at the high-energy end of the spectrum. This means each photon has a high energy; it can penetrate a long way into tissue and can cause damage if it gives up some of its energy to the tissue. You should also remember from Section 5.5.1 that X-rays are ionising radiation and therefore have the potential to cause cancer, although the risks are very low.

As X-ray photons pass through air they interact very little with the widely spaced air molecules. However, when they enter tissue, or any other solid or liquid material, there are three things that can happen to each photon. These are shown in Figure 6.7.

- The photon can pass straight through the tissue with no interaction of any kind (A).

- It can be absorbed in the tissue, releasing some energy (B).

- It can be scattered so that, when the photon emerges from the tissue it is travelling in a different direction (C). In this case there is usually some energy released in the tissue.

Combinations of these processes can also occur, for example scattering followed by absorption (D).

There is an extremely large number of photons in an X-ray beam used to image a patient. The overall effect of all these processes is to reduce the number of X-rays in the beam so that, by the time the beam emerges from the patient, there is only a fraction of the original number of photons. This reduction is described as **attenuation** of the beam.

This is all very well, but it does not explain why one can obtain an image such as Figure 6.6 which shows up the different tissue types in the chest.

● Can you suggest an explanation for the fact that it is possible to obtain an image that shows different tissues?

● If the amount of attenuation were different in different tissues, then there would be a difference in the number of photons reaching different parts of the detector.

This is exactly what happens in X-ray imaging. Denser materials, such as bone and metal, attenuate a beam of X-rays to a much greater degree than soft tissue and water. For medical imaging it is extremely important to know the relative attenuation that occurs in different tissues. A quantity called the **attenuation coefficient** is used to calculate this.

Activity 6.1   Understanding X-ray imaging

Allow about 45 minutes in total for this activity

This activity gives you a chance to explore the way in which the X-ray intensity varies with thickness and tissue type. Completing this activity is essential for your understanding of how X-ray images are produced.

Planar X-rays are useful in cancer imaging, often for a quick and easy initial assessment of a patient. They can be used:

- for chest X-rays (as in Figure 6.6), which will show any large abnormalities in the thorax (chest cavity)

- to look for large tumours and/or co-pathology, i.e. some other disease that is present and may affect the way in which the cancer is treated – for example, to look for tuberculosis in a patient with cancer

- for myeloma, a cancer of the bone marrow. Figure 6.8 shows an example of this.

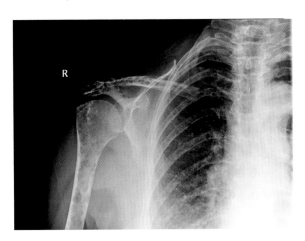

Figure 6.8   A planar X-ray of a patient with myeloma (Section 4.6.3). The cancer has damaged the bone cells and this has led to holes in the bone. (Source: University Hospitals Coventry and Warwickshire NHS Trust)

6.5.3 Computed tomography imaging

You have seen in Section 6.5.2 that planar X-rays are useful in some circumstances but they do have limitations.

- ● What do you think are the limitations of planar X-rays for imaging internal structures?

- ● The main limitation is that the image produced is a 2D projection of a 3D object. This means that some structures can be hidden behind others. It is also not possible to judge the depth of an object in the body.

There is another problem in that the attenuation coefficients of most soft tissues are very similar and so it is hard to distinguish different organs, or to distinguish tumour tissue within an organ from the normal tissue of the organ.

One of the ways to overcome these problems is to devise a **tomographic** method of X-ray imaging. Such a method produces images of slices of the body (the Greek word for slice is *tomos*). Successive slices can then be used to build up a 3D picture of the section of the body under investigation. Figure 6.9 shows a typical tomographic image, in this case an X-ray image of a slice through the abdomen.

Producing a tomographic image is not an easy thing to do; the mathematics needed was first developed by the Austrian Johann Radon in 1917 but the execution of the ideas had to wait until computers became available. The first tomographic X-ray scanner, designed for looking for brain tumours, was built in the UK in the 1970s and won a Nobel prize for its inventors

Figure 6.9 A typical tomographic (CT) image of the abdomen showing the intestines, liver, kidneys, a vertebra (bone of the spinal column) and ribs. It is conventional to view these images as if looking up from the patient's feet so the left side of the patient is on the right of the image. (The metastases in the liver will be discussed later in this section.) (Source: University Hospitals Coventry and Warwickshire NHS Trust)

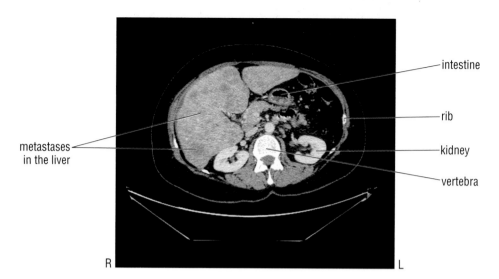

(Godfrey N. Hounsfield and Allan M. Cormack) in 1979. Development since then has been rapid but the basic principles are still based on the 1917 paper by Radon.

The aim of X-ray **computed tomography (CT)** scanning is to build up a 'map' of a slice of the body. Each pixel (picture element) in the image has an intensity that depends on its attenuation coefficient. Materials with a high attenuation coefficient, such as bone, are usually shown as white, and the intensity reduces as the attenuation coefficient reduces.

● Look at Figure 6.9. You should notice that the bones of the vertebrae are white. Can you think of a reason why the intestines show as black on the image?

● Black corresponds to a very low attenuation coefficient, most likely a material of very low density. In this case it is gas in the intestines.

An image like this is obtained by rotating an X-ray source around the patient and collecting information about the number of X-ray photons that pass through the patient in each of about 1000 different directions. From this information the computer can calculate back to a number (known as the Hounsfield number) for each pixel. (The Hounsfield number is simply related to the attenuation coefficient which you learnt about in Activity 6.1.) Figure 6.10 shows the principles.

The first CT scanners obtained images of one slice at a time. The patient was then moved through the gantry and another slice was imaged. This was rather slow and, for the thorax, could lead to inconsistencies in the images if the patient inhaled by a different amount for each slice. Modern scanners are able to move the bed at the same time as collecting the information so a set of data for the whole volume is collected. The speed of rotation has also increased and a modern scanner can image the whole chest in less than 30 seconds – much less than one breath-hold, even for sick patients. Because a volume set of data is obtained it is possible to reconstruct a 3D image of the region under investigation. Figure 6.11 shows reconstructed images of a chest, with the lung cancer clearly visible.

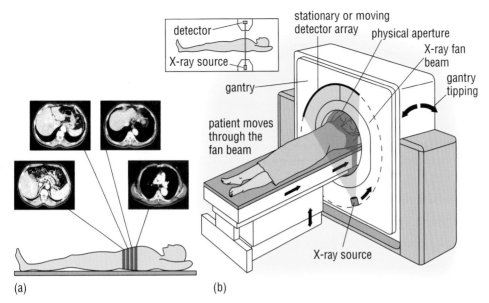

Figure 6.10 The principles of CT scanning. The patient lies on the bed which is moved through the aperture while the X-ray source rotates around the patient. The detectors measure the intensity of the transmitted X-rays and this information is used to calculate a Hounsfield number for each pixel and to produce images of the slices.

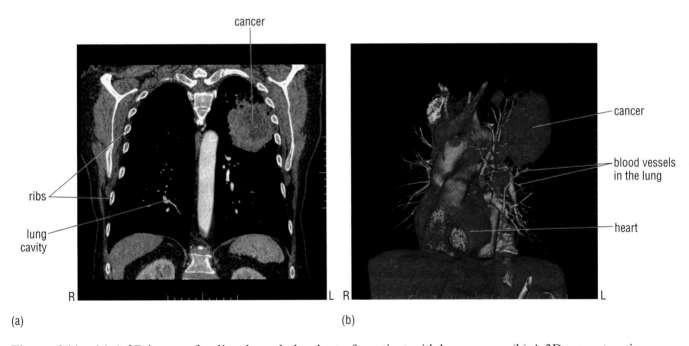

Figure 6.11 (a) A 2D image of a slice through the chest of a patient with lung cancer. (b) A 3D reconstruction of the chest of the same patient. (Note that the bones have not been included in this image.) (Sources: University Hospitals Coventry and Warwickshire NHS Trust)

CT imaging is more time-consuming and more costly than planar X-ray imaging and it also gives the patient a larger amount of potentially damaging ionising radiation. However, it has enormous diagnostic advantages over planar imaging. It is used in the diagnosis of a wide range of cancers. Often the diagnostic process is considerably helped by the use of **contrast agents**. These are substances that have either a much higher or a much lower attenuation coefficient than most soft tissues and are introduced into the patient in order to highlight certain organs.

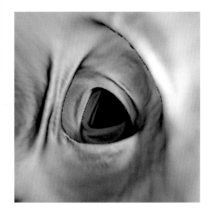

Figure 6.12 A 'fly through' view of the colon reconstructed from a CT colonograph with the colon inflated by carbon dioxide. Note that the resolution of this image is not high enough to see the surface texture of the colon. Video clips of images like this are on the course website. (Source: University Hospitals Coventry and Warwickshire NHS Trust)

Of course anything introduced into the patient must also be non-toxic and capable of eventually being expelled. Substances which are often used for contrast are iodine and barium (both very high density) and gas (very low density). Some examples of their use are:

- iodine-containing substances injected either into the bloodstream to show up the major blood vessels and organs such as the liver and kidneys, or into the urinary tract.
- barium-containing liquid given as either a drink (the 'barium meal') or as an enema to show up the gastrointestinal tract
- carbon dioxide gas blown in a controlled way into the colon prior to CT colonography, an examination of the colon to look for cancerous growths (see Figure 6.12).

As well as being very useful for diagnosis of a wide range of cancers, CT scans also play an important role in the management and treatment of patients with cancer. CT scans of the abdomen can show up lymph glands that have been affected by cancer (Figure 6.13) and also metastases in, for example, the liver (Figure 6.10). This enables the staging of cancers (see Section 4.4.4) using the TNM system.

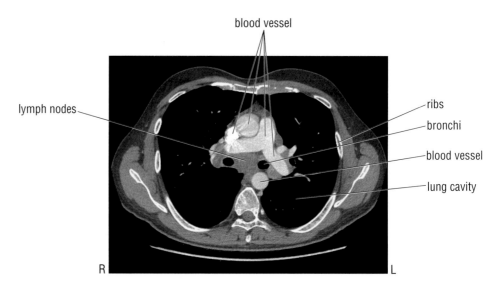

Figure 6.13 CT scan showing enlarged lymph glands. Note that the blood vessels show as light areas because a contrast medium has been injected into the bloodstream prior to imaging. (Source: University Hospitals Coventry and Warwickshire NHS Trust)

● Why do you think the metastases (secondary tumours) in the liver look different from the surrounding tissue?

● The metastases have a different attenuation coefficient from the normal tissue.

Last, but definitely not least, CT scans are essential in the planning of radiotherapy treatment for the vast majority of patients. This subject will be covered more fully in Chapter 9 but Figure 6.14 shows a CT scan with a superimposed plan of the treatment using two high-energy X-ray beams.

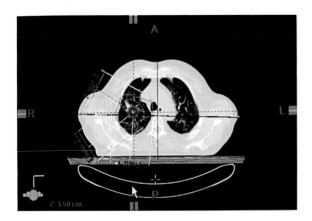

Figure 6.14 A CT scan with superimposed beams for lung radiotherapy treatment. (Source: Directorate of Radiology, Royal Berkshire NHS Foundation Trust)

Case study 6.2   Lin Ming's diagnosis

Ten years later, Lin Ming, now 51, begins to feel unwell, and has nausea and vomiting. He also feels as if his stomach has swollen. He goes to the provincial hospital with his wife and has some blood taken for laboratory tests. The tests show that he has liver malfunction, which is suggestive of a diagnosis of hepatocirrhosis (liver cirrhosis is a disease of the liver which may be caused by alcoholism or hepatitis). However, the doctors want to do further tests. Subsequently, using CT-imaging, one tumour of 12 cm diameter and a few smaller tumours are found near his hepatic portal vein. Tumours of this size and position are too difficult to treat by surgery. The doctors at the hospital then decide to carry out a liver biopsy over the area where the tumours are. Lin Ming undergoes all these tests without asking many questions and with a complete faith in the hospital doctors' abilities to cure him. Finally, a diagnosis is reached, advanced hepatocellular carcinoma.

The diagnosis of advanced hepatocellular carcinoma suggests an incurable terminal disease and many patients in China would have difficulties in accepting this prognosis. Often it is their relatives who are informed first. As soon as Lin's wife hears the diagnosis from the doctor, she is completely at a loss and does not know how to cope with the news. The doctor discusses with her whether it is appropriate to tell her husband the truth. After learning that Lin is an active and optimistic person, the doctor suggests breaking the news to him gradually. So at the point of diagnosis Lin Ming is hospitalised as a hepatocirrhosis patient.

6.5.4 Ultrasound imaging

Following the discovery of X-rays in 1895 and their rapid adoption as a medical imaging technique, they remained the only medical imaging technique for about 50 years. Several other techniques were developed after World War II, in some cases being built upon the technological developments that had taken place during the war. Ultrasound is a good example of this; it is based on the reflection of ultrasound from tissue interfaces in the body. Early ultrasound imaging used some of the electronic pulse technology developed for radar which is based on the reflection of low-energy electromagnetic radiation.

The frequency of a sound wave is the number of oscillations per second. The units used are hertz, abbreviated to Hz. One Hz means one oscillation per second.

The prefix M, for mega, means one million times. Thus a MHz is 1×10^6 Hz. (Refer back to Boxes 2.2 and 4.2 for more information on scientific notation and units.)

Ultrasound is, like audible sound, a pressure wave. The frequencies used for medical imaging are between 2 MHz and 10 MHz – well above the audible range of 10 Hz to 20 kHz.

In an ultrasound imaging system, pulses of high-frequency sound are transmitted into the tissue by a **transducer** – a device that converts an electrical signal into a pulse of ultrasound. The sound passes into the tissue and is reflected at boundaries between different tissues. The reflected waves return to the transducer as shown in Figure 6.15. When the transducer is not transmitting ultrasound it 'listens' for ultrasound pulses to be returned and can convert received ultrasound pulses back into electrical signals. The reflection and transmission of ultrasound is shown in Figure 6.15. As with radar, because the speed of the sound is known, the time taken for a pulse to be returned allows the distance it has travelled into the tissue to be calculated. In another parallel with radar, the pulses are sent out in different directions, so enabling a 2D image to be built up.

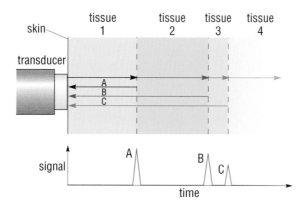

Figure 6.15 The principles of ultrasound imaging. Ultrasound pulses produced by the transducer are reflected by boundaries in the tissue and arrive back at the transducer where they are converted into electrical signals giving a series of electrical pulses (bottom trace). If the transducer scans across the patient, then a 2D image can be produced (as in Figure 6.16a).

When the ultrasound pulse passes through tissue it will be attenuated in a similar fashion to X-rays. As with X-rays, the attenuation coefficient is different in different tissues – in clear fluids such as water, urine or amniotic fluid (the fluid that surrounds the fetus in the womb), attenuation is very low. However, the key factor in ultrasound imaging is not the attenuation – that is simply a bit of a nuisance! Instead it is the amount of reflection at the boundaries between different types of tissue (also known as tissue interfaces). Table 6.2 shows the percentage of the ultrasound reflected at some different interfaces.

Table 6.2 Percentage reflection at the boundaries at different interfaces.

	Tissues			
	Muscle/fat	**Muscle/ bone**	**Muscle/ water**	**Muscle/gas**
percentage reflection	1.1%	25%	0.4%	99%

● Look at Table 6.2. What can you say about imaging parts of the body where there is bone or gas? Would you expect to be able to image the lungs or inside the skull?

● Almost all the sound is reflected at an interface with gas, and a large amount at an interface with bone. This means that the ultrasound will not penetrate beyond the bone or gas so it will be difficult to image behind them. So imaging inside the skull is very hard (except for the fetus where the bones are soft, or for babies where there is a gap, the fontanelle, in the bones on the top of the head.)

Consequently ultrasound is primarily a technique for soft tissue imaging. Because the equipment is portable and (relatively) cheap it is widely available and finds many uses. Perhaps the most well-known use is in obstetrics (the branch of medicine dealing with the care of women during pregnancy and childbirth) which was the first area in which it was widely used, but today ultrasound is used for many different purposes. A simple one is shown in Figure 6.16a, an ultrasound scan of a breast. This patient had had a breast X-ray (a mammogram) as part of a routine screening programme (see Section 6.7) and that had identified some form of lump in the breast. The ultrasound scan shows that this is in fact a harmless cyst. The cyst, which is full of fluid, shows up very clearly as a black object because there is no reflection or attenuation within the fluid. A tumour would have produced a far greater intensity of reflection and would have shown up as whiter than the other tissue. In recent years it has become possible to produce 3D ultrasound images; Figure 6.16b is an example and shows a bladder tumour.

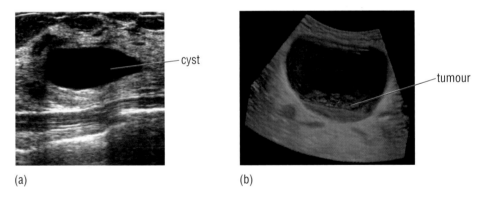

(a) (b)

Figure 6.16   (a) A 2D ultrasound scan of a breast, showing a harmless cyst. The ultrasound transducer is at the top of the image. The area below the cyst looks brighter because there is no attenuation of the sound as it passes through the cyst. (b) A 3D ultrasound scan of a bladder, showing a tumour. (Sources: (a) Department of Medical Physics and Radiology, Oxford Radcliffe Hospitals; (b) University Hospitals Coventry and Warwickshire NHS Trust)

Ultrasound images can be enhanced by using a well-known phenomenon called the Doppler effect. If you have ever listened to the note of a train whistle or an ambulance siren as the vehicle passes you, you are familiar with the Doppler effect. The note rises in pitch (an increase in frequency) as the vehicle moves towards you, and drops in pitch (a decrease in frequency) as the vehicle moves away again. The same effect can be used in imaging; the ultrasound is transmitted into the patient at a known frequency but if it is reflected by a moving object, such as a red blood cell, then the frequency of the ultrasound pulse is either increased or decreased depending on whether the blood is flowing towards or away from the transducer. This change in frequency can be detected and used in one of several ways, the most usual one being to display it as a change in colour of the moving object on the ultrasound image. Conventionally blue is used for objects moving away from the transducer and red towards. Figure 6.17 shows a typical Doppler ultrasound image.

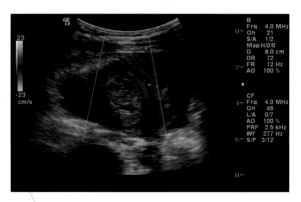

Figure 6.17   Ultrasound 2D scan of a section of the bowel where there is an intussusception (one part of the bowel invading another) due to an osteosarcoma. The Doppler colour imaging shows the blood flow in the bowel wall. (Source: University Hospitals Coventry and Warwickshire NHS Trust)

6.5.5 Magnetic resonance imaging (MRI)

Atomic nuclei were introduced in Box 5.5.

Magnetic resonance imaging is another tomographic technique and produces very high-quality images. It developed from nuclear magnetic resonance (NMR) – a technique used for analysis by chemists and physicists since its discovery in 1948. In 1973, Paul Lauterbur proposed a method whereby NMR could be used to form an image and MRI has developed steadily since then. Its basis lies in the behaviour in a magnetic field of the nuclei of the atoms, usually the hydrogen atoms, in the body. The patient has to be placed in a large uniform static magnetic field (Figure 6.18). Then pulses of rapidly changing magnetic fields are used to excite the nuclei of the atoms. The hydrogen nuclei in different tissues respond slightly differently to the radio-frequency fields. This enables the production of images in which different tissue types appear with different intensity. You may recall that, in CT, the brightness depends on the attenuation coefficient, so bone is light and air is black; in MRI it is much more complicated! By changing the sequence of the different pulses the images can be altered to show up different tissues.

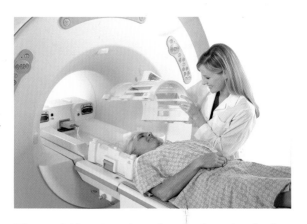

Figure 6.18   A patient about to have her brain imaged in an MRI scanner. The structure being placed over her head is a coil designed to pick up signals from the head. Once it is in place, the bed is moved so that the patient's head is in the centre of the scanner. (Source: GE Healthcare Technologies)

The technique is complicated, time-consuming and expensive but it yields high-quality images of slices in any direction in the body, plus 3D images when required. However, some patients may find the procedure claustrophobic because they have to lie in a long tube.

Applications of MRI are too numerous to list. It is excellent at showing soft tissue damage and disease; in cancer it can be used for diagnosis of metastases and for the staging of, for example, colorectal tumours. Figure 6.19 shows some typical images. One specialist use is in the diagnosis of breast cancer in high-risk younger women; the denser breasts of younger women are difficult to image using the standard X-ray mammogram so MRI is used for women with a familial history of breast cancer.

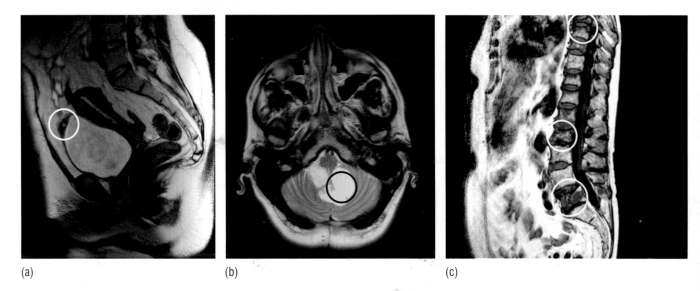

(a)   (b)   (c)

Figure 6.19   Some examples of MRI scans. (a) An adenocarcinoma at the top of the bladder (circled). (b) A brain tumour and accompanying hydrocephalus (a build up of fluids within the skull) (circled). (c) Collapsed vertebrae due to myeloma (circled). (Sources: University Hospitals Coventry and Warwickshire NHS Trust)

6.5.6 Radionuclide imaging

All the imaging methods discussed so far are used largely for examining the *structure* of the body. For example, CT scans give excellent images of all the organs and can easily reveal any anatomical abnormalities. Radionuclide imaging is very different in that its main purpose is to examine the *function* of organs, in other words to look at the physiology.

Radionuclide imaging involves the use of radioactive materials, so in order to understand this method you need to know something about radioactivity. If you are not familiar with this, please study Box 6.3 (overleaf) before going any further in the main text.

Stable and unstable isotopes

Some nuclei are stable, and can remain in that form indefinitely; others are unstable and will undergo radioactive decay to form some other nucleus. For example, a carbon nucleus with 6 or 7 neutrons is very stable indeed, but the other isotopes mentioned in Box 6.3, with 5 or 8 neutrons are unstable.

Nuclei that are unstable will decay, and such decay is known as **radioactive decay**. A nuclide (type of nucleus) that undergoes radioactive decay is known as a **radionuclide**. There are several types of radioactive decay that can take place,

Box 6.3 Atomic structure

In Section 2.3 you learnt that elements exist as atoms, and that atoms of different elements can combine to form molecules. In Box 5.5 you learnt that atoms are made up of a nucleus, composed of protons and neutrons, surrounded by negatively charged electrons. The nucleus is very dense and positively charged and is surrounded by a very light, 'cloud' of negatively charged electrons. The outer electrons are only very loosely bound to the nucleus and it is these electrons that take part in chemical reactions, forming the bonds mentioned in Section 2.3.

The nucleus is made up of two types of particles: protons, which are positively charged, and neutrons, which are, as their name suggests, neutral, i.e. not charged at all. The charge on each proton is exactly opposite to the charge on an electron so, in a neutral atom, the number of protons in the nucleus is exactly matched by the number of electrons around the nucleus. The number of protons in the nucleus therefore determines the number of electrons around the nucleus and consequently also determines the chemical behaviour of the atom. So the type of atom (i.e. the element) is determined by the number of protons in the nucleus. This number is known as the **atomic number**, usually given the symbol Z.

The simplest element, hydrogen, has only one proton in the nucleus, the next heaviest, helium, has two, and so on. Figure 6.20 is a schematic diagram of a carbon-12 nucleus – not to scale – showing the protons and neutrons in the nucleus and the electron cloud around the nucleus. In reality the nucleus is so small as to be invisible on this scale. Table 6.3 shows the number of protons in the nuclei of some common elements. It also shows the symbol that is conventionally used for that element.

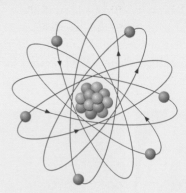

Figure 6.20 Schematic diagram of a carbon-12 nucleus. The positively charged protons (shown in red) and neutrons (green) form the very dense nucleus which is surrounded by a cloud of negatively charged electrons (blue). Note that this diagram is not to scale.

But what of the neutrons – what do they do? Almost all nuclei contain at least the same number of neutrons as protons; in the case of larger atoms the number of neutrons is larger than the number of protons. The neutrons maintain the stability of the nucleus. The mass of a neutron is approximately the same as the mass of a proton (both are about 1.67×10^{-27} kg) so each additional neutron increases the mass of the nucleus. It is possible to have atoms of the same element with different numbers of neutrons – these are known as **isotopes** of the element. For example, the nucleus of the commonest form of carbon contains 6 protons and 6 neutrons; however, there are other isotopes that contain 5, 7 or 8 neutrons. Physicists and chemists have a useful shorthand notation for writing about the different isotopes of the elements. As an example, look at the symbol for the common isotope of carbon:

$$^{12}_{6}\text{C}$$

Table 6.3 Symbols and atomic numbers of some common elements.

	Element						
	Hydrogen	**Helium**	**Carbon**	**Oxygen**	**Calcium**	**Iron**	**Lead**
symbol	H	He	C	O	Ca	Fe	Pb
number of protons (atomic number)	1	2	6	8	20	26	82

Here the C indicates that the element is carbon; the 6 tells you the number of protons in the nucleus; the 12 is the *total* number of protons plus neutrons. This number, rather than the number of neutrons, is given because it indicates the mass of the atom – approximately 12 times the mass of one proton or neutron. (The mass of the electrons is so small it has very little effect on the mass of the atom.) The top number (12 in this case) is therefore known as the **mass number** (N). The bottom number (6 in this example) is the atomic number (Z), which was described above.

● Write down the symbol for a nucleus of oxygen that contains 7 neutrons.

● You should have written $^{15}_{8}O$ because oxygen has 8 protons (Table 6.3) and the total number of neutrons and protons together is $7 + 8 = 15$. Another way of writing this that you will come across is oxygen-15; oxygen always has 8 protons so we really do not need to include that, so oxygen-15 gives just as much information as $^{15}_{8}O$.

Once you have got the hang of this notation you are well on the way to being able to write down the symbol for any nucleus.

the three most common being known as alpha (α), beta (β) and gamma (γ) decay. Table 6.4 is a simplified summary of the characteristics of these decay processes. You do not need to remember all these details. Note that alpha and beta decays produce charged particles whereas gamma decays produce gamma rays which, as you know from Section 5.5.1, are a form of electromagnetic radiation. There are two types of beta decay – beta plus (β$^+$) and beta minus (β$^-$).

Table 6.4 Characteristics of some common radioactive decay processes.

Type of decay	What happens	Emitted particle/radiation
Alpha decay	An alpha particle is emitted from the nucleus. This usually happens for heavy nuclei such as uranium.	An alpha particle consisting of two protons and two neutrons (actually a helium-4 nucleus). This is comparatively heavy and potentially damaging but travels only a very short distance.
Beta minus decay	A (negatively charged) electron is emitted from the nucleus. There are initially no electrons in the nucleus so this can only happen if a neutron (neutral) turns into a proton (positively charged).	A fast-moving (negative) electron is emitted. (This should not to be confused with the much less energetic electrons that form the outer part of the atom.) The fast-moving electron is potentially damaging.
Beta plus decay	A positron (essentially a positive electron) is emitted from the nucleus. This reaction only happens in synthetic nuclei (i.e. those that don't occur naturally).	The fast-moving positron is emitted from the nucleus but does not travel very far before it meets an electron. Two gamma rays are given off in opposite directions. This is used for PET imaging (see later in this section).
Gamma decay	The nucleus loses energy in the form of a photon of electromagnetic energy which is emitted from the nucleus. This usually happens immediately after an alpha or beta decay.	A photon of electromagnetic radiation in the gamma ray region of the spectrum (see Figure 5.7).

Half-life

When using a radionuclide for imaging or for treatment it is obviously important to know what kind of decay is taking place. But it is also important to know how rapidly the radionuclide will decay. Radioactive decay is a random process – it is never possible to predict exactly which nucleus in a large number of nuclei will decay next. However, what is known is that in a certain length of time, called the **half-life**, half of all the nuclei present at the beginning will have decayed. In each half-life period half of the nuclei will decay. So the number decaying per minute or per second is always decreasing. Figure 6.21 shows how the number of nuclei left, out of an initial sample of 100 000, decreases with time.

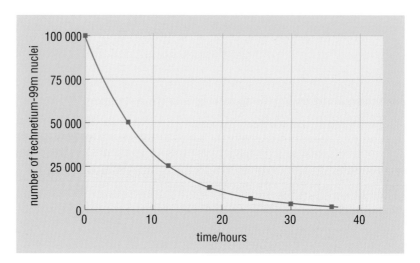

Figure 6.21   A graph of the number of nuclei of the radionuclide technetium-99m versus time, starting with 100 000 nuclei.

Technetium-99m is widely used in radionuclide imaging as will be explained on the next page.

● From the graph in Figure 6.21, what is the approximate half-life of technetium-99m?

● The time taken for the number of nuclei present to drop from 100 000 to 50 000 (i.e. to halve) is about six hours so this is the half-life. (Note that the number halves again in the next six hours, and so on.)

Radioactivity was discovered at the end of the 19th century – around about the same time as X-rays – and radioactive materials were used quite soon after that for *therapeutic* purposes, as they still are today (see Chapter 9). Radioactive materials were first used in *diagnostic* medicine in the 1930s as tracers – radioactivity was administered to the patient and the progress of the radioactivity could be traced through the body using a Geiger–Müller counter (a device for counting emitted radiation, invented in 1929). The really big step forward in imaging came with the development of the gamma camera in the 1950s. These technological developments ran in parallel with the creation of new methods for producing radionuclides, often as a by-product of the developing nuclear power industry.

We are going to consider the two slightly different versions of modern radionuclide imaging separately; we'll start with gamma camera imaging where the gamma rays given off by a radionuclide are imaged by a device known as a gamma camera. Positron emission tomography (PET), which uses a type of beta emission, will be considered later.

Gamma camera imaging

The principle of modern gamma camera imaging is shown in Figure 6.22. The patient is injected with a **radiopharmaceutical** – a substance that contains both a *radionuclide* and a *biologically active component* which will take the radioactive material to the organ that needs to be imaged. The patient is placed in close contact with the gamma camera (sometimes after a time delay to allow the radioactivity to be delivered to the correct organ).

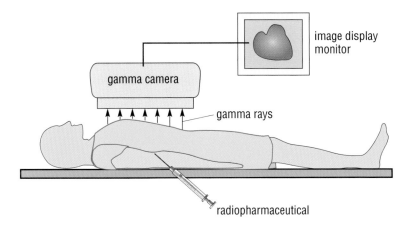

Figure 6.22 Gamma camera set-up, showing the patient close to the camera and the emitted gamma rays forming an image.

The image formed demonstrates the uptake of the radiopharmaceutical in the organ. This will depend on the metabolism of that organ and therefore shows the *function* of the organ.

The choice of radionuclide for these studies is important. The ideal radionuclide produces only gamma rays, without any alpha or beta emissions (see Table 6.4) as these are potentially more harmful and contribute nothing to the image. It also needs to have a suitable half-life – long enough to allow uptake and imaging but short enough that the patient does not remain radioactive for any longer than necessary. And the gamma ray energy needs to be suitable for the detector used. The radionuclide also needs to be readily available at a reasonable cost and be suitable for combination with a variety of agents to form the radiopharmaceutical. There is one radionuclide that is used for at least 95% of all gamma ray investigations and that is

$$^{99m}_{43}\text{Tc}$$

● The letters Tc are the standard abbreviation for the element technetium, an artificially produced radionuclide which is a by-product of the nuclear power industry. What do the numbers 43 and 99 indicate?

● 43 is the atomic number (Z) and indicates the number of protons in the nucleus. 99 is the mass number and indicates the number of protons and neutrons in the nucleus.

The letter 'm' is slightly unusual and tells you that the technetium-99 nucleus is produced in a metastable state. This means that the gamma decay that in most radionuclides would happen immediately is delayed; the gamma emission has a half-life of six hours. This fits in nicely with the criteria mentioned above – it is long enough to allow for administration and imaging, but not so long that it lingers in the patient's body for years.

● Can you think of one possible disadvantage of using a gamma-emitting radionuclide for diagnosis?

● Gamma radiation is a type of ionising radiation (Section 5.5.1) so there is a small possibility that imaging can lead to the development of a cancer many years later.

Other radionuclides that may be used for imaging are iodine-123, gallium-67 and krypton-81m (a gas used for lung imaging). Figure 6.23 shows an example of planar radionuclide imaging. Both patients have been injected with technetium-99m-phosphonate, a compound that will be taken up by the bones as bones contain phosphates. Regions of high metabolic activity will emit more radioactivity and appear black on the image. This technique is used on patients who have had a known primary cancer such as breast or prostate and who are suspected of having bone metastases.

Figure 6.23 Bone scans with Tc-99m. (a) A normal scan; the skeleton can be seen clearly on both front (anterior) and back (posterior) views, and there are no unexpected 'hot spots'. (b) A scan showing bone metastases; in addition to the skeletal outline there are regions of high radioactivity which indicate greater metabolic activity at the metastases. Note that the bladder shows up as radioactive; this is because the radionuclide is removed from the body via the kidney and bladder. (Source: University Hospitals Coventry and Warwickshire NHS Trust)

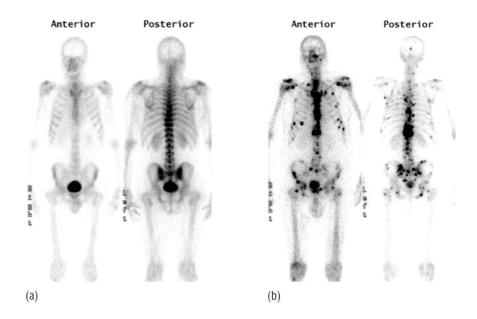

(a)   (b)

You'll notice that the images obtained from gamma camera imaging are not of the same high definition as from X-ray imaging or MRI. There has to be a balance between obtaining excellent images and giving the patient too high a dose of ionising radiation. However, it is important to remember that they are giving different information that could not be obtained any other way.

You have already seen how CT developed from planar X-rays; in the same way, a tomographic version of gamma camera imaging has now been developed. This is usually known by the acronym SPECT – single photon emission computed tomography – or occasionally SPET, leaving out the 'computed' as everything is computed these days! In a SPECT system one, two, or even three, gamma cameras are rotated slowly, more slowly than for CT, around the patient and the data from all the cameras are processed, in a similar way to the CT data, to give either images of slices or 3D images.

SPECT systems have been available for some time but in the last few years combined SPECT/CT systems have been gaining in popularity (Figure 6.24).

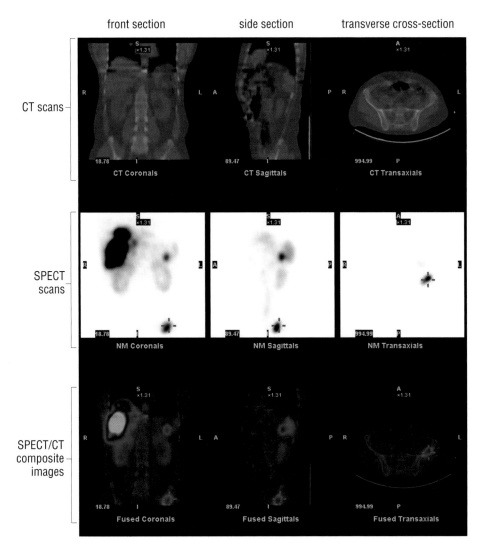

Figure 6.24 SPECT/CT images of the lower abdomen of a patient with metastases from a primary cancer in the pancreas. The pelvic secondary is marked in red and the yellow area in the lower left image indicates high activity in the liver. (Sources: University Hospitals Coventry and Warwickshire NHS Trust)

● Can you suggest what the advantage of combining SPECT and CT might be?

● The SPECT gives information about the function of organs; the CT gives information about the anatomy. If the two images are co-registered (superimposed) then the clinician can identify the exact position of any abnormalities.

There are many possible uses of a SPECT/CT system. One radiopharmaceutical, indium-111 pentetreotide (trade name Octreoscan) is useful because it binds to the receptor of a hormone called somatostatin. The action of somatostatin is to inhibit the release of other hormones by the endocrine system. Octreoscan is therefore useful in showing neuro-endocrine tumours. Figure 6.24 shows some SPECT/CT images of a patient taken using Octreoscan. The scans showed a tumour in the tail of the pancreas (probably the primary) and many small metastases in the liver. The SPECT scan also showed up a 'hot spot' in the pelvis (marked in red). Without the addition of co-registered CT it would not have been possible to have shown that the hot spot is in fact in the bone.

Positron emission tomography (PET) imaging

Table 6.4 listed two types of beta decay: in beta minus decay an electron is produced from the decaying nucleus; in beta plus decay a positron is produced. The positron has the same mass as an electron but an opposite (i.e. positive) charge. If an emitted positron collides with an electron, of which there are many in the body, then both particles are annihilated and their mass is converted into energy (as predicted by Einstein's famous equation $E = mc^2$, where E is energy, m is mass and c is the speed of light). Figure 6.25 shows what happens.

PET scanners are designed to detect the simultaneous emission of two gamma rays (energy 511 keV; see Figure 5.7) in opposite directions. The image can then be reconstructed to show the point of emission of the gamma rays, which is very close to the point of emission of the positron.

One of the very useful aspects of PET imaging is that the suitable radionuclides are mostly isotopes of elements that occur naturally in the body. This means that radioactive versions of normally occurring substances can be used as radiopharmaceuticals. These will be taken up in the same way as the non-radioactive version of the substance. Table 6.5 shows some of the most commonly used ones.

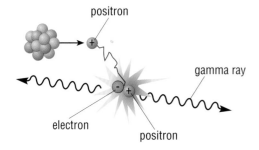

Figure 6.25 The positron produced by beta plus decay travels a short distance before colliding with an electron and emitting two gamma ray photons in opposite directions simultaneously.

Table 6.5 Suitable radionuclides for PET imaging, with their half-lives.

Radionuclide	Half-life
carbon-11	20 minutes
nitrogen-13	10 minutes
oxygen-15	2 minutes
fluorine-18	110 minutes

These radionuclides are produced in a cyclotron – a type of accelerator in which a chosen target is bombarded with charged particles.

● Can you see some disadvantages of the half-lives of these radionuclides?

● Most of them are very short. This means that the radiopharmaceutical must be prepared very quickly and administered to the patient immediately. The cyclotron will have to be close to the scanner.

Cyclotrons are expensive and complicated pieces of equipment and only a few specialist hospitals can afford to have one. For some time this limited the scope of PET. However, the more recent development of fluorine-18-based radiopharmaceuticals has made a big difference. With its longer half-life fluorine-18 can be transported from the cyclotron to another hospital. Fluorine-18 can be combined in fluoro-deoxyglucose which follows part of the same metabolic pathway in the cell as normal glucose. It is therefore a good indicator of metabolic activity, which is very high in cancer cells (see Section 2.6).

As the name suggest, PET is always done tomographically and produces similar images to those from a SPECT scanner. And again it is possible to combine modalities; PET/CT scanners are becoming increasing popular as a tool in oncology and are becoming standard in all large hospitals. Figure 6.26 (overleaf) shows an example of the use of PET/CT to look for metastases.

The main usefulness of PET scanning is not in the diagnosis of primary tumours but in the search for metastases. Whether or not a patient has metastases can have a large effect on the aggressiveness of the treatment and the management of the disease. For example, a patient with a known primary lung tumour is a candidate for lung resection (removal of all or part of the lung) which is a major operation with a long recovery time. However, if the PET scan reveals the presence of metastases the management of the patient treatment will be very different and he/she will be spared the trauma of a pointless operation.

Figure 6.26 An example of the use of PET/CT to look for metastases. The images on the far left are CT images, the ones in the middle column are the PET images and the those on the right are the combined PET/CT images. These show the primary tumour in the lungs, which possibly has a core of dead tumour cells due to lack of blood supply (Section 4.3), but no other evidence of abnormal uptake of the radiopharmaceutical. This patient might therefore be a candidate for surgery to remove the lung tumour. (Source: University Hospitals Coventry and Warwickshire NHS Trust)

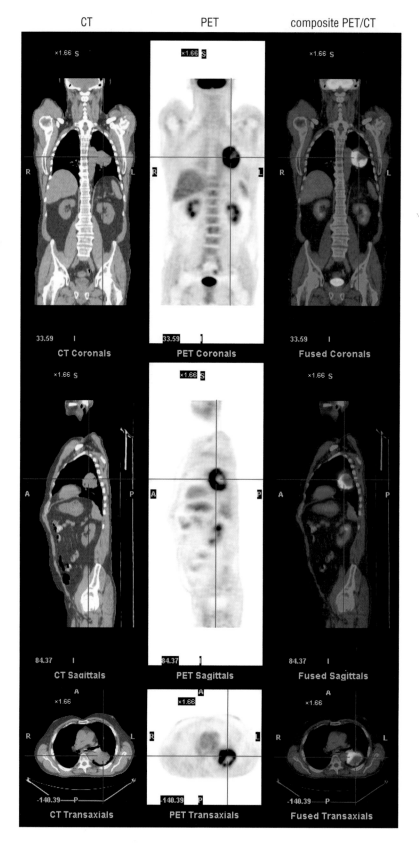

6.5.7 Which imaging method is best?

Having read all about the various possible imaging methods available you may be wondering how a choice is made between them. The choice will depend on a large number of factors. Some of these relate to the patient and the possible disease; others are factors such as the cost and availability of the different methods. Table 6.6 summarises some of the main advantages and disadvantages of the different methods.

Table 6.6 A summary of some of the features of the different imaging methods.

Imaging method	Advantages	Disadvantages	Main uses
Planar X-rays	Quick, cheap, readily available	2D images Contrast not very good Uses ionising radiation	Rapid assessment of gross features Mammography
CT	Excellent images of slices or 3D reconstructions Can use contrast agents to show blood vessels, etc. Relatively fast	Expensive Subjects the patient to larger amounts of ionising radiation Only available in larger hospitals in high-income countries	Wide range of diagnostic uses Staging Radiotherapy planning (see Chapter 9)
Ultrasound	Cheap, quick, readily available Easily portable No radiation hazard	Poorer-quality images Not suitable for all regions of the body	Looking for tumours and metastases in soft tissue Guiding biopsies (see Section 6.6.1)
MRI	Excellent images in any plane and 3D No radiation hazard	Very expensive and technologically complex Not suitable for patients with metal implants or heart pacemakers Only available in larger hospitals in high-income countries	Very wide range of diagnostic uses Increasingly useful for radiotherapy treatment planning
Gamma camera	Shows function rather than anatomy	Involves ionising radiation Not widely available, especially in low-income countries	Diagnosis of primary cancers Detection of metastases and staging
PET	Shows function rather than anatomy Especially useful for showing fast metabolism in tumours	Involves ionising radiation Very limited availability	Staging, diagnosis of metastases and monitoring of treatment

6.5.8 Imaging in the future

Table 6.6 summarised the pros and cons of current imaging methods, however imaging research leads to continual improvements to existing methods and even to methods. In this section we shall mention a couple of new developments that seem likely to play a role in cancer diagnosis in the future.

The first is a development of ultrasound known as elastography which essentially measures the elasticity of tissues. Its main use to date has been in the examination of the liver and the breast; in the latter case it may prove useful in distinguishing between benign and malignant tumours as malignant tumours tend to be much stiffer, i.e. less elastic. It is also beginning to be used for thyroid and prostate investigations (Chapter 12).

Infrared (see Figure 5.7) emissions from the body can be used to form an image and researchers have been working for many years on using this harmless method of imaging to look for 'hot spots' that may be associated with disease. However there are two major problems:

- patients need to be prepared very carefully for the scan and have, for example, to sit still in constant-temperature surroundings for some time before being imaged
- the infrared radiation will only penetrate through a limited thickness of the body so deeper problems will not be identified.

But infrared radiation is also used in a new technique called optical tomography. In this technique infrared light of two different energies is passed through the organ in question. As the name suggests, the technique produces an image of a slice. The differences in absorption of the two different energies yields information on the blood flow in the organ. Because of differences in the blood supply to cancers as compared to normal tissues (Section 4.3), this technique has potential applications in looking for cancers and has been suggested as a diagnostic technique for breast cancer.

There are many other possible ideas that could lead to new methods. It is hard to predict what new imaging technique may be round the corner – who would have predicted the genesis of MRI in the 1970s? There is bound to be some emphasis on techniques that do not use ionising radiation, although at the same time the wider use of techniques such as CT may see an increase in the average dose of ionising radiation to the population (Section 5.5.1).

6.6 Biopsies

From a diagnostic point of view, it is useful for clinicians to know whether the tumour is invasive or localised, its degree of differentiation, etc. This enables clinicians:

- first, to make a definitive cancer diagnosis
- second, to predict the probable outcome of a particular cancer in a patient, and
- third, to monitor the effectiveness of a particular treatment.

Much clinical information is obtained by looking directly at the potentially malignant cells with the aid of a microscope. In order to do this, tumour cells and some of the nearby tissue are isolated using a technique called a biopsy. A **biopsy** is a medical test in which the doctor removes a sample of tissue and sends it to a pathology laboratory to be analysed.

6.6.1 Obtaining the tissue

Biopsies may be performed using different techniques. Sometimes the procedure is relatively straightforward and can be performed in a primary health centre. For example, the Pap smear test, named after the doctor who first used this technique, Georgios Papanikolaus, merely involves scraping the tissue of the cervix to collect cells in a tube. In most cases, however, a biopsy is carried out in a specialist clinic. For superficial lumps or masses under the skin (e.g. breast carcinoma) a technique called **fine needle aspiration**, in which a thin hollow needle is inserted into the tumour to extract cells, is used (Figures 6.27 and 6.28). Fine needle aspiration is also applied to determine whether tumour cells have metastasised to nearby lymph nodes, in particular the lymph node or group of nodes nearest to the tumour, in which case it is called **sentinel lymph node biopsy**. As you may imagine, this type of biopsy requires knowledge of the exact location of the tumour, usually determined by imaging techniques, so that the medical team can determine which lymph node(s) are likely to be colonised first by the metastasising tumour cells. However, sentinel lymph nodes can be located more precisely by a variation of this technique which involves injecting either a radioactive substance or a dye, or even both, near the tumour site, prior to the biopsy. As the lymphatic system collects the interstitial fluid from tissues (Section 4.4.2), the sentinel lymph nodes will be the first to accumulate these substances and can then be easily identified with either a Geiger–Müller counter (a device for measuring ionising radiation) or by observing the location of the dye following surgery.

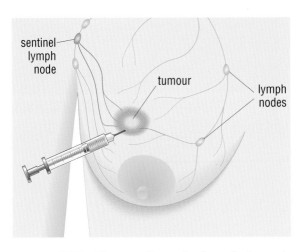

Figure 6.27   Fine needle aspiration of a lump in the breast of a patient.

A larger tissue sample can be removed if a core biopsy is taken. In a **core biopsy**, a larger needle is used (Figure 6.28) and a small cylinder of tissue is removed intact.

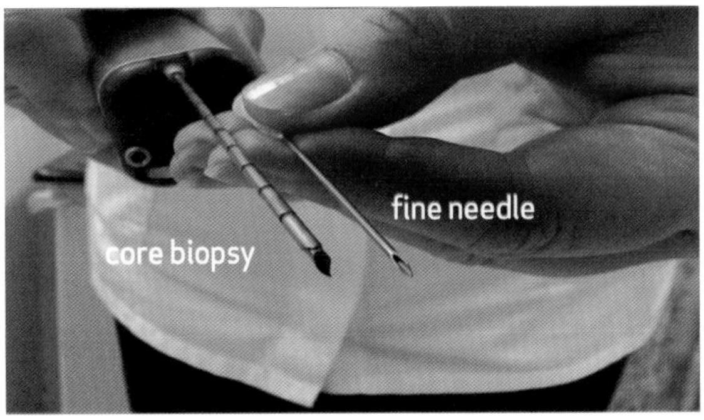

Ultrasound imaging (Section 6.5.4) is also used for guiding needle biopsies.

● The percentage of the incoming ultrasound that is reflected at a metal/soft tissue boundary is very high. How might this be useful in using ultrasound to guide biopsies?

Figure 6.28   A core biopsy needle and a fine needle. (Source: Milton Keynes Breast Screening Unit)

● The needle, which is made of metal, will reflect the ultrasound strongly and therefore will show up clearly on the image.

Ultrasound-guided biopsies can be used for liver, kidney and breast but one very common use is in the sampling of prostate tissue in cases of suspected prostate cancer. Figure 6.29a shows a diagram of the set-up used and Figure 6.29b shows a typical image, with the tumour tissue (arrowed). The biopsy sample will be taken from this tissue.

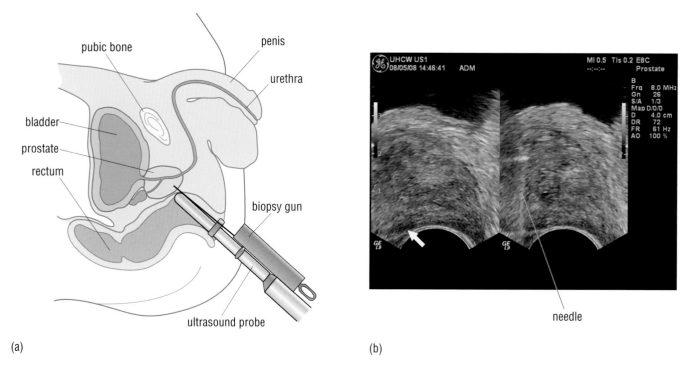

Figure 6.29 (a) Set-up for TRUS (trans-rectal ultrasound) biopsy. (b) Typical image showing needle and tumour (arrowed). (Source: (b) University Hospitals Coventry and Warwickshire NHS Trust)

For cancers affecting internal cavities such as the gastrointestinal tract, the lungs, and the reproductive and urinary systems, tissue samples, usually not larger than 5 mm long, are generally extracted using an endoscope (Section 6.3). In some other cases, the presence of a large tumour may have already been confirmed using, for example, imaging techniques. In this instance, the medical team may decide that the best treatment option is immediate surgery. In order to assess the tumour, tissue samples are then taken during surgery.

An **excisional biopsy** denotes an attempt to remove the whole tumour surgically. An **incisional biopsy**, also known as a wedge biopsy, is the surgical removal of part of a tumour. Incisional biopsies are used in some cases, for example, when tumour cells have spread to such an extent that hardly any healthy tissue is left. Surgery as a therapeutic tool will be dealt with in Chapter 7.

Case study 6.3   Trupti Shah's diagnosis

The doctor in the casualty ward examines Trupti carefully and seems particularly concerned by the fact that the glands in her neck are enlarged and, as her mother indicates, there is some odd bruising that does not look quite like the normal bumps of early childhood on her arms and legs. She sends Trupti's blood samples to be analysed for a full blood cell count. After a night in hospital, the doctors have managed to control Trupti's high temperature. However, the results of a blood test only increase the doctor's initial suspicion, and she tells Mrs Shah that further tests need to be taken. Trupti is discharged and referred as an outpatient to Great Ormond Street Hospital for Children in central London for two diagnostic procedures.

First, a bone marrow biopsy, in which a thin needle is inserted into the hipbone at the top of the pelvis and a sample of bone marrow is aspirated for further tests. Second, a lumbar puncture, in which a needle is inserted in her back to draw off some of the fluid that covers the brain and spinal cord. Both procedures are carried out under general anaesthesia in an operating theatre.

Trupti is very frightened every time she goes to the hospital, but the doctors who do the tests are very kind and caring and are able to reassure her. On both occasions, Trupti is sent home shortly after she wakes up from the procedure. Two weeks later, Trupti's parents are told the results from the bone marrow aspiration and the lumbar puncture which confirm what the doctors had originally suspected: Trupti has acute lymphoblastic leukaemia (ALL). The doctors gently tell her parents that she is very unwell due to her cancer but that there are no signs that the tumour cells have spread to Trupti's brain, which improves her chances of recovery. Nevertheless, Trupti will have to have intensive chemotherapy followed by at least two years' further treatment. She is immediately admitted to the hospital as an in-patient so her treatment can begin. After putting Trupti to sleep in the ward, Mr Shah returns to his wife's sister's house and tells his other children: 'Trupti is very sick but the doctors are helping her so she and mum had to stay in hospital tonight.' Trupti's siblings are shocked and confused by the news and at the sight of their dad crying. 'I just feel a little sad and a little tired today. It makes me feel better to cry and get it all out of my system. Now I feel better', says Mr Shah.

6.6.2 Histopathological assessment of tissue biopsies

Once the tissue samples have been collected and usually frozen to preserve the tissue architecture, a pathologist examines the tissue under a microscope to confirm the diagnosis of cancer, a procedure known as a **histopathological** evaluation (from histo-, meaning 'tissue' and -pathology, meaning 'study of disease'). Before this is done, the specimen is first thawed and then prepared by means of several physical and chemical processes so that different cellular structures can be viewed (Figure 6.30). The basic steps are similar for most histopathological investigations and mostly include a step called chemical fixation. Fixation is a chemical process that stops the destruction of tissue by the action of enzymes released from dead cells, and stabilises proteins and other major components of tissues so that, during subsequent processing, the cells retain as fully as possible their form in the live tissue.

Once the tissue is treated with a fixative chemical, the sample is then cut into thin slices called sections and arranged onto a glass slide. However, the structure of cells is difficult to visualise under the microscope unless they are first stained with dyes. One of the most common staining methods uses two dyes, haematoxylin and eosin. Haematoxylin stains mainly nucleic acids (DNA and RNA). As a result, haematoxylin preferentially stains cell nuclei with a blue/purple colour. Eosin stains most cell structures pink, including the cell cytosol and mitochondria (Figure 6.31).

Figure 6.30 The technique of histopathological evaluation of biopsies. Tissue samples are placed in a plastic cassette, which facilitates manipulation of the tissue, and then 'fixed' with chemicals to preserve the architecture of the tissue. The sample is embedded in wax to facilitate sectioning, then sections are arranged on a glass slide and, finally, stained with dyes before inspection under the microscope.

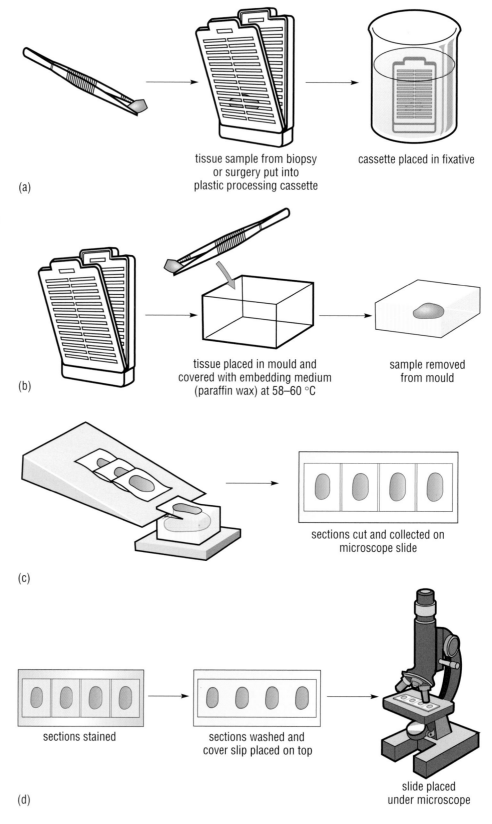

(a)

tissue sample from biopsy or surgery put into plastic processing cassette

cassette placed in fixative

(b)

tissue placed in mould and covered with embedding medium (paraffin wax) at 58–60 °C

sample removed from mould

(c)

sections cut and collected on microscope slide

(d)

sections stained

sections washed and cover slip placed on top

slide placed under microscope

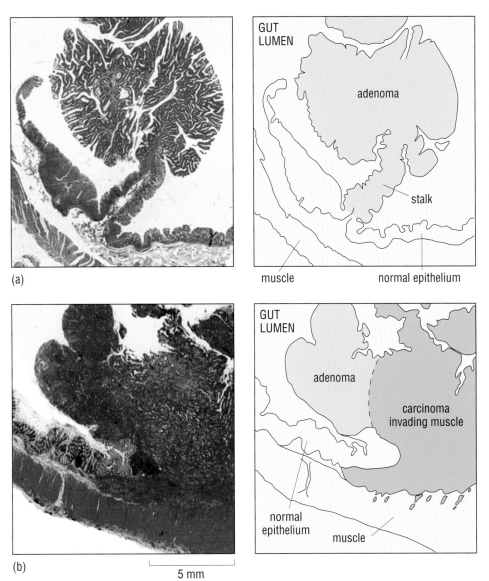

Figure 6.31 Cross-sections and diagrammatic interpretations showing the stages in development of a typical colon cancer following staining of a biopsy sample with haematoxylin and eosin. (a) A polyp from the colon. The polyp protrudes into the lumen – the space inside. The rest of the wall of the colon is covered with normal colon epithelium; the epithelium on the polyp appears mildly abnormal. (b) A carcinoma that is beginning to invade the underlying muscle layer. (Sources: Paul Edwards, University of Cambridge)

● In Figure 6.31b, can you suggest a reason why malignant tissue appears purple whereas normal tissue appears slightly pinker in the haematoxylin and eosin stained section?

● The purple colour is given by the haematoxylin dye which specifically stains cell nuclei. Malignant tissue contains a higher number of cells and therefore a higher density of cell nuclei. In addition, tumour cells are disorganised and rapidly dividing and they usually contain larger nuclei (Section 2.4). Therefore, haematoxylin will preferentially stain malignant tissue over normal tissue.

After examination of the specimen, pathologists write a histopathology report, which usually includes a general description of the tissue sample together with an indication of the differentiation and proliferative state of the tumour cells and whether they have invaded the tissue locally or have metastasised to the lymph nodes. This process is called **grading**, which helps in the classification of the tumour according to the staging systems described in Section 4.4.4. The commonest grading system is usually on a scale of low grade, intermediate grade, or high grade. There are very specific scientific terms used to describe the grading of a tumour in a histopathology report, some of these terms are summarised in Box 6.4.

Box 6.4 Medical terms used to describe the proliferative and differentiated state of cells in tissues and organs

Hypertrophy – increase in the size of an organ or tissue due to an increase in cell size, not to an increase in cell numbers. An example of hypertrophy is the increase in muscle mass observed following weight training (i.e. muscle cells become larger but their number remains constant).

Hyperplasia – an abnormal increase in the number of cells within a tissue or organ. Hyperplastic cells look normal and differentiated in an organ or tissue (Figure 6.32a).

Dysplasia – an alteration in the size and shape of normal cells. Dysplasia is the earliest form of a pre-cancerous lesion (Figure 6.32b).

Carcinoma *in situ* (CIS) – a neoplasm in which tumour cells have reverted to an undifferentiated state but still remain localised to the tissue of origin.

Invasive carcinoma – a neoplasm in which tumour cells have become undifferentiated and have spread to nearby tissue and/or have metastasised.

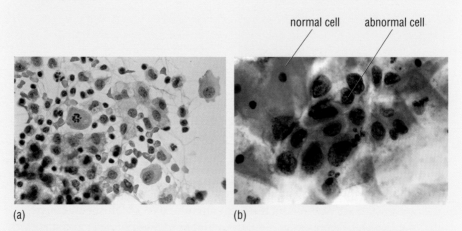

(a)   (b)

Figure 6.32   (a) Light micrograph of a section through lung tissue showing hyperplasia (increased cell number) in the pleura, the membrane that lines the lungs and inner chest wall. This condition is benign but some hyperplasias may be mistaken for cancer in a biopsy. (b) Light micrograph of a cervical Pap smear test showing severe dysplasia in epithelial cells (stained pink). Large dark-stained nuclei of dysplastic cells can be seen at the centre. These abnormal cells have little or no cytosol and few organelles and their shapes are severely distorted. (Sources: (a) CNRI/Science Photo Library; (b) Science Photo Library)

In some types of cancer, the pathologist performs further tests on the tumour samples which will help doctors evaluate whether the tumour cells will be sensitive to a particular treatment. For example, tissue samples of patients with breast cancer are usually tested for the expression of a growth factor receptor, HER2 (Section 2.9.2), and of receptors for hormones such as oestrogen and progesterone (Table 6.1), using a technique called **immunohistochemistry**. Following a biopsy and fixation of the tissue, sections are incubated with antibodies that specifically bind to the protein under investigation. A specific colour reaction reveals the cellular location of the antibody, and therefore of the protein it binds to. The tissue section can then be visualised under the microscope and cells that express the protein of interest will appear stained in a different colour from cells that do not (Figure 6.33). As described in Chapter 2, tumour cells may express higher levels of growth factor receptors than normal cells, leading to enhanced cell division. If breast tumour cells express high levels of either HER2 or oestrogen receptors, specific therapies that target activation of these receptors

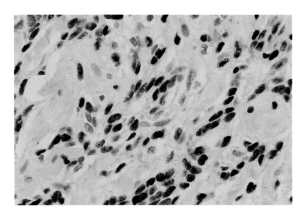

Figure 6.33 Immunohistochemical detection of oestrogen receptor in a uterine carcinoma biopsy. A purple staining indicates high levels of oestrogen receptor in tumour cells, whereas normal cells are not stained purple. (Source: Miettinen et al., 2000, Figure 3)

are more likely to be more effective for cancer therapy. This is the basis for selecting patients with HER2-positive tumours for therapy with Herceptin (an antibody that binds to the HER2 receptor and inhibits its activation) and patients with oestrogen receptor-positive tumours for therapy with a drug called tamoxifen (an inhibitor of the oestrogen receptor). Other techniques that can be used on biopsies include molecular techniques that isolate DNA from tumour cells and detect mutations in proto-oncogenes and tumour-suppressor genes (see Section 3.5.4).

Note this colour reaction is not the same process as staining with dyes (e.g. eosin) which stains all the cellular structures.

Case study 6.4   Dave Bayler's results from his tests

Dave is asked to come back to the hospital a week or so later for the histopathology results. The news the doctor gives him is not good. The growth first spotted by his general physician is a tumour; he, like his mother 30 years earlier, has cancer of the colon. The tumour appears to be fairly small, although it has started to spread through the muscle of the colon wall. The doctor says that the tumour cells are not normal looking. A word sticks in Dave's mind, 'adenocarcinoma'. Dave tries to ask all the questions that pop in his head but the doctor is reluctant to say at this stage whether his cancer has spread elsewhere and how aggressive it is or what the best treatment is. The tumour and nearby lymph nodes need to be urgently removed in order to have a concrete diagnosis. Dave hears the doctor refer to something called 'staging'. At this time, Dave feels extremely anxious, thinking of and identifying himself with his mother and sister, and especially because he does not know what to expect of his recently diagnosed cancer.

6.7 Screening for cancers

So far this chapter has dealt with the diagnosis of cancer in someone who presents with symptoms; however, we must also look at the possibility of screening for cancers. **Screening** is the testing of asymptomatic people (people without symptoms) to identify those who are likely to have an increased likelihood of developing a particular disease, or those who already have an early stage of the disease. Screening can be carried out on an **opportunistic** basis – that is when someone has gone to visit the doctor about something else and, while the patient is in the surgery, the doctor or nurse has taken their blood pressure or checked their urine. That kind of screening happens all the time, but the kind that makes the news headlines is what is described as **systematic screening**. That is where a population – not the whole population but a subset, such as all women over 50 – are routinely invited to attend for a screening test.

Such screening always sounds as though it must be a good idea, but this is not necessarily the case. One must stop and think whether the screening process is really justified. There are several different aspects that must be considered. We will list just some of them here:

- There must be sound medical reasons for doing the screening. In other words, if the result is positive, it must be possible either to prevent the disease from occurring, or to treat it more successfully if it is identified at an early stage.

- The potential damage caused by the screening test must be less than the potential benefits of carrying out the screening. Possible damage might be exposure to ionising radiation (see Section 5.5.1) as, for example, in breast cancer screening.

- The test needs to be acceptable to the people undergoing it. It must not be too invasive nor take up too much time. For example, a test that involved everyone having a general anaesthetic would not be considered acceptable!

- Where the test is being offered to large numbers of people by a government-run health service, there must be a cost benefit for the government; that is, the cost of running the tests and treating people who test positive must be less than the costs that would have been incurred had those people had to be treated at a much later stage of the disease. Economic costs, such as time taken off work by patients, can also be included in this calculation.

- When a screening test is introduced there must be enough skilled staff available to run the screening service *and* to cope with the increased numbers of patients who will be referred for treatment.

- Last, but by no means least, the test must be accurate enough to ensure that there are not too many people who are told they do not have the disease when they do, or who are told they do have the disease but turn out later not to.

This last point is very important and can be examined by looking at the possible results of a screening test. These are shown in Figure 6.34.

● In Figure 6.34 which category corresponds to people who are told that they have the disease when they do not. What might be the consequences of this result for them?

● False positives are people who test positive but do not have the disease. The consequences of this test result will inevitably be more tests, sometimes more invasive tests such as a biopsy, and occasionally perhaps, uncomfortable and unpleasant treatment for a disease they do not have. Even if the next round of tests shows that the person does not have the disease she/he will still have had a very anxious time while she/he thought that the result was positive.

	Person has the disease	Person does not have the disease
Positive test result	True positive	False positive
Negative test result	False negative	True negative

Figure 6.34   The possible results of a screening test.

● The other category of incorrect results is false negatives – people who are told they do not have the disease when they do. What are the consequences of this result for them?

● They have a false sense of security because they believe that they do not have the disease. It is quite likely that the disease will manifest itself by producing symptoms some time later and it may at that point be much harder to treat the disease.

Examples of some tests that may be used to screen for cancer are given below.

Cervical screening

The Pap smear test (Figure 6.32b) involves taking a few cells from the uterine cervix. These are then examined under a microscope for changes in the cervical lining which may be a precursor of cervical cancer. The introduction of regular tests for women of reproductive age in many countries of the world has led to a dramatic drop in the incidence of cervical cancer. (Cervical screening is the topic of Activity 6.2.)

Breast cancer screening using X-rays (mammography)

This test is also widespread in many high-income countries. It does not detect pre-cancerous conditions but does allow detection of breast cancers when they are very small and before they have metastasised (Section 4.4). This means a much better prognosis for the patient. However, the test uses X-rays so there is a small potential for damage – a very small percentage of the women who are tested will develop cancer as a result of the test (see Section 5.5.1). For this reason, breast cancer screening is not recommended below the age of 50 in most countries; above that age the risk of having breast cancer is greater and, because the women are older, the risk of developing a radiation-induced cancer some years later is reduced.

Faecal occult blood tests for colorectal cancer

This is a simple test carried out in the home; the person collects a small sample of faeces on a slide and sends it in for analysis. This is being rolled out as a routine test for people over 60 in the UK; however, it is not a very accurate test because not all types of colon cancer are picked up by this test; this means that there will be quite a large proportion of false negatives. Note that other conditions unrelated to cancer (such as haemorrhoids, peptic ulcers) may also result in blood being present in faeces, giving a positive result.

PSA blood test for prostate cancer

A blood test that can be carried out on men over 50 to look for prostate-specific antigen (PSA) which may be a marker for prostate cancer (see Section 6.4). While this test does identify men with prostate cancer it also, like the CEA test discussed in Section 6.4, gives positive results for some who do not, because there are other reasons for a higher-than-average level of PSA in the blood.

Genetic screening for BRCA genes

In Box 5.3, you learnt that there are many variants of the *BRCA1* and *BRCA2* genes within the human population but only a few can predispose an individual to develop breast and ovarian cancer – most breast and ovarian cancers are actually not associated with these gene variants. Indeed, the possibility of testing for the *BRCA1* and *BRCA2* gene variants associated with breast and ovarian cancer may be offered to women from 'high-risk' populations. These may include women from families with a history of multiple cases of breast and ovarian cancer, or women from families of Ashkenazi (Eastern European) Jewish background, a population that has a higher frequency of high-risk *BRCA1* and *BRCA2* gene variants, and hence a higher incidence of breast cancer, than the overall population. It is worth mentioning here that not every individual in such families carries the high-risk *BRCA1* or *BRCA2* gene variants, and not every cancer in such families is associated with these gene variants. The cancer screening tests explained earlier are aimed at detecting cancer at early stages so that they may be treated with a higher success rate.

In contrast, genetic testing aims to identify individuals who are likely to develop a particular form of cancer later in life. Genetic testing is performed on a small sample of blood or a mouth swab, and the DNA is isolated and analysed in a laboratory to detect the different variants of a gene. Whereas a negative result may have no consequences for the individual concerned and/or their relatives, a positive result may prompt other members of the family to carry out a genetic test. It is important to stress that a positive result does not mean that the person has or will have the disease. Rather, it provides information only about a person's risk of developing cancer but it cannot tell whether cancer will develop. As a result, a person who has tested positive for the *BRCA1* or *BRCA2* gene variants associated with breast cancer may choose to undergo more frequent screening tests for ovarian or breast cancer, or may contemplate the surgical removal of these organs as a preventive measure. However, a negative result does not mean the person will not develop cancer. For example, the risk of developing breast cancer is approximately 12% in the general population. This risk only falls to about 11% in those who have tested negative for the cancer-risk variants of *BRCA1* and *BRCA2* genes.

Activity 6.2   Cervical cancer screening

Allow about 25 minutes in total for this activity

Listen to the audio sequence *Cervical Cancer Screening* on the success of the UK cervical screening programme. (This is an extract from a BBC *Woman's Hour* programme broadcast in July 2004.) As you listen to the audio clip consider the following questions.

(a)   Why is the UK cervical screening programme thought to have saved so many lives since it was introduced in 1988?

(b)   What are the reasons given for not screening women under 25?

The answers to these questions are in the Answers section at the back of the book.

Case study 6.5   Jôao Rodrigues' screening and diagnosis

Seventy-six year old Brazilian Jôao Rodrigues can look back on a successful life. Born into a fairly poor São Paulo family and apprenticed into a small engineering company, he worked his way up through its ranks into, eventually, the position of managing director. He has now been retired for 10 years. He was greatly saddened by his wife's death 7 years ago, and his only son, also an engineer, has recently achieved his lifelong ambition of a job in California. Although he has many friends, particularly former business associates, and an active social life, he is often lonely.

Like almost all professional and business people in Brazil, Jôao has full medical insurance cover, and this has continued into his retirement. As part of this cover, he has been offered a screening test for prostate cancer annually since he turned 60. The PSA (prostrate-specific antigen) test is a simple blood test that measures the level of the protein PSA, which is produced by the prostate. A raised level of PSA in the blood is often a sign of prostate cancer, although PSA levels rise with age and raised levels are also associated with commoner, less serious conditions such as BPH (benign prostate hyperplasia) and infection in the prostate.

Last year, Jôao was told that his PSA level was slightly higher than would be expected for a man of his age and previous medical history, but that there was probably nothing serious to worry about. This year, however, the result is very different; his PSA level is measured to be 10 ng ml^{-1}, compared to a normal value of under 5 ng ml^{-1}. (The prefix n, for nano, means 10^{-9}. So the unit ng is 1×10^{-9} g.) Jôao is asked to make an immediate appointment at the A. C. Camargo Hospital in São Paulo for further tests, at this stage meant to rule out prostate cancer.

At the hospital, the doctor gives Jôao a digital rectal exam, inserting a gloved finger into his rectum and probing his prostate, looking for irregularities of size, shape and texture. What he finds there suggests that there is likely to be a problem. To confirm the diagnosis, he arranges for Jôao to have a transrectal ultrasound combined with a biopsy. In this procedure, an ultrasound probe is inserted into the rectum and the images obtained are used to guide the insertion of a needle to remove a small sample of cells. This is a short and simple procedure, and very uncomfortable rather than painful.

Two weeks later, Jôao is called back to the hospital to receive his results, and told that he does have prostate cancer. The cancer is quite small, restricted to the prostate gland. The biopsy results indicate that the cancer cells are rather abnormal although the cancer appears to be unlikely to grow and spread beyond the prostate very quickly. Elderly men like Jôao, diagnosed with slow-growing prostate cancers, will often be given no active treatment, but simply given regular tests and asked to monitor any possible symptoms. Jôao, however, seems to be on the borderline between low and intermediate grade prostate cancer and the doctor wants to explain to him different treatments he can follow. Jôao finds himself, still feeling well, but facing both a potentially serious illness and some complex decisions about its treatment.

6.8 Concluding remarks

In this chapter, we have introduced some diagnostic techniques that help healthcare professionals in the diagnosis of the disparate range of diseases known as cancer. Whereas the least specialised techniques are available throughout the world, many of the diagnostic techniques described require technologically demanding and/or costly medical equipment and hence their availability is largely limited to high-income countries. Similarly, once the diagnosis of cancer has been reached, the therapeutic path that a person with cancer may follow varies widely amongst different geographical locations and it may largely depend on the economic status of the individual. In Chapters 7 to 10, you will come across some of the therapies that are either currently in use for the treatment of cancers, or in the experimental stage resulting from recent advances in modern medicine. However, you should also take into account that, as with diagnostic techniques, the availability of many of these therapies to people with cancer is unevenly distributed.

Case study 6.6   Anneke has lung cancer

Anneke has suffered from a persistent 'smoker's cough' for many years, and learned to live with it. She therefore finds it difficult to pinpoint the time when she first became aware that there might be something else going on. Looking back, she remembers her first noticeable symptom being simply a change in the nature, and increase in severity, of that cough. By the time she is sitting in her doctor's surgery awaiting her first consultation, over six months later, she has noticed that her voice is becoming hoarse and she has lost some weight. She is feeling also generally unfit and beginning to wonder if she will have to give up cycling, and she is no longer as interested in cooking, or even eating, splendid family meals.

Anneke's cough, on its own, would not be a particularly worrying symptom in a long-term smoker, but combined with the other symptoms she mentions they suggest that there might be a serious problem. Her doctor examines her thoroughly and arranges an urgent appointment for her to have further tests at hospital and to see a specialist.

On Anneke's first visit to the hospital, she is given a chest X-ray, and a sample of her sputum (saliva) is taken and checked for the presence of cancer cells. The chest X-ray reveals a suspicious-looking mass in her left lung, which looks very much like a tumour, but the specialists cannot be sure and they order more tests to confirm the diagnosis. She has to return to hospital in a few days for a CT scan and a lung biopsy. She is asked not to eat or drink anything for a few hours before the scan, and given an injection of contrast medium which shows up the blood vessels more clearly on the scan. The lung biopsy is done at the same time as the imaging. For this, she is given a local anaesthetic and asked to hold her breath while a needle is inserted into the lung through her skin and chest muscles between her ribs to remove a sample of cells. She finds this slightly uncomfortable, but not at all painful, and is able to go home as soon as the tests are over.

A week later, she and her husband are sitting nervously in the oncologist's office, awaiting the results of the tests. A young doctor gently gives them the bad news: she has non small cell lung cancer (NSCLC). Her cancer is stage IIB – the cancer is fairly small but has grown into the chest wall, although it does not appear to have spread further. As she has been relatively fit, she will be offered surgery, and this might clear the cancer completely. She will also be given chemotherapy after the operation to reduce the risk of recurrence, but a cure cannot be guaranteed. After the first shock, Anneke and her husband resolve to deal with her cancer to their best ability. Her first action is to throw her cigarette packet away; she will never smoke again.

6.9 Summary of Chapter 6

6.1 The diagnosis of cancer involves many different tests aimed at, first, detecting an abnormal growth and, second, determining the degree of malignancy of a tumour.

6.2 Physical examination, whether external or internal (e.g. endoscopies), is an important procedure to alert healthcare professionals of the presence of a tumour.

6.3 General laboratory tests provide information about the health of an individual. Tumour markers, although limited in their usefulness, are being employed in the diagnosis of certain cancer types.

6.4 There are a wide variety of imaging methods available. They can be used for diagnosis, staging, radiotherapy treatment planning and treatment monitoring.

6.5 X-rays (including CT), ultrasound and MRI are mostly used to give details of anatomy. Radionuclide imaging gives very useful functional information. Combinations of anatomical and functional imaging methods are increasing in popularity; these include SPECT/CT and PET/CT.

6.6 Biopsies are used to obtain samples of tissue which are then evaluated by a pathologist for the presence of tumour cells and their spread.

6.7 Screening is the testing of target populations to detect cancer in early stages of the disease or, in the case of genetic testing, to determine the likelihood of developing a particular type of cancer later in life.

Questions for Chapter 6

Question 6.1 (Learning outcomes 6.1, 6.2 and 6.3)

Which of the following diagnostic tests could be carried out at a primary health centre? Give a reason for your answer. (i) A gastroscopy; (ii) a CEA blood test; (iii) digital rectal examination; (iv) an ultrasound scan of the breast; (v) a sentinel lymph node biopsy.

Question 6.2 (Learning outcomes 6.1 and 6.4)

Table 6.7 gives the attenuation coefficients of some different tissues/substances for diagnostic X-rays. (You can ignore the units.) Between which of them would you expect to get good contrast in a planar X-ray?

Table 6.7 Attenuation coefficients for X-rays through different substances.

	Tissue/substance					
	Blood	**Fat**	**Muscle**	**Bone**	**Air**	**Titanium implant**
Attenuation coefficient/cm^{-1}	0.214–0.222	0.190	0.212	0.629	2.24×10^{-4}	3.4

Question 6.3 (Learning outcomes 6.1, 6.4 and 6.5)

Which of the imaging methods described in this chapter expose the patient to a dose of ionising radiation?

Question 6.4 (Learning outcomes 6.1, 6.2 and 6.6)

(a) Why would the expression of oestrogen receptor by breast tumour cells determine the choice of treatment?

(b) What procedure(s) would you follow to determine whether tumour cells in a patient with breast cancer express the oestrogen receptor?

Question 6.5 (Learning outcomes 6.1, 6.2 and 6.7)

List some of the possible advantages and disadvantages of screening for a cancer. (Three of each is sufficient.)

References

Duffy, M.J. (2001) 'Carcinoembryonic antigen as a marker for colorectal cancer: is it clinically useful?', *Clinical Chemistry*, vol. 47, no. 4, pp. 624–30.

Duffy, M.J. (2007) 'Role of tumor markers in patients with solid cancers: a critical review', *European Journal of Internal Medicine*, vol. 18, no. 3, pp. 175–84.

Miettinen, M., Sobin, L.H. and Sarlomo-Rikala, M. (2000) 'Immunohistochemical spectrum of GISTs at different sites and their differential diagnosis with a reference to CD117 (KIT)' *Modern Pathology*, vol. 13 (10), pp. 1134–42.

National Institute for Health and Clinical Excellence (NICE) (2008) [online], http://www.nice.org.uk/nicemedia/pdf/CG027fullguideline.pdf (Accessed June 2008)

Further reading

If you would like to read further about this topic, please refer to the following publications.

Duffy, M.J. (2004) 'Evidence for the clinical use of tumour markers', *Annals of Clinical Biochemistry*, vol. 41(5), pp. 370–7.

Pollak, M.N. and Foulkes, W.D. (2003) 'Challenges to cancer control by screening', *Nature Reviews Cancer*, vol. 3, pp. 297–303.

CHAPTER 7

INTRODUCTION TO CANCER THERAPY

Learning outcomes

After studying this chapter and its associated activities, you should be able to:

7.1 Define and use in context, or recognise definitions and applications of, each of the terms printed in **bold** in the text.

7.2 Describe the structure and function of the multidisciplinary team.

7.3 Explain the differences between radical and palliative treatments.

7.4 List the three main types of therapy used to treat cancers.

7.5 Outline the advantages and disadvantages of various forms of therapy for cancer.

7.6 Describe the role that clinical trials play in selecting new treatments for cancer.

7.1 Introduction

In the previous chapter you were introduced to the diagnostic process. In this chapter, we will now examine how a diagnosis of cancer impacts upon the individual and the process of selecting the most favourable treatment option for that individual. We will also discuss the role that clinical trials play in determining the usefulness of cancer therapies.

The focus of this chapter will be primarily the cancer therapies available in high-income countries. However, as you saw in Chapter 1, variations in prevalence, mortality and survival rates in different countries can indicate differences in the quality of diagnosis and treatments available.

7.2 The diagnosis

Over the last three decades the public perception of cancer in the UK and other high-income countries has undergone a monumental shift from being largely very negative to one of positive optimism. A diagnosis of cancer used to be considered a death sentence and the 'Big C', as it was known, was spoken of in hushed tones and rarely ever in front of the patient. Indeed, it was common for the sufferer not to be told that they had a diagnosis of cancer. A transition in public attitude started in the 1970s when several prominent women in the public eye raised awareness by openly discussing their battles with breast cancer and the rights of patients. In more recent times, this change has been driven by improvements in cancer treatment and increased survival rates. Today, a diagnosis of cancer is not an automatic death sentence; indeed, most individuals diagnosed with cancer have an excellent chance of being cured.

Activity 7.1   To know or not to know the diagnosis

Allow about 20 minutes in total for this activity

In this activity you will read an article on global approaches to diagnostic disclosure.

Figure 7.1 illustrates the route that an individual with a suspected cancer is likely to take from diagnosis to treatment in the UK. This 'patient journey' through the hospital system is triggered when a person visits their general practitioner or healthcare professional with symptoms. As discussed in Chapter 6, depending on the nature of the symptoms, the healthcare professional may take some samples such as blood or urine for analysis and/or refer the patient to a specialist for further investigation. When the outcome of an investigation is known, a healthcare professional will then inform the person of the diagnosis and explain the next stages of their 'patient journey'. Clearly, the manner in which a patient is informed of their diagnosis is important (this is an issue that we will revisit later in this section); however, the way a patient reacts to their diagnosis varies greatly.

Figure 7.1   The 'patient journey' from diagnosis to treatment.

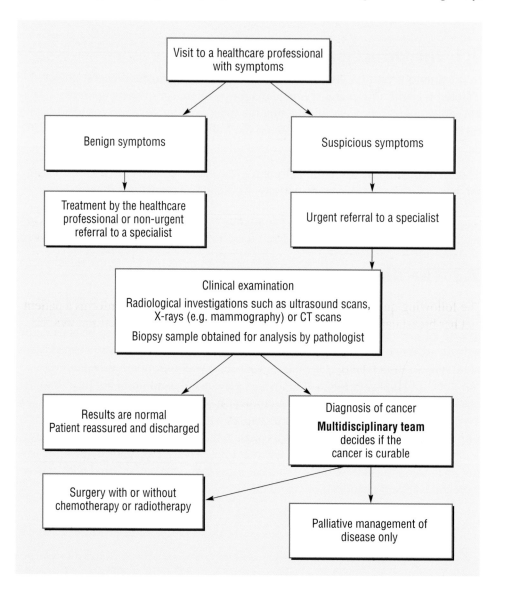

Once it became apparent that I wasn't going to scream, I didn't know what to say. What do you say? 'Oh dear'? 'Ooops'? 'What'? I moaned a couple of times, hoping that the moan would encourage the terror to come out of its hiding. I looked at Nigella, and at *Eastenders*, still taking in bits of the plot. I said 'I've got cancer' out loud as if this might explain everything, something. I apologised to Nigella. And that was about as much as I could do.

(Diamond, 1998, p. 38)

The above quote describes the reaction of the late journalist John Diamond to being informed of his diagnosis of cancer. He describes a range of different reactions to this. He expects to feel terrified and seems surprised that he doesn't. He apologises to his wife. He also seems to feel disbelief and bewilderment about his diagnosis.

●   What reaction might a person have on being told he or she has cancer?

●   There are many different reactions to a diagnosis of cancer. Often a person's reaction is influenced by personal experience of how friends and relatives have dealt with a similar diagnosis. Some people will feel frightened. Some may feel angry or that they have lost control of their life. It is possible to feel sad or lonely, whilst some people attempt to deny that there is anything wrong. Others will stoically accept their diagnosis and resolve to keep life as normal as possible.

You may have thought of other reactions to a diagnosis of cancer. The point here is that people will react in various ways to their diagnosis.

●   Can you think of any factors that may influence the way a person reacts to being told he or she has cancer?

●   The way in which the diagnosis is given may affect a person's feelings about having cancer. You may also have thought about the level of support a person has from friends or family. Knowing the prognosis will also affect the way individuals cope and adjust to a diagnosis of cancer.

The following quote describes the way in which a junior doctor informs a patient that her breast cancer has metastasised. The patient is alone and has not met the doctor before:

Unprompted, he began: 'I've got this report, let me read it to you. "Multiple metastases are present throughout both lungs as well as throughout the skeleton. The metastases are predominantly sclerotic, although extensive destruction around the SI joint is noted. The sclerotic changes are most likely due to breast carcinoma".'

(Ashford, 2008, p. 495)

The SI (sacroiliac) joint is at the base of the spine.

● What problems can you see with the way in which this patient is informed of her diagnosis?

● The patient does not have anyone with her, nor does she have any prior connection with the doctor giving her this news. He does not prepare her in any way for the news he is about to deliver. He uses medical jargon which the patient may or may not understand. For example, she is told that her cancer has metastasised; she may not know what this means; and she almost certainly won't know where her SI joint is located.

As mentioned earlier in this section, the way in which a person is told of a cancer diagnosis can have a significant effect on their well-being. When delivering a diagnosis, anxiety can be reduced by ensuring that the patient is given as much information as possible about the diagnosis, using terms that are clearly understood by the patient and with written information also available. Reassurance and discussing a patient's feelings when giving a diagnosis can also reduce future anxiety. People diagnosed with cancer are less likely to become depressed if the word 'cancer' is used and the severity of the situation is explained. Depression is also less likely if a patient is involved in making decisions about their treatment options.

Does the way in which a person reacts initially to their diagnosis make any difference to their health in the long term? There has been much research in this area and the consensus is that the way in which a person reacts and deals with the diagnosis can affect their psychological well-being during the course of the illness. In a study of women with breast cancer, patients who reacted to their diagnosis by avoidance or denial were found to have more psychological difficulties one year after diagnosis compared to those women who adopted a more positive attitude. This difference in psychological well-being was still present three years after the initial diagnosis.

There is also some evidence that the way in which a person reacts to diagnosis can influence their physical well-being. Patients who actively express their emotions around diagnosis were found to require fewer medical appointments and to report better physical health and quality of life than those who were unable to express their emotions. However, importantly, different methods of coping have not been shown to have any effect on long-term survival or the likely recurrence of cancer.

7.3 The multidisciplinary team

In the UK, the introduction of the **multidisciplinary team (MDT)** has standardised cancer treatment. Once a diagnosis is made, a member of the MDT will discuss all the suitable treatment options with the patient. The surgical option is usually explained first as this is often the best curative option (surgical approaches to cancer will be discussed in Chapter 8), but for some cancers, (e.g. laryngeal cancer, bladder cancer, prostate cancer or skin cancer), there are other equally curative options (radiotherapy and chemotherapy are discussed in Chapters 9 and 10, respectively). This can be a confusing time for someone who just wants the doctor to tell them the best treatment.

Box 7.1 lists the members of a typical MDT found in a UK hospital. Most cancer clinics and hospitals in high-income countries have a similar system for managing cancer cases. For example, compare Box 7.1 with Figure 7.2 which shows the members of an Australian MDT.

Box 7.1 The MDT

The typical MDT in the UK consists of the following core members:

- Pathologist (assesses the type of cancer and defines the grade)
- Radiologist (assesses the X-rays and scans and defines the stage)
- Diagnosing/surgical team (presents the patient's details to the meeting and considers surgical options)
- Oncologist (considers the radiotherapy and chemotherapy options as radical or palliative treatments, or also 'adjuvant' or 'prophylactic' treatments – these are explained in Section 7.4)
- Cancer nurse specialists (CNS) (assist the patient though the staging and treatment process and communications).

Additional members may also be present:

- Palliative care team, especially for a lung cancer MDT
- Research team.

The MDT generally discusses patients twice. The first meeting is to review the diagnostic biopsy and decide which further investigations are required to assess the extent of the cancer. The second meeting is to review these investigations to determine the stage of the cancer and decide which treatment options should be discussed with the patient in clinic.

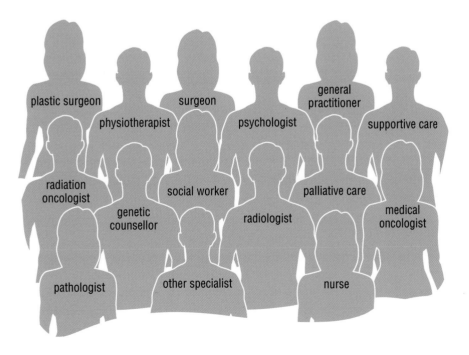

Figure 7.2 A typical multidisciplinary team in Australia.

7.3.1 The first MDT meeting

The role of the diagnosing team is to present the story or 'history' of the patient and their symptoms. This can be very helpful in deciding the best treatment. The treatment is usually based on established protocols but treatment will reflect a patient's particular set of circumstances. During this first meeting the role of the pathologist is to review the biopsy and confirm the type of cancer and the **grade** of cancer (Section 6.6.2). Grading is very different from the staging of cancer, which was discussed in Section 4.4.4. Grading is an assessment of how rapidly the cancer cells are changing, and this influences the treatment recommendation. Staging, on the other hand, defines the spread of the cancer. Depending on the type of cancer and the method used to collect the initial biopsy (e.g. a fine needle aspiration for breast cancer, Section 6.6.1), the stage of a cancer might be known before the grade is determined.

The commonest cancer-grading system uses a scale of low grade, intermediate grade, and high grade (Table 7.1).

Table 7.1 Cancer grades and their corresponding characteristic features.

Grade	Characteristics
Low grade (Grade 1)	Cells retain some of their original features. Slowly changing tumour with lowest chance of spreading.
Intermediate grade (Grade 2)	Cells are dividing slightly faster but some original cellular features remain.
High grade (Grade 3)	Densely packed cancer cells with dividing cells frequently seen. Rapidly changing cancer with the highest chance of spreading.

A notable exception to this is the grading of prostate cancer which uses a grading system devised by Gleason. There are five patterns in the Gleason system, numbered 1 to 5. When reviewing the prostate biopsy the pathologist assigns a primary pattern, between 3 and 5, reflecting the predominant pattern seen; this is illustrated in Figure 7.3. (Gleason patterns 1 and 2 are only detectable when reviewing the whole prostate after it has been surgically removed, so the lowest pattern seen on a prostate biopsy is grade 3.) The pathologist then assigns a secondary grade, which is the second most commonly seen pattern in the biopsy specimen, and the two Gleason pattern grades are added together to give the Gleason score. The lowest Gleason score seen on a biopsy is therefore 6. A summary of the treatment implications of the Gleason score is given in Table 7.2.

The role of the radiologist is to define the stage of the cancer (the TNM staging system was described in Section 4.4.4). At the first MDT discussion the radiologist will recommend which scans are required to complete the staging of the primary cancer. Usually a CT or MRI scan, and less frequently a bone scan, are helpful. The clinical oncologist reviews the grade and staging information available, with the diagnosing team to see if the treatment options can be discussed with the patient at this stage or whether they should wait until after further investigations. A recent addition to the MDT is the clinical nurse specialist (CNS) who plays an important role as a liaison between the patient and the MDT. It is becoming common practice for the CNS to communicate the diagnosis to the patient, to act as the hospital contact and to answer the patient's questions.

The identification, grading and staging of the tumour allows the treatment options to be refined. The commonest type of cancer is a carcinoma (epithelial cell cancer), which is usually best treated by surgery or radiotherapy. Less commonly, a lymphoma (cancer of the lymphatic system) may be diagnosed. Lymphomas are best treated with chemotherapy rather than surgery. Rarely, a sarcoma (supportive or connective tissue cancer arising from bone, muscle, cartilage, fibrous tissue or fat) may be diagnosed and this needs specialised surgery in a sarcoma unit.

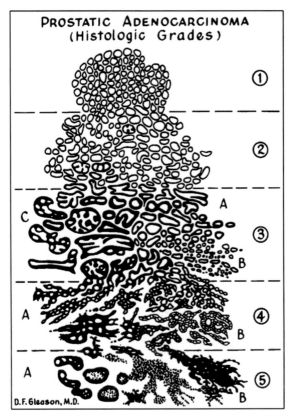

Figure 7.3 Gleason pattern grading. (Source: Humphrey, 2004)

Table 7.2 Gleason score grading on a prostate biopsy.

Grade	Gleason score	Properties of tumour	Treatment implication of the grade only
Low	6	Slowly changing tumour	May require treatment or active surveillance (the cancer is not treated but instead is closely monitored)
Intermediate	7		Requires treatment
High	8–10	High risk of spreading	Requires treatment and 2–3 years of hormone therapy to halve the chance of spread (see Chapter 10 for an explanation)

Activity 7.2   The role of the MDT: from diagnosis to treatment

Allow about 40 minutes in total for this activity

Now watch the series of video clips *The Role of the MDT: from diagnosis to treatment* in which a consultant oncologist talks about issues related to informing a person that they have cancer, the treatment options available and the role of the MDT.

Case study 7.1 Terri's diagnosis and first meeting with the MDT

On Terri's first visit to the hospital dermatology clinic, doctors examine her mole carefully and palpate the lump on her groin. The doctor appears to be worried by what they find. She is told that they need to perform a surgical procedure called an 'excisional biopsy' urgently, in which the mole will be removed and examined. She can have this immediately, as an outpatient, with a local anaesthetic. The local anaesthetic works well, and she feels very little pain; she is, however, beginning to get very worried about what might be wrong. No one has mentioned the word 'cancer', but she is becoming sure that her symptoms match what she has heard of melanoma, and the doctor's demeanour is not helping. She is told to go home and wait for the results.

The next week is the longest of her life, and the wait is ended abruptly by a phone call from a hospital nurse for an urgent appointment. In the hospital, she is told by the nurse that she has a malignant melanoma, and that the melanoma was around 3 mm thick. The nurse introduces Terri to several members of what she's told is called the MDT. She learns that she urgently must have a 'wide local excision' of the skin area where the mole was and that to cover the wound they will graft some skin tissue from her buttock. They also want to remove the lymph nodes from her left groin to check whether the cancer cells have spread. An appointment for surgery is made in three days' time.

7.3.2 The second MDT meeting

Once the patient has undergone further staging investigation their case is reviewed for the second time by the MDT. A CT scan of the chest and abdomen is the commonest scan used to detect secondary tumours in the lung and liver (the result of metastasis via the bloodstream). Blood-borne cancer cells can also metastasise to the bone and, less commonly, to the brain.

The bone scans shown in Figure 6.23 demonstrate 'hot spots' in the ribs, pelvis, hips and skull and is a typical pattern of spread for prostate cancer. When prostate cancer spreads, nine times out of ten it is to the bones. Other cancers that commonly spread to the bones include breast, lung, kidney and thyroid. It is unusual for bowel cancer to spread to the bones as it tends to go to the liver preferentially. (The likely sites of spread were discussed in Section 4.4.3.) The scanning techniques used to image the spread of cancer in the body have recently been improved by the introduction of SPECT/CT and PET/CT imaging systems (Section 6.5.6).

Routine brain scans are not required for most cancers, apart from lung cancer which has a high predilection to travel to the brain. So much so, that even if the brain is clear of apparent metastases, small-cell lung cancer patients are frequently offered 'prophylactic' (preventative) radiotherapy to the brain to reduce the chance of developing brain metastases.

The other way in which cancers can spread is via the regional lymph nodes. A CT or MRI scan can assess lymph nodes and also check whether the primary cancer is confined within the original organ or whether it has broken through the outer layer of the organ. In patients with prostate cancer this provides information about the likelihood of the cancer being completely removed surgically. This is particularly important in lung cancer, as only between 5 and 15% of lung cancers are surgically curable because of invasion into important local structures such as the heart or major blood vessels.

The pathologist will also review the cancers removed by surgery to see if the cancer has been completely removed or whether it is likely that there are some cancer cells left behind. If, when viewed under the microscope, cancer cells come right up to the edge of the specimen, it is likely that there are still cancer cells on the other side of the 'cut line' (Figure 7.4).

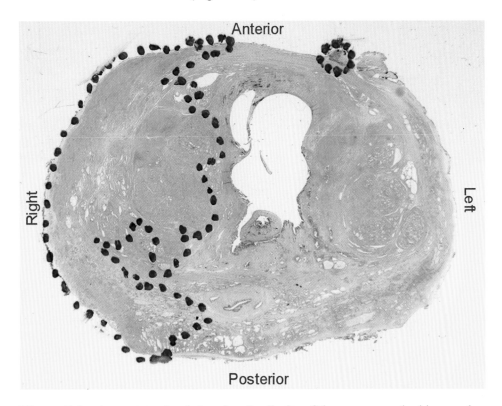

Figure 7.4 A prostate gland showing the limits of the cancer marked by a red dotted line. Note that the cancer is present right up to the edge of the specimen and consequently this patient received adjuvant radiotherapy to reduce the chance of metastatic spread. (Source: Royal Berkshire NHS Foundation Trust)

The MDT would then make further recommendations to reduce the chance of recurrence. The usual options, depending on the site or nature of the tumour, are either further surgery (e.g. with skin or breast cancer) or radiotherapy to the surgical site (e.g. with prostate or breast cancer).

At the second MDT discussion/meeting the radiologist presents the staging scans from which the prognosis and treatment can be assessed. It is useful to have a 'ball park' figure for the prognosis of each stage as well as the general definition for each stage (Table 7.3). Some cancers will have better prognoses than these figures, e.g. breast cancer and testicular cancer. Some cancers have a worse prognosis when comparing stage for stage, e.g. pancreatic cancer, oesophageal cancer and lung cancer.

Table 7.3 General staging and prognosis.

Stage	General definition	Approximate five-year survival rates/%
1	Confined to organ	80
2	Extends beyond the organ	60
3	Involves local/regional lymph nodes	30
4	Metastatic to lung, liver, bone or brain	5–10

7.4 Treating the cancer

The three main approaches for treating a cancer are surgery, radiotherapy and chemotherapy. **Surgery** is the use of manual techniques and instrumentation to remove or alleviate the effects of a tumour (see Chapter 8 for a fuller description). **Radiotherapy** is the use of ionising radiation in the treatment of cancers (see Chapter 9 for a detailed explanation). **Chemotherapy** (discussed in Chapter 10) is the use of drugs to kill cancer cells or reduce their number in the body. The first decision that needs to be made about all cancer treatments is about the treatment intent, i.e. the purpose of the treatment. The question that needs addressing is: 'Does this patient have a curable cancer or, if not, does the patient have symptoms that need treating? (Treatments that alleviate symptoms or complications of a disease are called **palliative**.)

7.4.1 Radical treatments

Radical treatments are either given for curative intent, where there is a realistic chance of cure, or they can be given for 'local control' of the primary tumour site to prevent the development of unpleasant local symptoms.

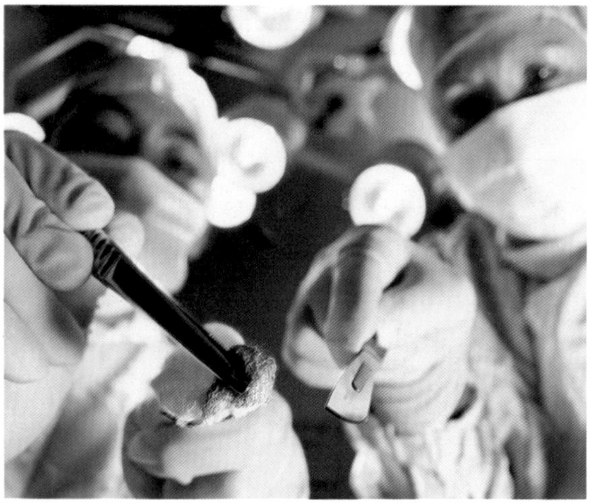

Radical surgery

Most radical treatments are surgical (Figure 7.5) and involve the removal of the primary tumour and, depending on the site, the nearest lymph nodes or other likely sites of spread. For example, ovarian cancer can spread to the uterus, Fallopian tubes, the other ovary and the omentum (a fatty 'apron' lying on top of the bowel within the abdomen). In this case a radical operation would involve removing all the likely sites of first spread so that the maximum chance of cure is obtained. As can be seen, radical surgery is a major operation with significant side effects and a prolonged recovery time is required. Radical operations are generally not suitable for patients with metastatic disease for whom a cure is not possible; these individuals are not likely to survive long enough to gain any benefit from the surgery (see Section 7.4.2).

Figure 7.5 Most cancers are treated using surgical approaches. (Source: Mark Thomas/Science Photo Library)

Radical radiotherapy

Radical radiotherapy provides an effective alternative to surgery for the curative treatment of a number of cancers. It is particularly useful where organ preservation is desired. A patient with laryngeal cancer has the same excellent chance of cure after radical radiotherapy as they have after a laryngectomy, i.e. the surgical removal of the larynx (voice box).

● In the case of laryngeal cancer, what advantage is gained by the patient should they opt for radical radiotherapy rather than surgery?

● There is an excellent chance they will not lose their voice. If they elected to have a radical laryngectomy, then they would have lost the ability to speak due to the surgical removal of the voice box (see Activity 7.2).

Radical radiotherapy treatments tend to be given on a daily basis, Monday to Friday, for about six weeks. The treatment lasts two minutes a day and patients have 10-minute appointments (see Figure 7.6) on an outpatient basis. Some cancers require a little more radiotherapy and others require less, depending on the intrinsic radiosensitivity of the tumour and several other factors such as the oxygen supply via the blood vessels.

Sometimes patients will not be medically fit enough to undergo a radical surgical operation but they can often still have radical, curative treatment in the form of radiotherapy. A common example would be lung cancer where the patient's lung function is poor due to a history of smoking. Such patients cannot tolerate losing any part of their lungs even if the cancer is only small and has not spread. In this circumstance, radical radiotherapy to the cancer is possible.

When a clinical oncologist plans the radiotherapy treatment, they go to great lengths to make sure that the cancer gets the effective treatment dose and that the normal surrounding 'critical structures' (in this case the normal lung tissue) receive a dose that is much less than the tumour receives and within the tolerance dose of the normal structure (see Chapter 9 for a detailed explanation of tolerance dose).

Radiotherapy only works in those tissues that are irradiated, which is why it is a good treatment when the cancer is only in one place and has not spread. Sometimes radical radiotherapy can be used as an adjunct to surgery to help reduce the chance of local recurrence after surgery. For example, if a woman develops breast cancer she may be faced with the choice of a mastectomy (complete removal of the breast) or a lumpectomy with radiotherapy (local excision of the primary tumour with a wide margin and intact covering of healthy breast tissue). Radiotherapy following lumpectomy reduces the chance of tumour recurrence to a level that is similar to that seen after the more radical alternative, a mastectomy. The latter is a disfiguring

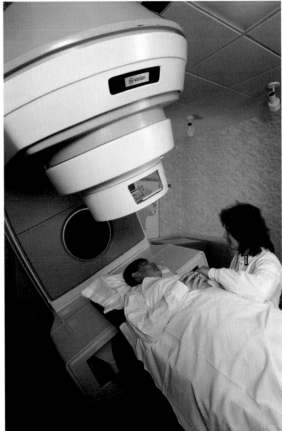

Figure 7.6   A patient about to undergo radiotherapy. (Source: Larry Mulvehill/Science Photo Library)

operation, and nowadays most women opt for a lumpectomy with adjuvant radiotherapy afterwards. Modern radiotherapy techniques have been developed to treat the breast cancer with very little noticeable after effect.

The side effects of radiotherapy can be split into acute and late, and within these two categories, general and specific; they are summarised in Table 7.4. Acute side effects are those that develop within weeks of starting the treatment. General tiredness may be noticeable by some patients particularly if they are having a large area treated, or if they are receiving treatment to the brain. This is caused by inflammation in the irradiated area and the symptoms usually persist for a couple of weeks after the treatment before fading. For most people, the inflammation should have completely settled within a month following radiotherapy. Some organs are very sensitive to radiotherapy and particular care is required with these. The lens of the eye can develop a cataract several years after treatment. Patients having head and neck radiotherapy need to be aware of this and the oncologist measures the dose the lens receives to see if the dose has been kept below the desirable tolerance.

Table 7.4 The side effects of radiotherapy.

Acute	Late
General	*General*
Tiredness	The general side effects of radiotherapy should have subsided by 1 month after treatment.
Lethargy	
Nausea (depending on site)	
Specific	*Specific*
Inflammation in the area treated (from the skin through to the underlying tissues and the exit site)	1 Atrophy (a wasting of the irradiated tissue, after about 18 months).
	2 Telangiectasia (thin fragile blood vessels appear at the site of irradiation, after about 18 months).
	3 Possible loss of function of an irradiated gland.
	4 Fibrosis (scarring/loss of elasticity, from 18 months).
	5 Possible small increased chance of second malignancies in the irradiated area after 15–20 years.

The gonads (testes and ovaries) are also very sensitive to radiotherapy and can result in reduced fertility, or even infertility, if care is not taken. When radiotherapy is given to the pelvis and abdomen in young men with testicular cancer, it may be necessary to offer semen analysis and sperm storage to them to maintain their fertility options before giving them curative treatment.

Radical systemic treatments: chemotherapy

Chemotherapy has the advantage that it treats both the primary site and the metastases. Chemotherapy, which is usually given via a drip into the bloodstream (see Figure 7.7), will find all the known sites of secondary spread and also any unknown secondaries which may be too small to see on the current scans. Unfortunately, chemotherapy is only curative in a minority of adult cancers such as leukaemia, lymphoma and testicular cancer. However, because chemotherapy finds 'unseen' cancer cells at a microscopic level, it lends itself very well to being used after surgery or radiotherapy (and so is called an **adjuvant treatment**) to reduce the chance of the cancer coming back systemically, i.e. affecting the body as a whole. (Adjuvant treatments increase the chance of a successful outcome.) From this point of view, chemotherapy adds a significant chance of cure and may be considered a radical treatment in this setting. For example, a woman with breast cancer who has a lumpectomy will be offered radiotherapy to the breast to reduce the chance of a local recurrence in the breast from say 15% to 5%, and she will also be offered chemotherapy to reduce the chance of metastases in the lung, liver, bone or brain.

● Which part of the body is most at risk of developing metastases in prostate cancer?

● The bones of the skeleton are most at risk of developing secondary tumours.

There are many different types of chemotherapy drugs and they are described in Chapter 10. Combinations of usually two or three different chemotherapeutic agents with different mechanisms of action are used together to reduce the chance of the tumour being resistant to the treatment.

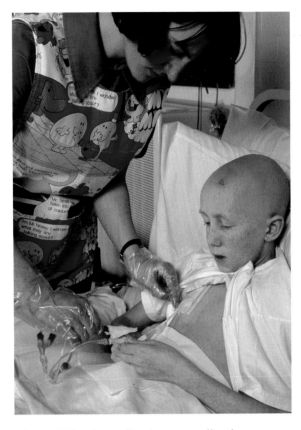

Figure 7.7   A paediatric nurse adjusting an intravenous line being used to deliver chemotherapy drugs to a young boy with leukaemia. (Source: Simon Fraser/Royal Victoria Infirmary, Newcastle/Science Photo Library)

7.4.2 Palliative treatments

In contrast to radical treatments, palliative treatments are usually quick and have few side effects associated with them. Relief of symptoms is achieved quickly with little or no toxicity. Here palliative radiotherapy and chemotherapy play a much bigger role than surgery.

Palliative surgery

Patients for whom a cure is not possible are likely to have symptoms from the metastases which require immediate relief. Only very occasionally does surgery provide the best palliative effect. For example, if a patient presents with metastatic thyroid cancer and the primary tumour is about to obstruct the trachea causing asphyxiation, a palliative tracheotomy (i.e. the surgical opening of the trachea to provide an additional airway) may provide short-term, immediate relief but a thyroidectomy (i.e. the removal of the thyroid) will provide longer-term relief when the metastases can be treated effectively by systemic radioactive iodine therapy, giving the patient a longer-term survival (this form of therapy will be discussed further in Chapter 9).

Palliative radiotherapy

Palliative radiotherapy is usually given as a single treatment and common applications are shown in Table 7.5. This treatment, while not curative, can significantly improve the quality of life for the patient.

Table 7.5 Use of palliative radiotherapy.

Site of cancer or symptom	Effect of palliative treatment
Bone metastases	Relieves pain quickly in 80% of cases
Brain metastases	Relieves headache and neurological symptoms
Haemoptysis (coughing up blood)	Dries up the bleeding
Cough or shortness of breath from lung cancer	Improves symptoms within weeks
Spinal cord compression causing paralysis	Can restore normal function to the legs

Palliative systemic treatments: chemotherapy

Chemotherapy can also be given to reduce the symptoms of cancer. Some tumours respond very quickly and there is rapid relief, e.g. lung cancer and lymphomas. The chemotherapy treatment is delivered into a vein and this treatment is usually given six times over a period of 4 months. (Such a treatment is known as a **regimen**.). A scan or X-ray check may be performed after the third cycle to see if the treatment is shrinking the tumour, but the most effective way of checking the progress is by talking to the patient prior to each visit to see if their symptoms are getting better!

Some types of cancer are sensitive to many chemotherapy drugs and different regimens can be used from time to time to keep the symptoms under control. Ovarian cancer is one such tumour where ascites (fluid in the abdomen) can be controlled by many different regimens. Chemotherapeutic treatments are advancing rapidly and some cancers, which were only recently thought to be chemoresistant (i.e. unresponsive to chemotherapy), such as some types of lung cancer can now be treated by a variety of regimens.

7.5 How is a treatment chosen? The patient and the oncologist

The role of the oncologist in the MDT meetings is to consider the treatment options which should be discussed with the patient when they return to the clinic. The options are recorded and documented in the notes. In some instances, there may be a great deal of choice. For example, a patient with a low-grade prostate cancer can chose between active surveillance (no initial treatment required), radical prostatectomy (major surgery to remove the prostate), or various forms of radical radiotherapy (teletherapy or brachytherapy; these treatments are explained in Chapter 9). There may be other radical treatments the patient may have heard about and wants to discuss such as cryosurgery, laparoscopy or robotic surgery. Alternatively, there may be very little choice of treatment, particularly if the cancer is very advanced. Here, systemic treatment such as hormone therapy or chemotherapy may be the only real option other than palliative care. In making the decision on the best treatment for the patient, the oncologist assesses both patient factors and tumour/cancer factors and these are summarised in Box 7.2.

Box 7.2 Cancer therapies and treatment decisions

Issues to consider for each cancer therapy

Surgery

Rapid resolution

Local treatment

The removal of organs or other body parts can lead to long-term consequences

Can cause disfigurement.

Radiotherapy

Organ preserving – an alternative to surgery

Adjuvant role to reduce the chance of local recurrences

Palliative role to improve quality of life

Side effects are mainly local.

Chemotherapy

Systemic treatment

Adjuvant role to reduce the spread of metastases

Palliative role to shrink tumours

Few curative roles

Significant and widespread side effects.

Factors affecting treatment decisions

Patient factors

Severity of symptoms

Current age and life expectancy

Concurrent illnesses may determine suitability for surgery

Patient preference (psychological factors, including patient's ideas, concerns and expectations).

Tumour/cancer factors

Grade of tumour (the 'aggressiveness' determines the risk of relapse)

Stage of tumour (determines radical or palliative approach)

Chance of response to treatment

Chance of recurrence

Possibility of second curative treatment regimens if the first treatment fails.

Case study 7.2   Jôao discusses treatment options

Jôao is asked to make another appointment with the oncologist to discuss the options available for treating his cancer as soon as possible. He attends the appointment alone; there has not been enough time for his son to fly back from the US to be with him, and somehow he doesn't feel able to talk to any of his former business colleagues about his cancer, however amicable their previous relationship. He deeply regrets that his son has had to move so far away to fulfil his ambitions.

At the appointment, however, he is greatly reassured. The doctor takes time to listen to him, and makes sure that he understands all the unfamiliar words. He is also able to reassure Jôao that, thanks to the screening, his cancer has been caught early and that the treatments he is being offered are very often extremely successful. His health insurance should cover all the treatment he needs, whatever he chooses.

The doctor explains that there are three possible routes that therapy could take: surgery, an operation to remove the whole prostate gland, known as a radical prostatectomy; radiotherapy, which destroys the cancer cells while minimising damage to normal tissue; and close surveillance, that is, no treatment but regular checks to monitor whether the cancer is spreading. Surgery is usually recommended only for men under 70, but as Jôao is generally fit for his age, it could also be an option for him (although not the first one, according to the doctor). Close surveillance could definitely be an option for men of his age but, on balance and taking into account that Jôao's cancer was borderline between low and intermediate stage, the doctor recommends a fairly new type of radiation therapy called brachytherapy that is available at the A.C. Camargo Hospital. This is sometimes called implant therapy; it involves inserting small radioactive metal 'seeds' into the tumour. These release their radioactivity over about six months. The main advantage of this treatment is its convenience; there is no need for patients to make regular (often daily) outpatient visits for repeated treatments, as is the case for conventional radiotherapy.

Jôao decides to opt for brachytherapy, as the oncologist suggested, and books an appointment for an ultrasound examination of his prostate gland. These images are used to determine the size and shape of the gland, and the associated tumour, and decide where the radioactive seeds will be placed. Jôao is also offered an appointment with a specialist counsellor to talk about his illness. Although he had always tended to dismiss the whole 'counselling' business, he decides to give it a go: he does, after all, want to talk to someone, his son is far too far away (and Jôao does not like talking on the phone), and he feels too embarrassed to mention it to any of his friends.

7.6 Consent

'Consent' is the agreement by a patient for a healthcare professional to provide care. This agreement can be non-verbal (i.e. implied consent) such as allowing a nurse or doctor to take a blood pressure reading, or it can be verbal or written (the latter, in cases that involve sedation or general anaesthesia). In order for consent to be valid, the person about to undergo treatment must:

- be competent to make that particular decision
- have received sufficient information to make the decision
- not be acting under duress.

When an adult lacks the mental capacity (temporarily or permanently) to give or withhold consent, no other person can give consent on their behalf. Treatment can, however, be given if it is deemed to be in their best interest as long as it has not been refused in advance (e.g. in a living will or advance directive). The provision of information is crucial to the consent process.

As mentioned in Section 7.3, before treatment can be started, the oncologist or surgeon, in conjunction with the CNS, will have a discussion with the patient about the various treatment options available as well as the risks and benefits of each treatment. The patient is taken through the procedures (they are often given an information leaflet about the treatment and sometimes a video of the procedure to take home with them) as well as given a detailed overview of what to expect during their stay in hospital or visit to the clinic, both before and after treatment. At this time, the person with cancer is usually asked to sign a consent form. The process for obtaining consent is usually done by the healthcare professional performing the treatment or by a doctor who is competent in performing the procedure. In the UK, a consent form is signed by all competent patients who are 16 years or older and are due to undergo a procedure involving a general anaesthetic or one that has significant complications. (In the case of children under the age of 16, consent is given by a parent or guardian.) The healthcare professional obtaining the consent also signs the form to indicate that, to the best of their knowledge, the patient has been given and understands the information necessary to make a considered judgement.

7.7 How do we know which treatments work best? Clinical trials

You may have wondered how it is known that certain cancer treatments are better than others. Some treatments have evolved over time through a process of trial and error, such as some of the procedures used in surgery, but the majority of procedures used today are based on the results of exhaustive testing. Potential new drugs and therapies are always being discovered or proposed; an example is the desert evergreen shrub chaparral (also called the creosote bush), which was used by native American Indians to treat cancer (Box 7.3). The most reliable way of testing a new treatment is by the use of a **clinical trial**. Such trials assess the effectiveness of a new treatment against existing treatments or against a control group. Another important aspect of clinical trials is that they are designed to test the safety of a new treatment. There is very little value in a treatment that cures the cancer only for the patient to die because of the toxicity or an unwanted side effect of the treatment.

Box 7.3 Ancient remedy 'shrinks cancer'

An ancient native American treatment for cancer has been shown to have a beneficial effect despite scepticism from the medical establishment.

Chaparral, an evergreen desert shrub, has long been used by native Americans to treat cancer, colds, wounds, bronchitis, warts, and ringworm.

But experts dismissed its worth, and warned it could be dangerous.

Now researchers at the Medical University of South Carolina have shown an extract may shrink some tumours.

Chaparral tea was widely used in the US as an alternative anti-cancer agent from the late 1950s to the 1970s.

However, the American Cancer Society said there was no proof that it was an effective treatment for cancer – or any other disease.

And the US Food and Drug Administration warned against its use after research showed it could damage the liver and the kidneys.

However, initial results from the latest study show that an extract of the shrub appears not only to be safe, but to have a positive effect.

The researchers tested a refined extract taken from chaparral called M4N.

They injected it into the tumours of eight patients with advanced head and neck cancer that had not responded to other forms of treatment.

The trial was primarily designed to test whether the extract was safe. The results were encouraging – patients seemed to tolerate it well, and there was no evidence of the serious liver damage previously associated with chaparral use.

However, the study also produced some evidence that the extract had begun to shrink the tumours.

The researchers now plan a larger study aimed at showing whether the drug really does work.

Trials important

Henry Scowcroft, science information officer at Cancer Research UK, said: 'Chaparral does not have a good track record as an anti-cancer treatment, but this finding is interesting and suggests that the active ingredients of the plant should be investigated further.'

'Plants are an extremely useful source of anticancer drugs. For example the drugs vinblastine and vincristine from the periwinkle plant are used to treat many different cancers.'

'And taxol, which is obtained from the bark of yew trees, is used to treat ovarian and breast cancer.'

'It is extremely important to test plant extracts thoroughly before they are routinely used in people, to make sure they have no harmful side effects.'

'This is why clinical trials of the M4N chaparral extract will be so important.'

(BBC News website, 11 August 2004)

Trials for new treatments go through a series of evaluation phases (from phase I to III).

Phase I trials are designed to assess the safety of a new treatment and generally involve a small number of participants, often healthy volunteers.

● Why do you think only a small number of participants are involved in a phase I trial?

● The aim of this phase is to test the acute toxicity of a treatment and it would be ethically unsound to expose more people than necessary to a potentially harmful treatment.

The role that clinical trials play in determining the safety of new treatments was amply demonstrated in 2006 when six healthy young male volunteers were given the drug TGN1412, a potential new treatment for chronic lymphoid leukaemia. The men were given a low dose of the drug (some 500 times lower than the dose found to be safe in animals) and all suffered a near-catastrophic failure in their main systemic organs. Thankfully, all six men survived and the trial was suspended.

Phase II: If a phase I trial is successful the treatment then enters phase II. In a phase II trial a larger group of participants, often several hundred, are tested and these usually include people with the cancer of interest. This phase examines the short-term benefits of the treatment as well as its side effects.

Phase III: The emphasis of phase I and II trials is safety. If a treatment passes these phases it then enters phase III. Phase III trials are designed to test the efficacy of the new treatment against existing ones and involve large numbers of patients. Sometimes, the trial will include a placebo group of participants. These are people who unknowingly receive a sham treatment.

● Why include a placebo group in a clinical trial?

● The placebo effect, an apparent improvement in health in the absence of 'real' treatment, will distort the results of any trial or experiment. By including a placebo group it is possible to separate statistically genuine responses from placebo ones.

Trials involving large numbers of participants are usually randomised and are called **randomised controlled trials**. In these trials patients are allocated to a treatment by a computer program designed to ensure that each treatment under

Figure 7.8 Research technicians in protective clothing using tablet trays to count pills (tablets) into plastic bottles for use in a clinical trial. (Source: Geoff Tompkinson/Science Photo Library)

test has a similar profile of patients (in terms of age, gender, severity of disease and general state of health). This allows a fair comparison to be made between the different treatments being tested. Importantly, during the trial neither the participants nor the doctors know which treatment a particular participant is to receive (Figure 7.8). Such studies are known as double-blind studies. (Blind studies are those where only the patient is unaware of the treatment assigned to them.)

● What is the significance of not knowing which treatment a participant is to receive during a randomised trial?

● If a participant or doctor knows or can choose a particular treatment, then the trial is subject to bias which can distort the results of the trial.

Phase III trials involve thousands of patients often spread over several hospitals and, in some cases, across many parts of the world. They are complex to administer but are essential if a treatment is to be appropriately assessed. Phase III trials can take several months or even years to complete. At the end of the trial a statistician evaluates the results, comparing the effectiveness of each treatment against the others assessed in the trial. If a new treatment is considered to be statistically better than the others available, then it is said to be clinically significant and is then usually approved as a treatment. (In the case of drugs, this often involves a regulatory authority.)

A trial may yield statistically significant results but that does not make it clinically significant. As an example, the Royal College of Radiologists ran a trial looking at two different ways of giving palliative radiotherapy for brain metastases. They compared a long course of 10 treatments over two weeks with a shorter course of just two treatments. The outcome was that there was a statistically significant survival advantage of eight days with the longer course of radiotherapy but this was not clinically significant when one considers the extra eight days spent travelling to hospital to have the treatments. Despite the statistical result of the longer course being better, the shorter course of radiotherapy has been adopted as a treatment option as there was no clinical advantage of the longer course!

When assessing the outcome of a clinical trial targeted at cancer it is not uncommon to ask the 'simple' question: 'Is this new treatment likely to increase the lifespan of the patient?' This question is answered by looking at the five-year relative survival rates of people with cancer using what is called the Kaplan–Meier method. The Kaplan–Meier survival plot is a visual and statistically relevant way of showing what happens to a study population over a period of time. An example of a survival plot is shown in the following chapter (Figure 8.2).

Activity 7.3   Clinical trials

Allow about 30 minutes in total for this activity

In this activity you will use the internet to investigate a clinical trial.

Case study 7.3   Terri decides to enrol in a clinical trial

The surgeons remove a large area of skin and tissue around the site of the mole, and also some of the lymph nodes in her groin; each of these will be examined separately to see if the cancer has spread. Terri wakes up after the operation feeling very groggy, and the leg where the mole was located and her left groin are swollen and painful. A day after, she's told the results from the tests: the doctors found cancer cells in two out of the five lymph nodes they removed from her groin; that is, the malignant cells have started to spread. Within the next few days, Terri has blood samples taken to monitor her general health and has several CT and MRI scans to check for the presence of secondary tumours in other areas of her body. No other tumours are detected and a Stage IIIC (or T3N2M0) is determined for Terri's melanoma. She is sent home to convalesce.

After a week, Terri returns to the hospital for a second appointment to discuss treatment options. The nurse from the MDT tells Terri that no secondary tumours were detected but, because there were metastases in the lymph nodes, there is a very high risk of the melanoma coming back in any of her vital organs. She's told that she can have some form of treatment to decrease the chances of the melanoma recurring but that at present there is not strong research evidence that this type of treatment may work. This kind of treatment is called 'adjuvant' therapy.

The nurse from the MDT talks to Terri about different treatment options for people with Stage III melanoma: radiotherapy to the groin area, chemotherapy, even running through a list of what Terri imagines are names of drugs, and some other names she cannot remember. The message is clear: it is up to Terri to decide which treatment she wants to follow, if any. Terri is confused; she is being bombarded with words she has never heard before. For, perhaps, the first time in her life, she feels completely out of control. She just about manages to walk out of the hospital, looks at the square of differently coloured skin below her knee and bursts into tears.

After a sleepless night, Terri has an idea. She remembers that one of the friends she goes to the opera with was, until she retired, a hospital consultant. She calls her friend, asks her round for a coffee, and pours out the whole story. Terri has chosen well: this friend is, as well as a distinguished doctor, a good listener. She gives Terri time to talk but then, gently and encouragingly, goes through all the possible options, explaining what the words mean.

Much reassured by her friend's support, Terri spends hours online, researching the various possible treatments that she has been offered after her operation. Following her friend's advice, she considers several options: no treatment; interferon, a cytokine that will boost her immune system and help her body's natural defences remove the cancer cells; and cancer vaccines, designed also to help her immune system fight against the melanoma cells. Each of these treatments has different advantages and disadvantages; with Terri's type of melanoma, she has been told, any option she chooses will give her a good chance of a long-term cure, but none will give her anything like a guarantee.

Terri finds the idea of boosting her own immune system to treat her cancer attractive, somehow more natural, but feels uneasy about not having any treatment at all. The side effects of the high-dose interferon that she will need include severe tiredness, depression, and possible heart or liver damage, and could be too much to bear. By contrast, cancer vaccines, the most experimental and recent therapeutic option, have minor side effects. However, she is confused by the apparently contradictory results from previous cancer vaccine clinical trials in different parts of the world; some gave very good results, whereas others had little, if any, effect on survival. Terri decides to base her decision on maintaining her quality of life and finally opts for trying a cancer vaccine, the treatment with the fewest side effects. At her next appointment, she tells the doctor her decision and asks whether a cancer-vaccine clinical trial is available in Australia. The doctor reassures her in her decision and says that there is currently a phase III cancer-vaccine clinical trial for which she would eligible at the Sidney Melanoma Unit.

7.8 Concluding remarks

Cancer therapy options are best discussed in the context of an MDT so that all treatment recommendations and options available are put to the patient after considering the cancer factors and the individual patient factors. The treatment decision, however, is ultimately made by the patient based on their understanding of the treatment intent and the side effects and risks of long-term complications.

7.9 Summary of Chapter 7

7.1   Informing a person that they have cancer should be managed in a sensitive and caring manner by the healthcare professional. Evidence suggests that individuals are better prepared to cope with a diagnosis of cancer if they are given as much information as possible.

7.2   In high-income countries the introduction of MDTs has standardised cancer treatment. The MDT consists of healthcare professionals who will stage, grade and treat the cancer and liaise with the patient. The treatment options are fully discussed with the patient prior to making a decision on the course of treatment.

7.3   Treatment of cancer has either a curative intent or is palliative. Curative treatments are radical but are often combined with adjuvant approaches to reduce the likelihood of recurrence. Palliative treatment is not curative but is designed to relieve the symptoms of the cancer.

7.4   Before commencing treatment, people with cancer are asked to give their consent for treatment. In doing so, they agree that they have been fully informed of their treatment choices and the benefits and disadvantages of their chosen treatment.

7.5   Before any new treatment is made widely available it first undergoes a series of clinical trials to assess its clinical significance and safety.

Questions for Chapter 7

Question 7.1 (Learning outcome 7.2)
Briefly describe the role of staging and grading in the diagnosis of cancer.

Question 7.2 (Learning outcome 7.2)
What is the role of the MDT in the management of a patient with cancer?

Question 7.3 (Learning outcome 7.3)
What distinguishes a treatment as being radical or palliative?

Question 7.4 (Learning outcome 7.3)
Give an example of a palliative treatment that is life-saving.

Question 7.5 (Learning outcomes 7.4 and 7.5)
Briefly describe the main advantages and disadvantages of the three main forms of cancer therapy.

Question 7.6 (Learning outcome 7.6)
Distinguish between the roles of phase I and phase III clinical trials.

References

Ashford, R. (2008) 'A memorable patient', *British Medical Journal*, vol. 336, p. 495.

BBC (2004) *Ancient remedy 'shrinks cancer'* [online], BBC News 11 August 2004. http://news.bbc.co.uk/2/hi/health/3555566.stm (Accessed June 2008).

Diamond, J. (1998) *C: Because Cowards get Cancer Too*, London, Vermilion.

Humphrey, P.A. (2004) 'Gleason grading and prognositic factors in carcinoma of the prostate', *Modern Pathology*, vol. 17, pp. 292–306.

CHAPTER 8

SURGERY IN CANCER TREATMENT

Learning outcomes

After studying this chapter and its associated activities, you should be able to:

8.1 Define and use in context, or recognise definitions and applications of, each of the terms printed in **bold** in the text.

8.2 Give examples of the use of surgery in the diagnosing and treatment of cancer.

8.3 Explain the difference between conservative and radical surgical management in cancer.

8.4 Explain the advantages and limitations of laparoscopic versus open surgery in a patient with cancer.

8.5 Describe the possible side effects and risks of surgical treatment.

8.1 Introduction

Surgery is the oldest form of cancer treatment and is the focus of this chapter. For many types of cancer it offers the greatest chance for a cure, especially for those cancers that have not spread to other parts of the body. For those of you who have an interest in the origin of words, surgery comes from the Latin *chirurgia* meaning 'hand work'. Today, surgery is defined as the use of manual and instrumental techniques to investigate or treat a patient's pathological condition. In later chapters in this book, you will learn more about other techniques, such as radiotherapy and chemotherapy, used in the treatment of cancers. However, most people with cancer will undergo some form of surgery during their treatment.

The term 'cancer surgery' encompasses a broad spectrum of surgical techniques that are used to repair or remove a part of the body in the treatment or diagnosis of cancer. Sections 8.2–8.4 will introduce some of these techniques. Sections 8.5 and 8.6 will be centred on the process and implications associated with the surgical treatment of a patient with cancer, and Section 8.7 looks at therapies for eliminating cancer tissue that cannot be surgically excised. The chapter concludes with a comparison of cancer surgery availability in different parts of the world.

8.2 Surgical approaches in the treatment of cancer

Chapter 7 introduced surgery as the primary tool in the treatment of cancers. In this chapter, you will learn that surgical techniques used to treat cancers are not just simply a case of 'cutting the cancer out' but are also involved in its diagnosis, prevention and palliative care. Most people when they think about surgery conjure up mental images of the surgeon's knife and spurting blood. These images could not be further from reality. Today, surgery is all about precision and minimal trauma; employing a wide variety of techniques ranging from cryosurgery to robotics! In this section, we will discuss in more detail the various approaches used by surgeons to treat cancer in the UK and other high-income countries.

8.2.1 Surgery as a diagnostic and staging tool

Surgery is used in the diagnosis and staging (discussed in Section 4.4.4) of most common solid cancers such as those found in the gastrointestinal tract (the gut), breast, lung and organs of reproductive and urinary systems. To make a diagnosis, tissue samples are first collected. In Section 6.6.1, you learnt how fine needle aspiration and core biopsy techniques are used to collect tissue samples for analysis by the pathologist. The diagnosis of breast cancer is usually confirmed by performing a core biopsy, commonly in the outpatient clinic of a hospital and with the use of a local anaesthetic to avoid discomfort. However, not all tumours can be easily reached by using a needle alone and in such cases a surgical approach is required. The most common procedures such as wedge biopsy and excisional biopsy are performed in the operating theatre. A wedge biopsy is generally used to diagnose liver cancer and involves removing a 'wedge' of the affected tissue for analysis by the pathologist. An excisional biopsy involves removing the entire tumour for analysis, such as the removal of a small tumour from the bowel or the skin. An example of a skin excisional biopsy can be seen in Figure 8.1 and in the video sequence that is part of Activity 8.1 (Section 8.5.1). Prior to surgery the surgeon marks the skin with a pen to delineate the extent of the margin. After excision, the tumour is examined by a pathologist to confirm whether the margins are healthy (i.e. free of malignant cells).

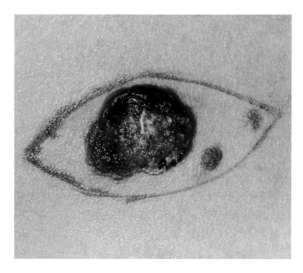

Figure 8.1 Malignant melanoma with the margins marked in ink prior to an excisional biopsy. (Source: James Stevenson/Science Photo Library)

8.2.2 Curative surgery for primary disease

Often the best approach when treating cancer surgically is to remove the whole tissue containing the tumour together with an intact covering of normal tissue. It is important that the **margin** of healthy tissue removed is free of malignant cells (this margin is sometimes referred to as the resection margin).

● Why is it important that the margin is free of malignant cells?

● The best chance of a cure is complete removal of the malignant tissue. If the margin contains malignant cells, then it is likely that not all of the cancer may have been removed, increasing the likelihood of recurrence of the malignancy and spread to other tissues.

Complete removal of a tumour is not without risk. The surgeon has to make sure that he or she is not subjecting the patient to a major surgical procedure only to leave malignant tissue behind that will lead to a recurrence of cancer. The type and location of the tumour will determine the extent of the margin removed with it. For example, in cancer of the oesophagus, the tumour cells spread longitudinally (along the tube of the oesophagus) beyond the visible limits of the tumour itself and it is important that the surgeon takes an adequate margin along the oesophagus to avoid leaving behind tumour cells. On the other hand, in colorectal cancer, tumour cells do not spread longitudinally, but radially (away from the source of the primary cancer, much like ripples that radiate away from the splash caused by a pebble thrown into a pond), so it is important to take away surrounding tissue in the pelvis when removing a colorectal cancer.

When a tumour is removed it is examined by the pathologist to assess the margin for the presence of malignant cells. Clearly, the desired outcome is a margin free of malignant cells. Such margins are called 'healthy' or 'clear' margins' (in the USA these are also called 'negative' margins) whereas margins that contain cancer cells are called 'dirty' margins (or 'positive' in the USA). Any situation that falls between a healthy or dirty designation is called a 'close' margin. If a margin is dirty or close, and if it is surgically possible, the surgeon will remove more tissue until a healthy margin is achieved. However, this is not always achievable and radiotherapy or chemotherapy is then used to destroy any residual malignancy. For some cancers, a clear margin does not always mean the body is free of the cancer as some malignant cells may have already spread to other parts of the body via the bloodstream and lymphatic system.

The importance of margins is illustrated in Figure 8.2. Initially it was argued that women diagnosed with advanced (grade IIIC: see Table 4.3) ovarian cancer would not benefit from aggressive surgery because it would not increase their lifespan. A study of 194 women in the USA with advanced ovarian cancer who underwent surgery to treat their condition clearly demonstrated that the major factor determining survival was the amount of residual disease left at the end of the surgery (Aletti et al., 2007). Women with healthy margins did much better than those with dirty or close ones.

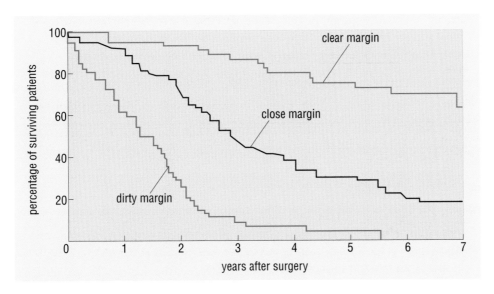

Figure 8.2   The graph shows the percentage of women surviving a number of years after they had undergone aggressive surgery for ovarian cancer. Patients with clear margins had a much better outcome than those with close or dirty margins. These data illustrate the need to ensure, whenever possible, that adequate margins are taken when the cancer cannot be cured by surgery. (Data adapted from Aletti et al., 2007, Figure 1)

So far the surgical approaches to cancer that we have discussed can be categorised as **conservative surgery**, such as only the removal of the tumour and the surrounding margins. However, often a more radical approach is required. An American surgeon named William Halsted (1852–1922) developed the concept of **radical surgery** for the curative treatment of breast cancer. He surmised that in order to remove a breast cancer, it was important that the draining lymph nodes and the intervening tissue were also removed.

● What is a draining lymph node and why is it necessary to remove it?

● Interstitial fluid drains into the lymphatic capillaries (these were introduced in Section 4.4.2) and then into the regional lymph nodes (the draining lymph nodes). Malignant cells can spread from the primary tumour along the lymphatic system and this is why it is important to remove the draining lymph nodes and intervening tissue; reducing the possibility of both metastatic spread and local recurrence.

Today, the concept of removing the tumour, intervening tissue containing the lymphatic vessels and the regional lymph nodes is applied to most solid tumours such as those found in the stomach, colon and pancreas. Indeed, radical surgery forms the basis of the modern approach to curative cancer surgery.

In many cases, surgery alone can bring about a complete cure. An example of this is shown in Figure 8.1 where a melanoma (skin cancer) is removed together with a margin.

Case study 8.1   Julie has thyroid cancer

Julie's family doctor suspected that the lump in her neck might be a thyroid cancer, but she could not be quite sure, so she referred her for tests. Two weeks later, Julie is in an outpatient clinic at St. Bartholomew's Hospital in London. She is feeling perfectly well, if extremely anxious. At the clinic, the oncologist takes a sample of Julie's blood and goes through her medical history. Until now, this has been totally uneventful, and Julie finds some of the details asked for, such as childhood immunisations, difficult to remember. Although, or perhaps because, she has always been very fit, she is not used to thinking much about her health. The oncologist also passes a fine needle into the lump, guided by a small ultrasound scanner, to draw out a sample of cells.

A week later, Julie is called into the clinic again to collect the results. She feels very anxious and asks her partner to go to this appointment with her. They both receive the bad news together: the cells were cancerous, and Julie needs to have an operation to remove her thyroid gland (called a thyroidectomy). Although this news is frightening, the doctor tells Julie that thyroid tumours do not spread quickly. Indeed, Julie's cancer is fairly large, but it is completely contained within the thyroid gland. She is reassured by the news that, although she will have to have an operation, this will almost certainly remove all the cancer and she will be completely cured.

At her first hospital appointment, the surgeon explains that although the surgery to remove the thyroid is quite straightforward, there is a small risk that a nerve leading to her vocal chords can be damaged during the operation because it passes so close to the thyroid gland. If this happens, Julie's voice could be permanently affected.

After the operation, Julie wakes up feeling very uncomfortable because she has a pressure bandage over the front of her neck to reduce the bleeding – but she was expecting this so she is not alarmed. She is lying propped up so that she can breathe more easily, and is very relieved to find that her voice sounds normal (although at first it is a bit painful for her to talk). A few hours later, however, she is beginning to recover from the operation and, within a day, she is able to go home. Her partner Jane takes a day off work to look after her but she does not seem worried as Julie appears her normal self.

Julie also has to start taking daily hormones to replace those that have been produced by her thyroid gland. Initially, while she is still being treated, she is given liothyronine sodium. Had her parathyroid glands, located behind the thyroid, been damaged by the operation she would also have had to start taking calcium supplements.

8.2.3 Curative surgery for secondary disease

Unfortunately, obtaining a surgical cure is not always possible but where local recurrence and/or metastases occur surgery can still offer benefits. You learnt in Chapter 4 that certain types of cancer can give rise to metastases in other parts of the body. For example, colorectal cancer can lead to metastases elsewhere, including in the liver (see Figure 4.6). These secondary cancers tend to occur a few years after the original surgery to remove the primary cancer located in the colon and can be treated by a second surgical operation to remove the liver metastases. Malignant melanoma (skin cancer) can sometimes metastasise to regional lymph nodes after the primary tumour has been surgically removed. For example, a tumour removed from a leg may metastasise to the lymph nodes located in the groin and can be treated by a radical removal of the groin lymph nodes. The therapeutic effectiveness of surgery in the treatment of secondary disease depends on the stage of the secondary tumours; however, in most cases it has a positive effect on five-year relative survival rates (Section 1.2.4).

8.2.4 Reconstructive surgery in cancer

Radical removal of malignant tissue in cancer surgery may result in changes in the body (such as the loss of a breast to treat breast cancer) that can produce severe negative psychological effects in some individuals, which affect healing and the ability to return to normal life. The need to alleviate the effects of radical surgery in cancer has led to the development of reconstructive surgery. Following the removal of an entire breast it is now possible to reconstruct a 'new' breast using the patient's own abdominal wall muscles or muscles from their back. If skin has been lost during breast cancer surgery, this too can be countered by using inflatable tissue expanders to stretch the healing skin and to create a space to allow the insertion of a silicone breast implant. Nipples can also be reconstructed and an example is shown in Figure 8.3. Another example is the reconstruction of the pharynx or oesophagus using tissue taken from the walls of the stomach (you met these structures in Table 4.4).

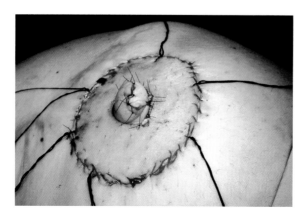

Figure 8.3 Reconstructed nipple and areola (the area of pigmented skin that surrounds the nipple) immediately after surgery to remove a tumour. A skin flap on the patient's breast was used to form the false nipple and a skin graft from her thigh was used to make the areola. (Source: Auro Fermariello/ Science Photo Library)

8.2.5 Debulking surgery

Often it is not possible to remove all of a tumour, usually because it is located within or near an important organ that could be damaged. In such cases, the surgeon will reduce the size of the tumour. This is known as **debulking surgery**. This increases the chance that radiotherapy or chemotherapy could then be used to destroy the remaining malignant tissue. For example, debulking is commonly used for treating tumours located within the brain.

8.2.6 Palliative cancer surgery

Depending on the form of cancer or the severity of the disease a surgical cure is not always possible. However, surgery still has a role to play in such cases and can be used to alleviate symptoms. Tumours of the gastrointestinal tract can often lead to obstruction affecting digestion and the normal functioning of the gut. In such cases a procedure called a bypass is performed. The part of the bowel immediately before the blockage is brought to the abdominal wall surface to form a **stoma** (an opening) where it is connected to a bag to collect the evacuated waste products of the gut (when this involves the colon the procedure is called a **colostomy**) and this is illustrated in Figure 8.4. A colostomy may be a temporary or a permanent intervention and this is determined by the extent of the tumour and its location. A permanent colostomy is required when the lower colon or rectum has been removed.

Malignant obstructions can also be relieved by inserting a tube called a **stent** at the site of the obstruction using an endoscope. A stent is a collapsible metal lattice tube that when in place is expanded to open the obstructed passageway.

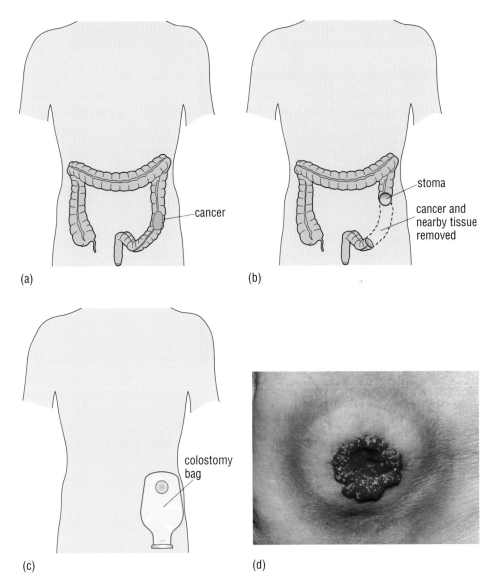

Figure 8.4   (a) A tumour has caused an obstruction in the colon. (b) The section of colon containing the tumour is removed and a stoma created. (c) A colostomy bag is then connected to the stoma to collect the evacuated contents of the gut. (d) A photograph of a stoma in a patient who has undergone palliative surgery for a cancerous obstruction of the colon. (Source: (d) Science Photo Library)

● What is an endoscope and why do you think it is used to insert a stent?

● An endoscope is a thin lighted flexible tube containing a small camera and allows investigation via the body orifices (Section 6.3). They also contain small surgical instruments which may be manipulated by remote control. A stent is used to open a blocked passageway or vessel and because it comes in a collapsible form can be introduced into the body via an orifice and guided to the site of blockage by an endoscope.

Figure 8.5 shows a stent used to relieve an obstruction caused by cancer of the oesophagus.

Figure 8.5 The view seen by an endoscope showing a metal stent holding open an oesophagus affected by cancer. The cancer had blocked the oesophagus, causing vomiting and difficulties in swallowing. The placement has forced open the oesophagus allowing food to pass to the stomach. (Source: David M. Martin MD/ Science Photo Library)

Surgery may also be used to help relieve symptoms and reduce the need for repeated treatment even though it may not affect the final outcome. For example, patients with incurable stomach cancer often experience repeated bleeding from the site of the cancer. In such cases, surgery is used to remove that part to the stomach; this stops the repeated bleeding and so avoids having to receive repeated blood transfusions in hospital.

8.3 Surgery: open or minimal

Broadly speaking, surgery for cancer can be divided into open or minimally invasive surgery. **Open surgery** is the traditional method of entering the body cavities in order to remove tumours. The three main cavities in the body are the abdomen, the thorax and the skull. A **laparotomy** is the surgical opening of the abdominal cavity and is the traditional technique for gaining access to organs such as stomach, gall bladder, liver, small and large bowel (intestines). This form of surgery is still the mainstay of major cancer operations in the abdomen (see Figure 8.6). A *thoracotomy* is the surgical opening of the chest and is used to gain access to cancers of the lung and upper oesophagus. A *craniotomy* is the opening of the skull and is used to gain access to cancers of the brain and of the lining of the brain.

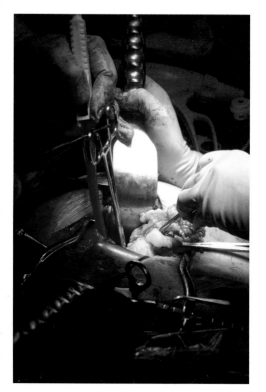

Figure 8.6 Surgeons performing bowel surgery on a person with colon cancer. The patient's abdomen has been cut open and the surgeons are removing malignant tissue from the lining of the colon. This procedure is carried out only if the cancer is detected early. (Source: AJ Photo/Science Photo Library)

Case study 8.2   Dave has open surgery and a colostomy for colon cancer

Dave is told that he needs an urgent operation to remove his cancer and nearby lymph nodes. As the tumour has grown through the wall of the bowel, it will not be possible to simply remove the cancer from the bowel lining; he will have to have part of the bowel itself removed. This will mean he will have to have a colostomy, in which the surgeons make an opening called a stoma in the wall of his abdomen, to which the upper end of his remaining colon is joined. He will have to wear a bag attached to the stoma to collect faeces.

Before Dave comes into hospital for his operation, he is put on a very strict diet to clear out his bowels, with laxatives for the last two days. He is also given an antibiotic to help prevent post-operative infections. The operation is quite a major one, and Dave wakes up afterwards feeling very unwell. He is given strong pain killers to control the pain (morphine via a continuous intravenous infusion), which help, and he gradually begins to feel better. At first, he is unable to eat or drink at all; he starts with sips of water, and within four or five days he is eating a very light diet.

The results from the lymph node biopsies are back. They are, indeed, negative, containing no cancer cells. Dave's cancer is described as Duke's stage 2, or, using the TNM system, T2N0M0: the tumour has penetrated the bowel wall, but there are no lymph nodes involved and no distant metastases. In the United States, over 70% of patients newly diagnosed with this type of colon cancer will survive for at least five years. Had his wife not encouraged him to visit the doctor when she did, his cancer would undoubtedly have spread into the lymph nodes and then into other organs. The prognosis for patients who already have advanced, metastatic colon cancer when they are diagnosed is far worse.

After his operation, Dave is given adjuvant chemotherapy to kill any remaining cancer cells and prevent the cancer from returning. Chemotherapy is started before Dave is discharged from hospital following his operation. He is given a drug called 5-fluorouracil, which is one of the drugs that kill rapidly dividing cancer cells by inhibiting DNA replication. This drug cannot be given orally; Dave has a narrow tube called a central line inserted into one of the veins in his chest, and the drug is infused into his vein through this. The tube is put in under a local anaesthetic and his chest feels rather sore afterwards.

Dave goes home about ten days after the operation. He is still feeling very tired, and rather sick from the chemotherapy, and he is finding it very difficult to get used to the colostomy bag. He is helped by a specialist nurse who visits him at home. During a very long convalescence, his wife and family, and friends from his church and neighbourhood are a great source of support. Several months after the operation, he is a great deal better, although not quite back to his previous self, and he has something else to worry about: he still needs to take expensive medications, and his inadequate health insurance is about to run out.

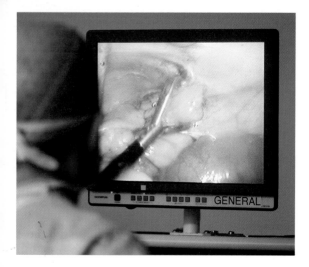

Figure 8.7 A screen displaying an image of laparoscopic surgery, being watched by the surgeon performing the procedure. The surgeon is removing a small section of the colon for diagnostic analysis. (Source: Mark Thomas/ Science Photo Library)

Minimally invasive surgery is a combination of modern technology (usually employing an endoscope) and traditional surgical techniques with the aim of achieving minimal trauma to the human body and mind. It is now widely accepted that this form of cancer surgery (often called **keyhole surgery**) is less disabling and less disfiguring to the patient. It also has the bonus of shorter times in postoperative recovery and facilitates the return to normal life. Minimally invasive surgical techniques can be divided into the following categories:

Laparoscopy

This technique uses a laparoscope, a device similar to an endoscope (a laparoscope is sometimes referred to as an abdominal endoscope). Using the laparoscope, a camera is introduced into the abdominal cavity through a small incision (cut). The cavity itself is inflated with gas (carbon dioxide) to provide space so that the laparoscope can be easily manoeuvred and to allow the structures inside the abdomen to be visualised. This technique has greatly helped in obtaining tissue samples for diagnosis of cancer because it is possible to see exactly where the tumour lies, even though the incision is very small. An example of a laparoscope being used to collect tissue is shown in Figure 8.7. Laparoscopy is also gaining ground in curative surgical procedures involving the stomach and other abdominal organs.

Thoracoscopy

A camera is introduced into the chest to gain access to the lungs, oesophagus and heart. This enables the surgeon to remove the cancer through a much smaller incision than that would be required for open surgery.

Endoluminal endoscopy

A flexible or rigid camera is introduced into hollow organs or systems such as the oesophagus or colon. This technique enables the surgeon to make a diagnosis and obtain tissue samples without having to perform major surgery to gain access to the site of the cancer.

Perivisceral endoscopy

This technique allows a surgeon to gain access via one of the orifices to organs that cannot be easily reached through one of the body's natural cavities (e.g. abdomen and thorax); the prime example being access to the kidney.

Although the techniques of minimally invasive surgery are gaining popularity it must be noted that they also have limitations. As the surgery is being carried out with the aid of a camera, it takes considerable training to develop the necessary hand–eye coordination to work with a 2D image. The added disadvantage is that of a lack of navigational aids to judge the depth on the 2D image. Also, the tactile sensation that a surgeon would normally expect when using a scalpel or other manual instruments is missing and is another drawback that the surgeon must cope with (imagine peeling an orange without the sense of touch!). In some advanced hospitals, complex surgical procedures that would normally have been tackled using open surgery are now being performed by robots in the minimally invasive setting. This innovation allows the surgeon to perform the operation from another site in the hospital or even outside the hospital; offering the opportunity of life-saving surgery to patients in remote locations or in hospitals that lack appropriately trained surgeons.

8.4 Special techniques in cancer surgery

Surgery continues to evolve, a process driven by a better understanding of cancer and the emergence of new and better techniques to treat it. Along with the traditional and minimally invasive procedures discussed earlier in this chapter, cancer surgeons now employ several other techniques that help with performing operations.

Of these emerging techniques, the one that truly captures the imagination is the use of lasers. A laser is a highly focused and powerful beam of light energy that can be used to 'cut' and/or 'ablate' (destroy) a tumour. The beam is delivered via an optic fibre cable that is often an integral part of an endoscope. These are very fine and flexible cables (light guides) that can be easily guided to the site of the tumour, usually through a body cavity. Lasers can be used to debulk advanced tumours that are obstructing the larynx (voice box) or oesophagus and to destroy small tumours in the small bowel. Because the light guides are relative narrow they can easily be inserted into the urethra to gain access to the bladder where they are used to treat bladder tumours. Figure 8.8 shows a cervix after it has undergone laser treatment for the removal of pre-cancerous cells. The burn pattern left by the laser can be easily seen.

Cancers can also be destroyed by being frozen. This technique is called **cryosurgery** and involves the use of liquid nitrogen to freeze and kill abnormal cells. The temperature of liquid nitrogen is approximately −196 °C.

● Is liquid nitrogen colder than a kitchen freezer?

● Yes, the typical kitchen freezer is usually set at −20 °C.

Liquid nitrogen is sprayed onto the tumour to freeze it. After freezing, the dead tissue, containing the tumour, sloughs off leaving a disease-free base. This technique has the advantage of being relatively pain-free and, importantly, minimises blood loss. Cryosurgery is commonly used to treat low-grade skin cancers and to remove cancer of the trachea.

Surgery can also be aided by the use of sound waves to locate the tumour. Ultrasound probes (Chapter 6) can be used to identify the site of the tumour and anatomical landmarks such as blood vessels. This is useful 'on-site' information, particularly when there is doubt about the extent of the tumour and the level of invasion into adjacent tissues.

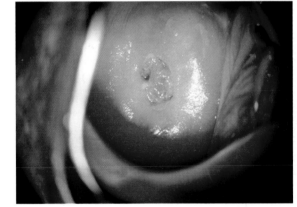

Figure 8.8 The cervix after successful laser treatment to remove pre-cancerous cells. The cervix is a healthy pink colour, but the cervical canal is considerably enlarged due to the destruction of the pre-cancerous cells by the laser. The concentrated source of high-intensity light radiation destroys cells directly under the beam, whilst leaving adjacent cells undamaged (the burn path of the laser is visible at the centre of the image). (Source: Science Photo Library)

X-rays can also help to identify the site of a tumour. Standard X-rays are used to localise breast cancers that are not easily located using the sense of touch. A small metal wire, which is readily seen on an X-ray, can be used to mark the site of the tumour, reducing the need to perform a large operation on the breast in order to look for the tumour.

Surgery in general continues to innovate and advance. Technological advances in other fields such as robotics, optics and physics have made certain surgical procedures feasible and relatively trauma-free for the patient. A recent innovation that is based on such spin-off technologies is called **natural orifice transluminal endoscopic surgery (NOTES)**. This has made it possible to perform surgical operations without any abdominal scars but through natural orifices such as the mouth, vagina or anus using an endoscope. The surgical incision made to gain access to the tumour is through the internal wall of the natural orifice (i.e. transluminal; passing across the lumen or passageway). Its use is still experimental and the benefits for cancer surgery are currently not known. However, spin-off technologies are bound to be used to further minimally invasive cancer surgery.

Case study 8.3   Naheed has laparoscopy for colon cancer

At the hospital, Naheed immediately underwent a colonoscopy (a camera test to examine the large bowel). The colonoscopy showed that Naheed had a small tumour in her caecum (the junction between the small and large bowel situated on the right side of the abdominal cavity). Naheed was then referred onto a colorectal surgeon at the hospital after having a CT scan of her chest and abdomen to stage the tumour as well as to identify any spread to the lungs or liver (you were introduced to the use of CT scans in the diagnosis of cancers in Chapter 6). The scan showed the tumour to be localised with no evidence of distant spread. The colorectal MDT came to the consensus that Naheed's tumour was operable and subsequently at a meeting with the consultant surgeon and the CNS, Naheed was given the treatment options available to her. These included either laparoscopic (keyhole) surgery or open surgery or if she had strong views regarding an operation, chemotherapy. The surgical team explained to Naheed that she had a very good chance of a cure from the cancer as it appeared to be at an early stage and had not spread to distant sites in the body. After consultation with her family, Naheed decided to choose the laparoscopic operation to remove the cancer.

Naheed was then invited to a preoperative check clinic where a doctor from the surgical team carried out basic medical tests on her to ensure she was fit to withstand an operation. Some blood was also taken to test the amount of haemoglobin in her body as well as to check that her kidneys were functioning properly. Finally, blood was taken to be crossmatched on the day of the operation. This test enables the blood bank to match stored blood with Naheed's blood type so that in the eventuality of major haemorrhage during surgery, replacement blood can be given to Naheed. Naheed was then given a medication to take on the day before her operation to empty her bowel. Naheed was admitted to hospital the night before the operation and a junior member of the surgical team made a final check to ensure that she was fit to go ahead with the procedure.

On the morning of the operation, Naheed met with her anaesthetist. The doctor explained how she would be putting Naheed to sleep for the operation. She also explained that she would insert an epidural anaesthetic into Naheed's spine for pain control after the operation. The anaesthetist also told Naheed about the various lines and tubes that would be used to monitor her physiological status during the operation. Before she was sent down to the anaesthetic room, Naheed was also given a medication to calm her nerves and help her cope with the stress of the day.

After she had been anaesthetised, Naheed's operation was carried out using the laparoscopic (keyhole) method. This involved four small incisions and one medium sized incision on her abdomen. The operation was successful and the surgeons were able to take away the part of the bowel with the tumour as well as rejoin the bowel without any trouble.

Naheed was quite drowsy on the night of the operation but was pain free as the epidural anaesthetic was working well. She was looked after in the high dependency unit (HDU) for the first night. The next morning, Naheed was allowed to drink fluids and encouraged to walk around the ward. As the amount of pain experienced by patients who have undergone laparoscopic surgery is much less than those who have had an open operation, Naheed was very pleasantly surprised to find that she could walk to the toilet and around the ward without too much trouble. She was also very pleased with the size of the scars from the operation. The four scars were only about 2–3 cm long while the larger scar was about 5 cm across and hidden under her bikini line. Naheed joked that she would be able to wear a bikini on holiday later in the year without being embarrassed about the scars from her operation! By the second day after the operation, Naheed was back on a ward and the epidural anaesthetic had been removed. She was now regularly taking strolls down to the café and newspaper shop. Her surgical team had started her on a soft diet of ice-cream and soup. This was stopped for a day as Naheed felt nauseous after she had taken some ice-cream but was restarted on day three without any further problems. On day four Naheed was passed fit by the physiotherapists who had taken her through a series of exercises to ensure she was taking regular deep breaths and was active whilst in hospital. The final test was Naheed's ability to climb a flight of stairs without unduly exhausting herself. She passed this without too much trouble.

After she was seen by her surgical team for a final time (who ensured the wounds had healed well, that Naheed had started to open her bowels (pass faeces) and that her blood tests were in order), Naheed was discharged home with an appointment to come to the clinic in a few weeks time. She was also given contact details of the nurse specialist so she had someone to call in case she became unwell or had questions about her condition. Naheed's thoughts about her stay in hospital include, 'I did not know you could do such operations through such small incisions'. 'I did not realise that I could walk around the ward on the day after surgery! I was expecting to be bed bound and in pain.' 'My husband's aunty had an open operation a few years ago and was in hospital for two weeks; I am going to be enjoying the sunshine in my garden and mowing the lawn in less than a week after having my operation!'

8.5 The process of surgical therapy in the treatment of cancer

Sections 8.5.1–8.5.6 will focus on the process of treating a patient with cancer.

8.5.1 If a tumour is operable

In Chapter 7, you were introduced to the role of the MDT in managing the care and treatment of the person with cancer. It is the MDT that decides if a cancer is suitable for surgery. Regardless of whether the patient is a candidate for surgery, they are invited to a clinic to discuss the diagnosis as well as the consensus decision of the MDT and further treatment options. If the person's cancer is thought to be a good candidate for surgical removal, they are then placed on an urgent waiting list to have an operation.

The ideal for any form of cancer surgery is the complete removal of malignant disease from the body. Most operable cancers diagnosed at a relatively early stage can be treated in this way. In instances where metastases are confined to areas adjacent to the tumour (e.g. the adjacent lymph nodes and vessels), these are removed at the same time as the removal of the primary tumour or sometimes in a second operation. Even if there are widespread incurable metastases, removal of the primary tumour can relieve the local effects of the cancer (such as compression of nerves or important blood vessels or bleeding from the site of the tumour).

● Is this an example of surgery to cure a primary disease?

● No, it is an example of palliative cancer surgery, i.e. it is to relieve the symptoms experienced by the patient.

Surgery might be required in an emergency setting such as when a patient with incurable bowel cancer is admitted with a bowel obstruction due to the tumour. They will need to undergo urgent surgery to relieve the obstruction. The success of any cancer treatment is measured in survival terms rather than whether the disease is cured or not (this was discussed in Chapter 7). The five-year relative survival is used as the yardstick of success in cancer therapy and in some cases does not imply that the disease has been cured. Some tumours such as breast cancer can recur after an interval of 20 years or more, while others such as bowel cancer tend not to recur if the patient has been free of disease for more than five years.

Activity 8.1   Skin cancer surgery

Allow about 30 minutes in total for this activity

Now watch the short video clip *Skin Cancer Surgery* in which you will follow the journey taken by Dorothy Bloyce, a 67-year-old woman from a farming family in Wiltshire, as she is treated for skin cancer.

8.5.2 The effects of major cancer surgery on the human body

Most surgical interventions in the treatment of cancer are 'minor' operations performed in the outpatient clinic or done on patients who have been admitted to a general surgical ward. Patients requiring 'major' surgery will have to be admitted to hospital. A major operation on the human body can be viewed as an assault on the general well-being of the patient. At the time of surgery and in the immediate aftermath, the body undergoes a series of responses at the site of the operation (locally) and in the body as a whole (systemically). All these responses are characterised by the need of the body to:

- compensate for starvation: preceding surgery and in the postoperative period; patients are asked to fast prior to surgery to prevent vomiting during the operation; vomit could cause the patient to choke to death and any vomit inhaled into the lungs could cause pneumonia
- provide additional energy and building blocks for tissue repair
- conserve salt and water: surgery by its very nature produces damage and this induces local inflammation (swelling) and fluid loss; the body also responds to the trauma of surgery by releasing hormones into the bloodstream, often in response to a reduction in the amount of blood circulating in the body caused by fluid loss or bleeding.

8.5.3 Preoperative preparation of the patient prior to major cancer surgery

Taking into account the assault and shock to the body during major surgery, it is important to ensure that the patient is carefully prepared to obtain a satisfactory outcome after major cancer surgery. This part of the patient's experience involves the doctors of the anaesthetic team. The anaesthetists are the doctors who will sedate the patient for the duration of the operation and also monitor and maintain the vital functions of the patient during surgery; they will also provide pain control, both during the operation and during the period in the intensive care unit (ICU) or HDU immediately after the operation. The anaesthetist makes a risk assessment about whether the patient is able to undergo a major surgical procedure and make a full recovery without serious effects to any of their body systems.

In order to make sure the person is fit enough to withstand a major surgical procedure, the patient is invited to a preoperative assessment clinic after the MDT has decided that the patient's cancer is curable through surgery. At the clinic, the patient is assessed by a doctor who takes a thorough medical history to identify concurrent medical problems, such as a previous myocardial infarction (heart attack) or coexisting lung disease, which may have a significant impact on the patient's ability to withstand a major operation. The patient is also subjected to a rigorous clinical examination to determine whether they have any undetected medical conditions (such as hypertension, i.e. high blood pressure) and the anaesthetist makes a note of the regular medications taken by the patient, as well as whether they have any allergies to drugs which may affect the response to the anaesthetic the patient receives.

Based on information gained in the preoperative clinic, the patient is then sent for further investigations to determine whether any special precautions need to be taken during surgery and in the immediate recovery period. In general, patients who are relatively young and do not have any previous medical problems do not require major investigations. Older patients (the majority of the patients with cancer) need a battery of tests to ensure that they are suitable for major surgery and these are summarised in Box 8.1.

Box 8.1 Tests used to assess cancer patients prior to surgery

A blood sample is taken and then sent for various tests. A full count of the number of blood cells is carried out to ensure the patient does not have anaemia.

The levels of urea and electrolytes (salts) in the blood are measured to give an estimation of the patient's kidney function and blood glucose is tested to check that the patient does not have diabetes.

Chest X-ray and/or lung function tests are carried out to ensure the patient does not suffer from any form of lung disease that will impair their ability to breathe during and after the operation.

An electrocardiogram (heart trace) and/or treadmill test are used to ensure the patient does not have an underlying heart condition such as a previously undiagnosed heart disease or irregular heartbeat.

More recently, cardiopulmonary exercise testing (CPX) has been shown to be a better indicator of how well a patient's heart and lungs will cope with major surgical procedures. This test involves getting a patient to ride an exercise bike and measuring the amount of oxygen consumed and carbon dioxide produced while the level of exercise is gradually increased. The information gained from the test enables the anaesthetist to determine whether a patient is at a high risk from heart- and lung-related complications during and after major surgery.

In addition to the tests listed in Box 8.1, the anaesthetist also uses the ASA (American Society of Anaesthesiologists) scoring system to determine a rough estimate of a patient's suitability to undergo a major cancer operation. This system is based on a score of I to V as shown below:

Systemic diseases are those that affect many organs.

I   Healthy patient

II   Mild systemic disease

III Severe systemic disease

IV   Severe systemic disease that is a constant threat to life

V   A patient who is not expected to survive 24 hours.

Only after the person has been fully appraised with regard to their general health and specifically in relation to their cardiopulmonary system (heart and lungs) does the anaesthetic and surgical team give the green light to proceed with the operation. In some cases, a person waiting for surgery may be asked to take some form of corrective action to reduce the risk of complications during surgery; for example, an overweight individual may be asked to lose weight prior to their operation.

8.5.4 After the operation

Care of the patient after major cancer surgery is divided into three major periods.

1   The recovery period in the immediate aftermath of a major cancer operation including care on the HDU or the ICU

2   Care on the general ward up to discharge from the hospital

3   Care in the community and at home.

Immediately after surgery the patient will require very close monitoring in a dedicated recovery area such as an HDU or ICU (see Figure 8.9). These areas are usually situated next door to the operating theatre, and the patient's vital signs, including their breathing and their circulation, are monitored by a healthcare professional assigned to that particular patient. This enables any immediate problems to be identified and action taken as appropriate. To ensure a smooth recovery from the operation, the patient's anxiety and pain are also controlled by the administration of drugs. The intensity of the monitoring undertaken is dependent on the nature of the procedure performed and the general well-being of the patient prior to surgery. As an example, a woman with breast cancer, who is having a lump removed from her breast, is not monitored as intensely in the immediate postoperative period as someone who has had an operation to have

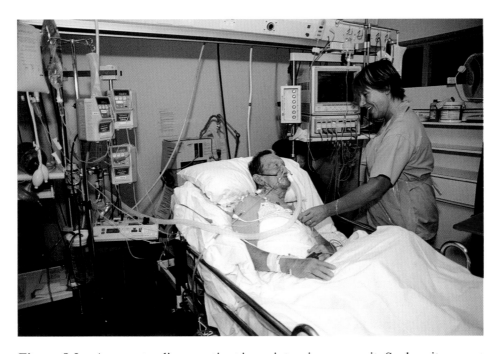

Figure 8.9   A nurse tending a patient in an intensive care unit. Such units provide constant care for patients during severe illness or after major operations. (Source: John Cole/Science Photo Library)

cancer removed from their liver. Similarly, a young and fit patient who does not have any pre-existing medical conditions does not need as intensive monitoring as an older patient with a whole range of medical problems such as high blood pressure, heart disease or chronic bronchitis. In general, immediate postoperative management of the patient after major surgery includes the following:

Airway management: Patients who arrive in the recovery ward immediately after surgery usually have an endotracheal tube in place (a tube placed in the trachea and attached to a ventilator to help them breathe whilst they are under a general anaesthetic). This artificial airway is left in place until the person can breathe on their own when they are fully awake. During this time, the patient is given oxygen to breathe and the oxygen level in their blood is constantly monitored to ensure that their tissues are adequately oxygenated.

Circulation: In the immediate postoperative period blood pressure is monitored at 15-minute intervals. If the patient lost a large amount of blood during the operation the blood pressure is monitored continuously via a sensor placed into an artery. The operation wound and drainage tubes that help remove excess bodily fluids are also monitored for haemorrhage (excessive bleeding).

Fluid loss: Before the patient is returned to the ward, their total fluid loss (blood, tissue fluid, urine, water vapour, etc.) is calculated and replaced during and immediately after the operation, usually via a saline drip (a salt solution, the concentration of which is similar to that in blood) placed into a vein (intravenous).

Temperature: People recovering from surgery may have difficulty in maintaining their body temperature, so core body temperature is measured regularly.

8.5.5 Care on the ward

Patients are generally discharged from the recovery area after they are able to maintain their vital functions independently. This also includes the fact that they should be fully conscious, and have stable respiratory and cardiovascular readings. On the ward, the initial observations performed by the staff on the patient are much the same as those in the recovery area. The frequency is gradually reduced as the patient recovers from the effects of the surgery. The surgical team visits the patient daily and reviews their whole status including their vital observations, condition of the wound, fluid balance (fluid taken in the form of intravenous and oral fluid as well as fluid excreted such as urine, fluid through drains, sweat and also insensible losses (i.e. water loss we are not aware of) through the skin and from the respiratory tract), drug prescriptions and nutritional status. It is also the job of the surgical team to keep the patient abreast of the ongoing management of their condition, including the findings at the operation and future management plans such as expected date of discharge, need for chemotherapy or radiotherapy and further outpatient appointments.

8.5.6 Pain control after major surgery

Patient recovery after major cancer surgery cannot be smooth without adequate **analgesia** (pain control). **Pain** in itself is defined as an unpleasant sensory or emotional experience associated with actual or potential tissue damage. Pain occurs when tissue damage during surgery causes the release of substances (pro-inflammatory substances) that stimulate the nerve endings of the neurons that give rise to the sensation of pain. Blockade of this sensory pathway, and thus the perception of pain, by various pain medications forms the basis of postoperative analgesia. Pain is a complication of surgery and its relief is an important part of the recovery process. Surgery of the chest or the upper abdomen can cause pain which limits the patient's ability to breathe deeply or cough. Pain also increases the activity of that part of the nervous system involved in the 'flight or fight' reflex (the body's natural response to danger) and this causes an increase in heart rate and blood pressure. These factors put an increased strain on the heart and occasionally trigger a myocardial infarction (heart attack) in patients with a pre-existing heart condition. Patients suffering pain find it more difficult to get out of bed and walk about. If a patient remains too immobile there is an increased risk of developing life-threatening blood clots, especially in the veins of the legs; a condition called deep vein thrombosis (DVT; airline passengers on long-haul flights who spend many hours in the same position are susceptible to this condition).

A variety of techniques and drugs are used to provide postoperative analgesia after major cancer surgery. It has been shown in repeated studies that patients who are well-informed about the procedure they are about to undergo and are aware of the nature of the postoperative pain and the modes of analgesia available are better able to cope with it after major surgery. Therefore, it is essential that an anaesthetist counsels the patient before the operation and explains the methods of analgesia available after the operation and that they jointly agree a postoperative pain management plan.

The major class of drug to treat postoperative pain continues to be the opioids (e.g. morphine). These can be given via the mouth in the form of tablets or syrup. For patients who are unable to take oral analgesia (e.g. those who have had major abdominal surgery), the drug is given by the intramuscular route (injected into a large muscle) or intravenous route. In recent years, there has been a growth in popularity of intravenous opioid patient-controlled analgesia (PCA) following major cancer surgery. This method allows the patient to self-administer small doses of opioid when he/she feels pain. The drug is administered via a special pump which delivers the drug into the patient's vein when a button is pressed, as shown in Figure 8.10. Each time the patient activates the pump, a preset dose is administered. The pump has a timer that prevents a further dose being administered within a specified interval and thus reduces the risk of opioid overdose.

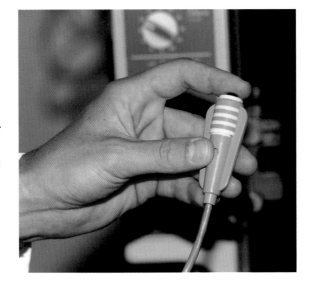

Figure 8.10 The control unit of a pump that can be used by patients to self-administer the pain-killing drug morphine. By using a pump such as this, patients are able to give themselves doses of morphine when they need to. The machine is set up such that it should be impossible to administer an overdose. (Source: BSIP/Platriez/Science Photo Library)

● Do you think that PCA would result in patients administering more or less analgesia than staff would otherwise have given them?

● Research has repeatedly shown that patients self-administer smaller doses of pain-killing drugs. The reason is believed to be that because the patient knows that pain relief is instantly at hand, should they need it, they are less anxious about the pain and this in turn reduces the experience of pain.

In addition to opioids, local anaesthetics are also used to block the conduction of nerve impulses involved in the signalling of pain. They are particularly useful in wounds and are frequently used in conjunction with PCA. Local anaesthetics can be administered into the wound, as nerve blocks, or administered into the epidural space around the spinal cord and provide excellent pain control in major thoracic (chest) or abdominal cancer surgery. The latter is called an epidural block. Opioid analgesia can be complemented by the use of other medications such as non-steroidal anti-inflammatory drugs (NSAIDs, e.g. ibuprofen) and other drugs such as paracetamol.

Case study 8.4   Anneke's surgery

Within a month, Anneke is in hospital again, for an operation to remove a lobe of her left lung (a lobectomy). This is a major operation. The surgeons have to open her chest wall and cut through several ribs to gain access to her lungs. During the operation her lungs collapse and her respiration has to be assisted by machines to keep her blood oxygenated. Anneke feels very ill when she wakes up. Her family are quite frightened on their first visit after the operation, as she is joined up to tubes to drain fluid from the wound. She makes a good recovery, however, and is allowed home after two weeks as she has her retired husband to look after her and daughters living locally. Even before she goes home, a physiotherapist gives her gentle exercises to do to help her recovery.

As soon as she is fit enough, she is back in hospital as a day patient to start her chemotherapy. She is given a combination of three drugs, mitomycin C, ifosfamide and cisplatin, infused through a fine tube into her arm. This is uncomfortable but not particularly painful. After the chemotherapy, she feels very tired and rather sick, and has no appetite, but these effects gradually wear off. After six such chemotherapy 'cycles', each involving one day's chemotherapy followed by a three-week recovery period, the doctors have some good news for her: her lungs seem to be clear of cancer cells although she will have to be monitored very regularly and carefully for any signs of the cancer coming back.

8.6 Risks of cancer surgery

As discussed in Chapter 7, a patient only proceeds to surgery once consent has been obtained for the procedure to be carried out. At the time of signing the consent form, the patient is made fully aware of the risks associated with their particular operation. The major risk associated with surgery is haemorrhage. Tumours often have an excellent blood supply (see Section 4.2) and excessive bleeding can occur at the site of tumour removal or from a blood vessel that was tied (ligated) in order to reach the tumour. The risk of haemorrhage can last for a few weeks after the operation.

In many forms of cancer surgery, a reconstruction of the organ affected by the tumour is carried out once the cancer is removed. In colon cancer for example, once the cancerous colon is removed, the two ends of the remaining colon are reattached to re-establish continuity of the bowel. This approach is also used to reverse a temporary colostomy. The type of join is called an **anastomosis**. A risk associated with an anastomosis is leakage of the gut contents from the region of the reconnected bowel; a phenomenon called **anastomotic leak**. Figure 8.11 shows an example of such a leak from a colorectal anastomosis detected by X-ray using a contrast medium. The leakage of the contrast medium from the joint into the abdominal cavity can be clearly seen. Various factors determine the success of an anastomosis, the major ones being an adequate blood supply to the area that has been joined, the tension on the area of the join and the lack of local infection at the site of the anastomosis.

● Can you think of another reason why an anastomosis might become leaky?

● A dirty margin.

Another and perhaps more serious cause of anastomotic leakage is the presence of tumour residue or malignancy at the joint, once again emphasising the importance of healthy margins in the surgical treatment of cancer.

As mentioned in Section 8.5.6, DVT (the formation of blood clots in the veins in the legs) is a risk associated with surgery. These blood clots occur if the flow of blood is slow or sluggish such as when a patient is bedbound. This risk is increased even further after surgery as patients are immobile in bed due to pain from the surgery and the complications associated with having a major procedure. In order to minimise the risk of DVT and pulmonary embolism (caused by a smaller clot which breaks off from a clot in the leg vein and travels into the veins of the lungs), all cancer patients undergoing major surgery are given thromboembolism deterrent (TED) stockings, which increase the flow of blood in the legs, and also blood-thinning drugs (such as heparin) both prior to surgery and during their stay in hospital. Research has shown that these measures markedly reduce the rates of DVT and pulmonary embolism in patients who have undergone major surgery (Wille-Jorgensen, 2003).

Infection is an ever-present danger after surgery, particularly at the point of entry into the body (the incision wound). (An example of an infected wound can be seen in Figure 8.12.) Also, as mentioned in Section 8.5.6, a patient undergoing major cancer surgery of the chest or abdomen will find that they experience a certain amount of pain when sitting up or while taking deep breaths immediately after the operation. In the immediate aftermath of major surgery (especially if the operation is long requiring the patient to be under the influence of anaesthetic for a long time) there is a certain amount of lung collapse at the base of the lungs. If the patient does not make a significant effort to expand the lungs by taking regular deep breaths in an upright position, they are at a significant risk of developing a chest infection.

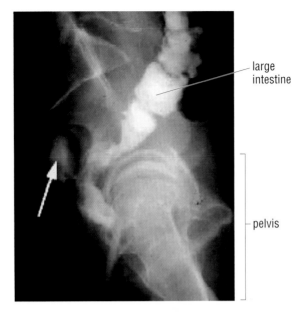

large intestine

pelvis

Figure 8.11   X-ray of the pelvic region of a patient with an anastomosis taken after the ingestion of a high-contrast meal. An anastomotic leak can be seen (arrowed) to the left of the image. (Source: Royal College of Surgeons Edinburgh)

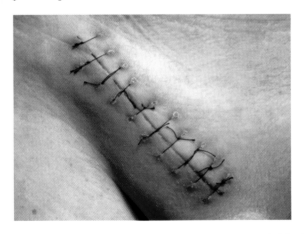

Figure 8.12   Inflammation and 'crusting' of dried pus around the stitches closing this surgical wound are typical signs of post-operative hospital-acquired infection. (Source: Wellcome Library)

Each operation for a particular form of cancer carries with it risks specific to the organ affected by the disease. A patient who has had a section of colon removed may experience loose stools for life. The colon plays a major role in reabsorbing water from the faeces and a smaller colon is less efficient at performing this task. In some cases, cancer surgery requires the removal of an entire organ. An example of this is seen in cancer of the pancreas where removal of the pancreas removes the insulin-producing cells from the body and leaves the person with life-long diabetes. Another risk associated with surgery is damage to the nerves. Surgeons try to spare as much nervous tissue as possible. However, for some cancers, especially those such as an acoustic neuroma for example, that affect cranial nerves, nerve damage associated with surgery is unavoidable. In the case of acoustic neuroma the patient loses hearing on the operated side of the head.

Activity 8.2   Surviving cancer

Allow about 30 minutes in total for this activity

Now watch the video sequence *Surviving Cancer* describing the experiences of the pantomime actor Dominic Gray as he battles with an aggressive cancer of the face.

8.7 Tissue transplantation

There is a class of cancers that cannot be removed by surgical means. These are the cancers that affect the blood such as leukaemia, a family of cancers of the white blood cells of the immune system. White blood cells originate from a population of special cells found in the bone marrow, known as stem cells (Section 2.8.1), which possess the ability to continually produce new white blood cells by cell division and differentiation (examples of bone marrow stem cells are shown in Figure 8.13). Leukaemia arises when the stem cell population becomes malignant.

The traditional method for treating leukaemia is to destroy the existing bone marrow and to replace it using the stem cells harvested from a donor. The malignant bone marrow is destroyed using either chemotherapy, radiotherapy or a combination of both. The form of radiotherapy that is used is called 'total body irradiation' (TBI), which is designed to kill all of the bone marrow cells. (You will learn how radiotherapy is used to treat other forms of cancer in Chapter 9.) In the early days of bone marrow transplantation the donor bone marrow was collected from the hip bone using a wide-bore needle; a minor surgical operation carried out under general anaesthesia. Once harvested, the stem cells from the bone marrow are collected and then injected into the bloodstream of the patient. The stem cells migrate to the bones where they establish new cancer-free populations of cells that restore the bone marrow and produce new blood cells.

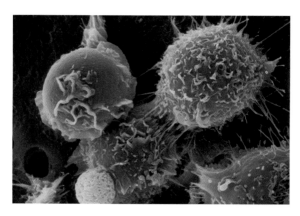

Figure 8.13   Scanning electron micrograph of bone marrow stem cells. The cells are about 20 μm in diameter. (Source: Andrew Leonard/ Science Photo Library)

Advances in medical technology and the understanding of the biology of stem cells have radically changed the way stem cells are harvested. It is now possible to harvest them directly from the blood of the donor without the need for minor surgery and a general anaesthetic. This approach is called peripheral stem cell donation. Prior to collection the donor is given drugs that cause their stem cells to filter out of the bone marrow and into the bloodstream where they are then harvested in the form of a blood donation. Other sources of stem cells are also being developed including the collection of stem cells from the umbilical cord of newborn babies.

8.8 Cancer surgery: a global perspective

This chapter has given a broad perspective of the types of cancer surgery available in a high-income economy such as the UK. However, there is a wide discrepancy in access to treatment between the high- and low-income countries of the world. The WHO recently reported that surgery (including cancer surgery) was a neglected part of healthcare provision in low-income countries; mainly because it was viewed as being reliant on sophisticated equipment and expertise, and of course expensive. Currently, the main impediment for the delivery of surgical care in low-income countries is the lack of trained surgeons and the migration of locally trained surgeons to the high-income countries. For example, in Uganda, there are fewer than 100 surgeons practising in a population of 24 million. For comparison, in 2001 there were 5214 consultant surgeons working in England and Wales with a population a little over 52 million. In Uganda, the majority of surgeons work in urban areas leaving large parts of the countryside with little or no surgical provision. Other countries, such as Gambia and Malawi, have no qualified anaesthetists and have to 'import' them from other countries to provide basic surgical care to patients. Provision is mixed in South-East Asia: here surgeons are concentrated in the major hospitals of large cities. In small towns and villages, very little surgery is performed because of inadequate equipment and the reluctance of local surgeons to perform complex procedures because of poor training.

8.9 Concluding remarks

Surgery is the most common treatment used in the fight against cancers. It has both a curative and palliative role. Whilst this chapter has focused on the effects of major surgery on the body (Sections 8.5 and 8.6 and Activity 8.2); the majority of surgical interventions for cancer are minor operations, often performed in the out-patient clinic such as the excisional biopsy carried out for skin cancer in Activity 8.1.

8.10 Summary of Chapter 8

8.1   Most forms of therapeutic intervention for the treatment of cancer involve surgery.

8.2   Surgery is used in the diagnosis and staging of cancer. It is used for the curative treatment of both primary and secondary disease. When a cure is not possible, surgery can be used to aid other therapeutic interventions, such as the debulking of tumours prior to radiotherapy or chemotherapy. Surgery also has a palliative role in the treatment of cancers and the side effects of treatment. Surgery is also used to reconstruct parts of the body damaged by cancer treatment.

8.3 Surgical strategies for the removal of cancer can be conservative or radical in nature. The radical approach is designed to remove all possible traces of the cancer and includes the removal of regional lymph nodes and lymphatic tissues.

8.4 Traditional approaches to surgery involve the opening of the body's cavities to access the tumour, whereas more modern approaches use less invasive techniques, such as endoscopy.

8.5 An individual about to undergo surgery for cancer is fully assessed by the team of healthcare professionals who will perform the operation and provide postoperative care. Strategies for controlling postoperative pain are agreed jointly with the patient and the anaesthetists. After major surgery a patient is monitored to ensure the maintenance of vital signs and to reduce complications that may arise as a consequence of the treatment.

Questions for Chapter 8

Question 8.1 (Learning outcome 8.2)

What is an excisional biopsy and how does it differ from surgery to cure primary disease?

Question 8.2 (Learning outcome 8.3)

Using breast cancer as your example, briefly describe how a surgeon would treat this condition using (a) a conservative approach and (b) a radical one.

Question 8.3 (Learning outcome 8.4)

List the advantages and limitations of keyhole surgery compared with open surgery.

Question 8.4 (Learning outcome 8.5)

List the major side effects and risks associated with any surgical treatment.

References

Aletti, G.D., Gallenberg, M.M., Cliby, W.A., Jatoi, A. and Hartmann, L.C. (2007) 'Current management strategies for ovarian cancer', *Mayo Clinic Proceedings*, vol. 82, pp. 751–70.

Wille-Jorgensen, P., Rasmussen, M.S., Andersen, B.R. and Borly, L. (2003) 'Heparins and mechanical methods for thromboprophylaxis in colorectal surgery', *The Cochrane Database of Systematic Reviews*, no. 4, CD00121.

RADIOTHERAPY

9.1 Introduction

Radiotherapy can be defined as the use of ionising radiation in the treatment of malignant disease. It can be used both as radical treatment, where the aim is to remove the cancer cells completely, and as palliative treatment, where the aim of the radiotherapy is to reduce pain and other discomfort. Radiotherapy is, after surgery (Chapter 8), the most widely used and effective means of treating cancers; it is estimated that over 50% of all patients with cancer require radiotherapy at some time during their illness (Delaney et al., 2005) and that, in the UK, it forms part of the treatment of 40% of all patients whose cancer is controlled (NRAG, 2007). In Section 5.5, it was mentioned that ionising radiation can damage cells and can actually *cause* cancers; however, radiotherapy makes good use of this potential for damage and uses far larger doses of ionising radiation to *kill* cancer cells. Section 9.2 of this chapter will explain how cells respond to radiation and how it is possible to do more damage to tumour cells than to normal cells. It will also explain what is meant by the term 'dose' in the context of ionising radiation.

The terms 'radical' and 'palliative' were introduced in Chapter 7.

Sections 9.3 to 9.5 will look at the different methods of carrying out radiotherapy. Radiotherapy involves large quantities of ionising radiation so it is appropriate to then discuss briefly, in Section 9.6, the measures that need to be taken to protect the staff and the patient's family and visitors; these measures are known as **radiation protection**.

Unfortunately the procedures described in this chapter are not available to everyone so we shall conclude the chapter with a look at the provision of radiotherapy around the world.

There are two main categories of radiotherapy:

The Greek *tele* means 'at a distance'.

- external beam therapy or **teletherapy** (Section 9.3) where the source of radiation is some distance from the body
- internal radiotherapy, where the source is inside the patient, sometimes for a long period, in other cases for only a few minutes. There are two types of internal therapy:

This word comes from the Greek *brachy* meaning 'nearby'.

brachytherapy, where a sealed source is placed close to the tumour, and

unsealed source radiotherapy, where the patient is given a tablet, a drink or an injection containing radioactive material which will be distributed around the body.

These will be the subjects of Sections 9.4 and 9.5 respectively.

9.2 How does radiotherapy work?

You will recall from Chapter 6 that when X-rays pass through tissue they can be either absorbed or scattered. In each case there is some loss of energy. The amount of energy lost by each photon is very small but it is potentially dangerous because the photon energy is high enough to cause ionisation (see Section 5.5.1). For this reason X-rays, and other high-energy radiation such as gamma rays, are known as ionising radiation. The study of the effects of ionising radiation on tissues is a large and complicated subject known as **radiobiology**. In this course we can only touch on some of the results of this work.

Research has shown that it is damage done to DNA (rather than to other components of the cell) that kills cancer cells, so assessing the extent of DNA damage is crucial in determining the amount of cell killing done by radiation. You saw in Chapter 5 that the incoming radiation can cause either one or both strands of the DNA double helix to be broken (Figure 5.9).

The aim of radiotherapy is 'to damage every single potentially malignant cell to such an extent that it cannot continue to proliferate' (Munro and Gilbert, 1961). This means either killing the cell or removing its potential to divide and proliferate. Of course one also needs to keep the radiation dose to normal tissue as low as possible.

9.2.1 Units of dose: the gray

In the context of radiotherapy, the word 'dose' tends to be used instead of 'radiation dose'. In the rest of this chapter we shall just refer to 'dose' when we mean 'radiation dose'.

Before you can understand radiotherapy it is essential to be familiar with the way in which the dose of radiation is measured. There are several different measures of dose, depending on whether one is interested in the damage done to a particular organ, or in the overall chance of someone developing cancer, or in some other effects due to radiation. In radiotherapy the measure of the dose needed is simple – it is the amount of energy absorbed per kilogram of tissue, and this is expressed in units of **grays** (Gy), where

$$1 \text{ Gy} = 1 \text{ joule per kilogram (J kg}^{-1})$$

● Can you remember what the superscript '−1' means in the expression J kg^{-1}?

● You should remember from Chapter 2 that the superscript '−1' means the same as 1 over that quantity. (See Box 6.2)

The gray (named after the physicist Louis Harold Gray, one of the pioneers of radiobiology) is a very large unit – the doses received in diagnostic X-rays are measured in milligrays or thousandths of a gray. In contrast, the doses delivered to tumours in radiotherapy treatment are usually tens of grays.

9.2.2 Cell survival curves and dose–response curves

To understand how well radiation can kill cells it is usual to draw a **cell survival curve**. This is a plot of the percentage of cells surviving against the dose of radiation as shown in Figure 9.1.

● In Figure 9.1, what dose of radiation is required to kill 90% of the cells using X-rays?

● If 90% of the cells are killed, then 10% of the cells survive. On Figure 9.1 the dose required for 10% of the cells to survive is 8 Gy.

Cell survival curves differ for different types of cell (e.g. prostate or brain cells) and for different types of radiation. This is shown in Figure 9.1 where you can see that the curve for heavy-ion radiation is very different.

● Which is likely to be more effective at killing these cells – heavy ions or X-rays?

● The heavy ions will be more effective because cell survival drops off much more rapidly. Only about 4 Gy is required to kill 99.9% of the cells.

Inducing DNA damage in 90% or even 99.9% of tumour cells is unlikely to be enough to lead to what is known as local control of the tumour, i.e. the tumour is controlled in size and does not spread. For local control, damage to DNA within tumour cells must lead to the eventual death of those cells; moreover, for successful radiotherapy treatment, this cell death must occur in all of the cells within the tumour. If a small percentage of cells within the tumour survive radiotherapy treatment, there will be gradual regrowth of the tumour over time.

There are two processes that dictate whether there will be cell survival or death following DNA damage.

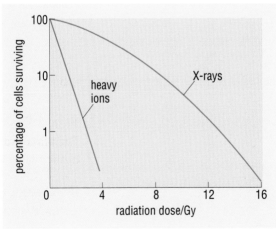

Figure 9.1 A cell survival curve for two types of radiation. Note that the vertical axis goes up in steps of ×10 rather than linearly. A surviving percentage of 100 means that all the cells survive.

- Single-strand or double-strand DNA damage (Figure 5.9): In a cell, DNA breaks are repaired by biological processes within the cell nucleus. Single-strand DNA breaks are quite simple to repair as the cell can use the remaining undamaged DNA strand as a template. In double-strand breaks, there is no complete template. Consequently, single-strand breaks are normally sublethal while double-strand breaks usually lead to cell death.

- DNA repair rates in tumour and normal cells: Tumour cells normally have a reduced capacity for DNA repair (see Section 3.5.4 on genetic instability of tumour cells); in other words, they take longer to repair a damaged strand of DNA. This means that a second radiation treatment applied later the same day, or 24 hours later, is more likely to cause accumulation of DNA damage in tumour cells than in normal cells.

The faster recovery of normal cells can be used to advantage and is the reason why radiotherapy is often given in **fractions**, i.e. a large number of small doses, each of which is a fraction of the whole dose, rather than one very large dose. For the majority of patients these fractions are given daily.

The effects of irradiation on a tumour can be best assessed by drawing a **dose–response curve** which shows the probability of local tumour control for different doses; this is known as **tumour control probability (TCP)**. Figure 9.2 shows one such curve.

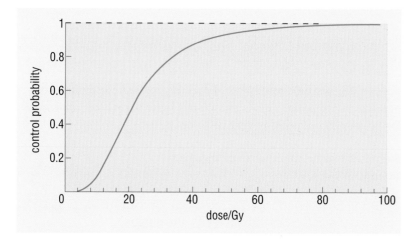

Figure 9.2 A dose–response curve. The greater the dose given, the higher the probability of a local tumour control. (A probability of 1 represents certain tumour control, i.e. the tumour does not grow or spread.)

- Looking at Figure 9.2, approximately what dose would be required to have a 90% chance of controlling the tumour?

- A 90% chance corresponds to 0.9 on the vertical axis. Reading across this gives a dose of about 44 Gy on the horizontal axis.

From this curve you might think that the obvious thing to do is to give the tumour a very large dose of radiation to ensure that a control probability of 1 is reached. However, to do this would be to neglect the effects of radiation on normal tissues. The next section will explore this idea more fully.

9.2.3 Normal tissue response and the therapeutic window

Ideally radiotherapy would be given in such a way that a large dose would be received by the tumour tissues and no dose at all by any normal tissues. However, since tumours are surrounded by normal tissues, this is impossible to achieve, although, as you will see later in this chapter, some methods come closer to doing this than others.

Damage to normal tissue is therefore inevitable, but needs to be kept to a minimum. There are many effects that can occur, some of them occurring relatively early on in the treatment, others not manifesting themselves until some time after treatment has finished, in some cases months or years later. Rapidly renewing tissues such as the bone marrow, which produces new blood cells, the lining of the intestines, and the skin are the first to be affected. Effects in other tissues such as the nervous system and lungs take longer to appear. Table 9.1 lists some of these effects with the onset dose for X-ray therapy (i.e. the minimum dose needed to cause the effect) and the time of appearance of the effect.

Table 9.1 Some side effects of X-ray therapy. (Data from Emami et al., 1991.)

Tissue	Side effect	Onset dose (for X-ray therapy)	Time of appearance
skin	transient erythema (sensitivity and pain upon touch)	2 Gy	2–24 hours
skin	temporary epilation (hair loss)	3 Gy	3 weeks
skin	main erythema (redness to skin)	6 Gy	1–2 weeks
skin	permanent epilation	7 Gy	3 weeks
skin	dry desquamation (skin flaking)	14 Gy	4 weeks
kidney	organ failure	17 Gy	up to 5 years
skin	moist desquamation (ulceration)	18 Gy	4 weeks
colon	organ failure	45 Gy	up to 5 years
spinal cord	myelopathy (paralysis)	47 Gy	up to 5 years
skin	necrosis	53 Gy	up to 5 years

Any of these side effects lead to what are known as normal tissue complications of radiotherapy. The probability of these occurring is the **normal tissue complications probability (NTCP)**. It is possible to draw a graph showing the probability of normal tissue complications as a function of dose (Figure 9.3). Such a curve needs to be compared with the dose–response curve introduced in Figure 9.2.

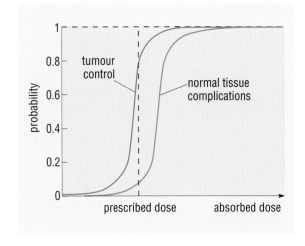

Figure 9.3 Dose–response curves for tumour and normal tissue.

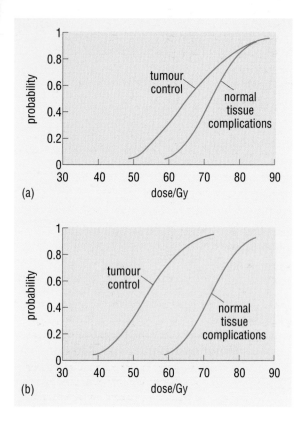

(a)

(b)

Figure 9.4   Dose–response curves for tumour control and normal tissue complications for two different (hypothetical) treatment regimens.

● At the prescribed dose shown on Figure 9.3, what is the tumour control probability? And what is the probability of normal tissue complications?

● From Figure 9.3, the prescribed dose corresponds to a tumour control probability of about 0.8 and a probability of normal tissue complications of less than 0.1.

Clearly the aim of the clinician who prescribes the radiotherapy treatment must be to succeed in controlling the growth of the tumour while not causing too many undesirable side effects in normal tissues. One way to do this is to deliver the radiotherapy in fractions, as mentioned in Section 9.2.2. For example, if the tumour is to receive a dose of 60 Gy this might be delivered in daily fractions of 2 Gy over 6 weeks (Monday to Friday). This allows time for the normal tissues, which have received a smaller dose than the tumour, to repair and recover between doses. As you can imagine, there is much debate about the details of different fractionation regimens but the aim of new regimens is always to improve on the TCP and reduce the NTCP as far as possible.

● Look at Figure 9.4. Which treatment regimen is most likely to lead to control of the cancer without normal tissue complications?

● The regimen in Figure 9.4b where the NCTP curve is far to the right of the TCP curve. If the two curves are far apart, the dose that will control the tumour will have a low probability of causing normal tissue complications.

This is a demonstration of the **therapeutic window** – the difference between the tumour control dose and the tolerance dose for normal tissue effects.

9.2.4 Long-term risk of developing cancer

While the main emphasis in radiotherapy is on tumour control and the avoidance of normal tissue complications that may occur in the days and months following treatment, there is one other, longer-term, risk that is always present. That is the risk you learnt about in Chapter 5 of developing another cancer because of the radiation given to normal cells in other parts of the body. Such cancers can take up to 20 years to develop so, for most people with cancer, they are not an immediate issue and control of the cancer that they have at present is their biggest concern. However, there is one group of patients for whom this is more of a concern and that is children.

When children have radiotherapy there is greater chance that they will live long enough to develop a radiation-induced cancer. Very great care needs to be taken to keep the doses to other organs as low as possible while still achieving the short-term aim of the radiotherapy which is of course to control the cancer.

9.3 Teletherapy

Teletherapy, as mentioned in Section 9.1, is carried out using a source of radiation that is some distance from the body. It can be done using a variety of different types of radiation but, at present, by far the majority is done using X-rays. You may find this surprising as the cell survival curve shown in Figure 9.1 suggests that a beam of heavy ions is likely to be more effective. However, the production of heavy-ion beams is technologically much harder, and therefore more expensive, and there are as yet only a few heavy-ion therapy machines available for routine treatment in the wealthiest countries of the world. (See Section 9.3.5.)

9.3.1 Linear accelerator

The earliest teletherapy machines used sources of radioactive cobalt (cobalt-60) which emits 1 MeV gamma rays. However, in most countries these have been superseded by high-energy X-ray machines which deliver photons with energies of up to 20 MeV. A typical machine, which uses a linear accelerator to accelerate the electrons used to produce the X-ray beam, is shown in Figure 9.5a and the schematic diagram in Figure 9.5b shows how the beam is produced. Electrons are emitted from a hot filament (the electron gun) and are accelerated through a high voltage and directed (using a magnetic field) on to a metal target. When the electrons hit the metal target, high-energy X-rays are produced. The key feature that allows the production of such high-energy X-rays (with a much higher energy than that used for diagnostic purposes) is the acceleration of the electrons in a straight line (i.e. linearly). As a consequence these machines are known as linear accelerators, or **linacs**.

You met the electronvolt (eV) as a unit of energy in Figure 5.7. The symbol 'M' in front means one million (you met some of the other possible prefixes in Box 4.2). Each gamma-ray photon emitted by a cobalt-60 source has an energy of 1 million electronvolts.

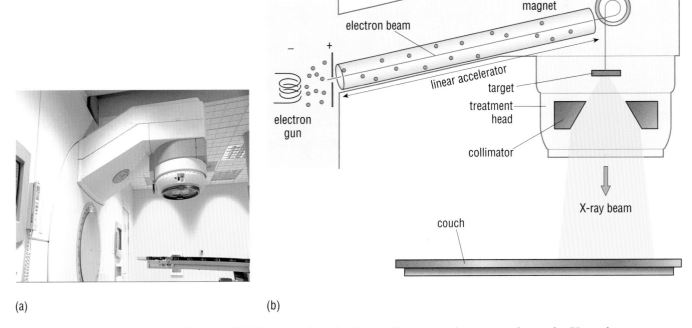

(a)   (b)

Figure 9.5   (a) A linear accelerator. (b) Diagram showing how a linear accelerator produces the X-ray beam.

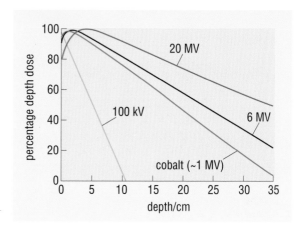

Figure 9.6 Depth–dose curves for different energies. On diagrams such as these the dose is always relative to the maximum dose.

As the X-ray beam is applied externally, the amount of energy that can be deposited in tissue (the dose) decreases as the depth of the tissue increases. But this effect varies with the X-ray energy. Figure 9.6 shows **depth–dose curves** for some X-rays of different energies. On these diagrams the dose is always given relative to the maximum dose. For example, the maximum dose for a 500 kV X-ray beam is deposited near the surface; for a 10 MV beam the dose is maximum about 2.5 cm from the surface. (As you have already learnt, photon energies are measured in electronvolts (eV). However, when referring to linacs, physicists talk about the voltage that is used to accelerate the electrons so they refer, for example, to a 10 MV beam. The maximum energy of the photons produced by this beam is 10 MeV, although most photons have a considerably lower energy.)

It may seem odd that the maximum dose does not occur at the tissue surface. There are sound physics explanations for this but we shall not enter into them here – the key point to note is that the maximum dose is below the surface and not at the surface. This effect is put to good use when high-energy photon beams are used for treatment; because the maximum dose is below the skin, there is a skin-sparing effect which reduces the dose to the skin. This results in fewer side effects such as skin reddening (Table 9.1) and therefore means less discomfort for the patient.

- From Figure 9.6, under what circumstances do you think that 200 keV (or some appropriate energy) X-rays might be useful?

- 200 keV X-rays only penetrate a short distance and give the highest dose close to the surface. They are therefore most useful for treating superficial cancers such as skin cancers.

If you refer back to Figure 5.7 which shows the electromagnetic spectrum you will see that both X-rays and gamma rays are at the high-energy end of the spectrum. Both can have a wide range of energies – the difference between X-rays and gamma rays is their origin: gamma rays are from the atomic nucleus (Section 6.5.6) and X-rays are produced by processes involving the atomic electrons. Generally X-rays have the lower energy, but it is possible to produce very high-energy X-rays.

These comparatively low-energy beams are indeed very useful and very effective in the treatment of many skin cancers, only requiring one application and giving an excellent cure rate. For tumours located deeper within the body higher-energy beams are used but even so, with only one beam, it is not possible to give a large dose to a deep-seated tumour without giving a higher dose to normal tissues nearer the body surface and in the path of the beam. The solution to this problem is to use several beams from different directions which all irradiate the tumour but which give a lower dose to other tissues. The diagram in Figure 9.7 shows how several beams can be used to target a tumour in the body while giving lower doses of radiation to the surrounding tissues.

9.3.2 Treatment planning

Figure 9.8 only shows a simplistic diagram of the way multiple beams can be used in teletherapy. It's not hard to imagine that this is in fact a very complicated process. The first step is to have good images of the patient – these are usually

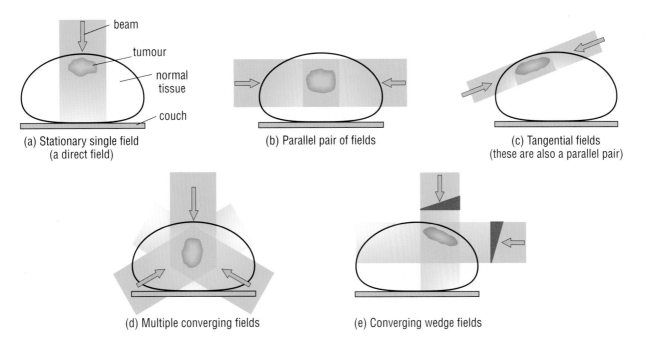

Figure 9.7 Diagram showing how the use of multiple beams can allow the largest dose to be given to the tumour. The amount of shading represents the intensity of the beam. (Wedges are explained in Section 9.3.3.)

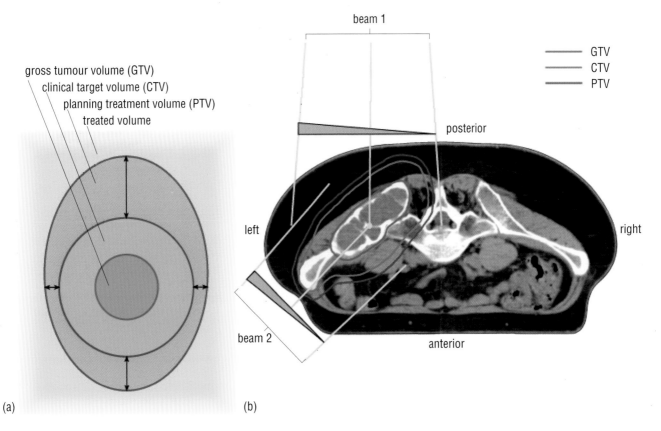

Figure 9.8 (a) The three target volumes outlined in green, blue and red. (b) The same target volumes marked out for a pelvic tumour on a CT scan. The planning is done in 3D but this diagram only shows one slice. (Anterior means the front of the body, posterior the rear.)

CT slices (see Section 6.5.3) covering the region of the body where the tumour is present. The clinician then delineates three important regions as shown in Figure 9.8:

- the gross tumour volume (GTV) – the extent of the tumour that can be seen, palpated or imaged

- the clinical target volume (CTV) – the GTV plus a margin to allow for subclinical tumour cells around the periphery of the tumour

- the planning treatment volume (PTV) – the CTV with another margin added to allow for the inevitable setting-up errors and organ movement.

The treatment must now be planned in such a way as to give the prescribed dose to the whole of the tumour and as low a dose as possible to the normal tissues, particularly the organs that are more sensitive to radiation, and therefore more prone to damage, than others. These organs are known as organs at risk (OARs) and include the spinal cord, the rectum, and the lungs. The beam angles, sizes, energies and the amount of radiation delivered by each beam (known as the beam weighting) are chosen to give the best possible **treatment plan**. In the early days of radiotherapy the calculations needed to optimise the treatment were done by hand; nowadays they can be done by very sophisticated computer programs. After checking, the information is transferred to the linac control system so that the radiotherapy can be delivered exactly as prescribed. Figure 9.9 shows an example of a treatment plan for prostate cancer. The dose received by different regions is calculated as a percentage of the prescribed dose and points that receive the same dose are connected by **isodose lines** – rather like the contours on a map.

The prefix 'iso' means 'the same'. Hence 'isodose' means the same dose.

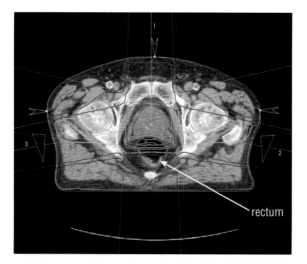

rectum

Figure 9.9 Treatment plan showing isodose lines. Note that since the radiotherapy treatment is done on a flat bed the CT scan must also be done on a flat bed so that, when treatment is given, the organs are in exactly the same position as they were on the scanner. (The colours used for the lines can vary – these colours don't relate to those in Figure 9.8.) (Source: Department of Medical Physics, Oxford Radcliffe Hospitals)

- Why do you think the beams have been arranged in the way they have?

- The beams have been arranged so as to avoid passing a beam directly through the rectum (outlined in red) and the spinal cord, both of which are very sensitive to radiation.

9.3.3 The multileaf collimator and image-guided therapy

Until quite recently the dimensions of the X-ray beam from the linear accelerator were defined simply by two sets of jaws, known as collimators (Figure 9.5), perpendicular to each other (Figure 9.10a). Metal wedges could also be used to absorb some of the radiation on one side – this could be used to compensate for dense tissues or for the oblique shape of the body surface (see Figure 9.10b). More recently **multileaf collimators (MLCs)** which move in and out of the beam (Figure 9.10c) have allowed the beam to have a much more complicated shape. The individual leaves of the MLC can be moved during treatment allowing what is known as **intensity modulated radiotherapy (IMRT)**. This enables the beam to conform more closely to the tumour.

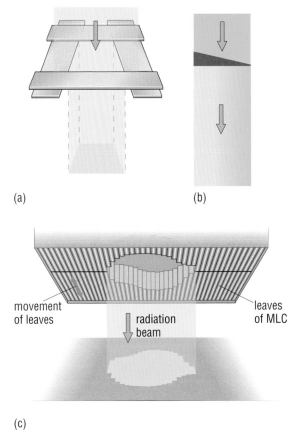

(a)

(b)

(c)

Figure 9.10 (a) The collimators define the beam size in two directions. (b) A wedge allows the intensity to be varied across the beam. (c) The multileaf collimator has much more flexibility and can be moved during treatment.

The most modern treatment planning systems allow the dosimetrist (the person who is carrying out the planning) to see a 3D view of the plan as shown in Figure 9.11. On the computer this view can be rotated so that the set-up can be viewed from different angles.

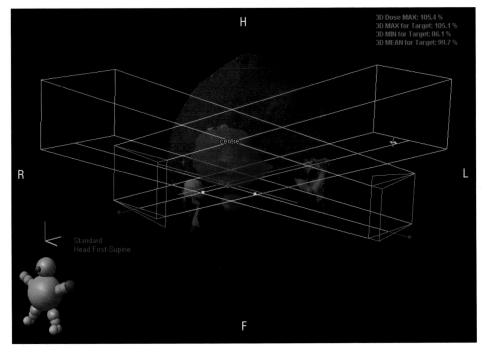

Figure 9.11 A 3D plan for a brain tumour. The radiotherapy is for a brain tumour (shown in red) which is above the eyes (shown in purple and blue). The orientation of the patient is indicated by the little green person in the bottom left of the page; from this you can see that the two beams are entering the patient from the front and from his left. The outlines of the beams are shown in yellow, and wedges (shown in orange) are being used to change the intensity of the beam in different regions. Care has been taken to reduce the dose to the eyes as much as possible as they are radiation-sensitive. (Source: Royal Berkshire Hospital)

If one initial CT scan is used to plan the therapy then there is always the possibility that patient and organ movement may mean that the radiation is not applied exactly where required. One way to avoid this is to image the patient at each treatment, or even continuously during the treatment. This is known as **image guided radiotherapy (IGRT)**. It can be introduced on standard linear accelerators but there is also one company, Tomotherapy™, which produces a radiotherapy machine which behaves rather more like a CT scanner with a linear accelerator built in. This allows continuous imaging of the patient as treatment takes place.

● Can you think of one possible disadvantage of IGRT?

● The X-rays used for imaging will give the patient a greater dose of ionising radiation.

The possible harm that this might cause has to be balanced against the benefits of better treatment.

For brain tumours there is another alternative method known as a gamma knife. This is not actually a knife, but a system which focuses the radiation from approximately 200 radioactive sources (usually cobalt-60 and arranged in a hemispherical pattern) very accurately on to the tumour. To achieve this, the patient's head has to be maintained in precisely the same position throughout the treatment; this is done by placing it in a metal frame and then imaging the patient and frame; markers on the frame then can be used to achieve very precise (sub-millimetre) alignment in the gamma knife machine. This treatment, also known as stereotactic radiosurgery, can be used for brain metastases.

9.3.4 Assessing the plan

All plans are carefully checked to ensure that the dose to normal tissues, especially sensitive ones, is as low as possible and that the dose to the tumour is as prescribed for the whole tumour. One way of doing this is to draw a cumulative dose–volume histogram (DVH). Figure 9.12 shows some examples.

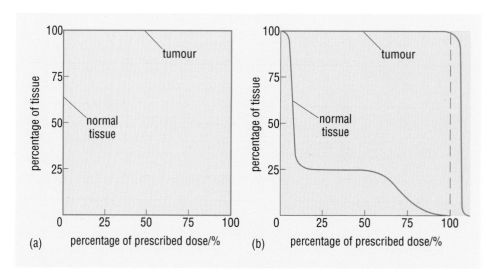

Figure 9.12 Cumulative dose–volume histograms: (a) the ideal situation; (b) a more realistic situation.

In a cumulative DVH the horizontal axis shows the dose (as a percentage of the prescribed dose) and the vertical axis shows the total volume of tissue that receives that dose or more. The ideal, but unachievable, situation is shown in Figure 9.12a – here the whole volume of the tumour receives 100% of the prescribed dose and the normal tissues receive no dose at all. In reality the dose is not the same throughout the tumour; Figure 9.12b shows a more realistic situation; here the curve for the tumour begins to drop off just before the 100% dose, indicating that there are parts of the tumour that only receive about 98% of the prescribed dose. The line goes beyond the 100% dose showing that some parts of the tumour receive more than the prescribed dose of radiation. The normal tissue does receive some dose but most of it receives less than 20% of the prescribed dose.

A dose higher than 100% for part of the target means that those tissues receive more radiation than was prescribed. For example, if the prescribed tumour dose is 50 Gy and part of the tumour received a dose of 120%, then that corresponds to a dose of 120% of 50 Gy = 60 Gy.

- The guidelines for treatment recommend that the tumour tissue should receive between 95% and 107% of the prescribed dose. Is this satisfied for the treatment shown in Figure 9.12b?

- Yes. A very small percentage of the tumour receives slightly less than 100% of the dose (top left of the dotted 100% line): the green line to the right of the dotted line is at approximately 106%. So most of the tumour receives about 106%. Only a very tiny percentage of the tumour receives more than this (bottom right).

Cumulative dose–volume histograms such as these are very useful for 3D planning as they sum the effects over all the tissues involved.

Activity 9.1   Teletherapy

Allow about 45 minutes in total for this activity

You should now study the three video sequences on *Teletherapy*.

1   *Treatment regimens*: in this sequence Paul Rogers, an oncologist, talks about the different possible treatment regimens that can be used.

2   *The linear accelerator*: Paul Whittard, head of radiotherapy physics, shows you round the linear accelerator and explains how it works and how the patients are positioned for treatment. (*Note*: electron beam treatment is a different mode of treatment that is not considered in this course.)

3   *Patient treatments*: in this sequence you can see two patients having their treatment. The first is a lung cancer patient; note the tattoo marks that have been put on his body when the CT scan was taken and which are now used to line him up with laser markers, thus ensuring his correct positioning in the beam from the accelerator.

(*Note*: The term FSD stands for 'focus to skin distance' and is the distance between the point where the X-rays are produced and the patient's skin. Knowing this value is important so that the treatment is exactly as predicted by the plan.)

The second patient is having treatment for head and neck cancer. Because accuracy is so important in the treatment of head and neck cancers, patients are fitted with a mask which clips to the bed and holds the head and neck in exactly the same position for each treatment. (*Note*: the simulator mentioned in this sequence is a machine that is set up in a similar way to an accelerator but which images the patient to check that the beam is going to irradiate the cancer correctly.)

After you have watched the sequences, describe what you think the treatment session might feel like from a patient's point of view. What processes has he had to go through before treatment starts? What will happen to him during a session?

Comments on this activity are given in the Answer section at the end of this book.

9.3.5 Therapy using heavy particles

Proton and heavy-ion therapy

You should remember from Chapter 5 that protons are the heavy, positively charged particles in the nucleus of all atoms.

There are many ways that teletherapy may develop in the future. X-ray therapy, as you have learnt, is constantly being improved. One of the most promising, and one which is already being used in some countries, is proton radiation. The depth–dose curve for protons is very different from the depth–dose curve for X-rays – it has what is know as a Bragg peak named after its discoverer, the famous physicist W.H. Bragg. Figure 9.13 shows the depth–dose curve for 10 MV X-ray photons and for 150 MeV protons (large blue peak).

Figure 9.13 The depth–dose curve for protons and for X-ray photons. The green line is the depth–dose curve for 10 MV X-ray photons, the largest blue curve is the depth–dose curve for 150 MeV protons and shows the Bragg peak at about 15 cm. If the energy of the protons is reduced (by passing it through some other material before the patient) then the Bragg peak can be moved, as shown by the smaller blue curves. If the patient is treated with a range of different energies then the overall depth–dose curve can be spread out to be as shown by the red curve labelled the 'spread-out Bragg peak'.

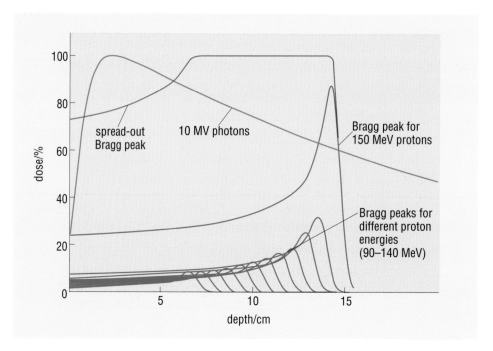

● Looking at these depth–dose curves, what advantage do you think protons might have over X-rays?

● For protons the largest dose is deep within the body, so it ought to be possible to give a large dose to a deep tumour while sparing the overlying tissue.

If the proton energy is changed, the depth of maximum dose is changed. By changing the beam energy the Bragg peak can be scanned across the target so that the end result (the sum of the blue curves in Figure 9.13, labelled the spread-out Bragg peak) is a uniform dose to the tumour and a very low dose elsewhere.

One might wonder why proton therapy has not superseded X-ray therapy long ago. The answer lies in the difficulty of producing the high-energy protons required for proton therapy and the guidance systems needed to irradiate the patient. Several accelerator systems have however been built, most notably in USA, Japan and Switzerland, and have shown themselves to be very successful.

Other heavy ions can also be used in the same way as protons and these have even sharper Bragg peaks. They are also very effective at cell killing (see Section 9.2.2). However they have only been used in a few clinical trials.

Neutron therapy

Another particle that can be used for teletherapy is the neutron and work on using these has been carried out since the 1950s; however results have generally not been encouraging. A more useful way of using neutrons is in what is known as boron neutron capture therapy (BNCT). In this technique the first step is to accumulate boron-containing chemicals in the tumour. This is done using a boron-containing pharmaceutical. The patient is then irradiated with neutrons which react with the boron:

boron + neutron $\longrightarrow$ alpha particle + lithium nucleus

Alpha particles were described in Section 6.5.

The fast-moving alpha particle will then deliver a high dose of ionising radiation to the tumour. Initial work on this technique was not very successful but recent results from Japan look more promising, so it may well find a place in the radiotherapy of the future, especially for some difficult-to-treat brain tumours.

9.4 Brachytherapy

9.4.1 What is brachytherapy?

Brachytherapy uses radioactive sources (see Section 6.5.6) that are placed in or near the tumour. In this way a much larger dose can be given to the tumour and usually a much smaller dose to other tissues. It is not always possible to carry out brachytherapy but many ingenious ways have been devised to get the source as close as possible to the tumour.

Activity 9.2   Brachytherapy

Allow about 25 minutes in total for this activity

Now watch the video sequences introducing *Brachytherapy*. These sequences were recorded for the Open University by Andrew Doggart who is a practising radiotherapy physicist, specialising in brachytherapy, at the Royal Berkshire Hospital in Reading.

As in Activity 9.1, describe what you think the treatment session might feel like from the patient's point of view. What processes has she had to go through before treatment starts? What will happen to her during a session?

Comments on this activity are given in the Answer section at the end of this book.

Andrew Doggart described several brachytherapy techniques which use an applicator to position a radioactive source next to the tumour. In these examples the radiation source is placed inside a body cavity – this is known as intracavitary brachytherapy. In the example shown in the video sequence the very intense source (iridium-192) was placed in the applicator for only a few minutes. This is known as *high dose rate* (or HDR) therapy. It is also possible to use *low dose rate* (LDR) therapy where a less intense source is placed in the patient for a longer period – usually several days.

● Suggest one advantage and one disadvantage of using LDR instead of HDR.

● A disadvantage of LDR is that the patient has to have the applicator inserted for a much longer period. This can mean that the patient has to be kept in isolation and in bed in a specially shielded room, with the sources removed whenever a nurse or doctor needs to enter the room.

   One advantage of this type of treatment is that the source used is less intense and therefore there is less risk of an accident to staff and fewer problems when the sources have to be changed.

HDR brachytherapy is, as was explained in the video sequence, an important technique for the treatment of gynaecological cancers. It can also be used for palliative treatment of lung cancers. In this case a tube is inserted into the trachea (airway), as in endoscopy (Section 6.3), under X-ray observation and the radioactive sources then pass along the tube to reside for a few minutes near to the tumour.

Apart from using an applicator to insert the source into a cavity or into a lumen, Andrew Doggart also mentioned two other types of brachytherapy.

● Can you name them?

● One of them involves placing the source close to the tumour – this is known as mould brachytherapy. This technique was the first type of brachytherapy used but is rarely used these days as low-energy X-rays can achieve exactly the same result much more simply and less hazardously.

   The other technique is interstitial brachytherapy, where the sources are placed in the tumour itself, sometimes permanently.

9.4.2 Prostate brachytherapy

As you saw in the video sequences, one of the most widely used interstitial techniques is prostate brachytherapy, usually with iodine-125 as the source (see Table 9.2).

Table 9.2 Radionuclides used in brachytherapy.

Radionuclide	Energy (emission type)	Half-life	Typical uses
caesium-137	0.662 MeV (gamma ray)	30 years	Temporary intracavitary and interstitial
iodine-125	0.028 MeV (mean) (X-ray)	59.4 days	Permanent implants/ interstitial for prostate especially, but also other sites
iridium-192	0.3–0.6 MeV (gamma ray)	73.83 days	Temporary implants of head, neck, breast and other sites. Intracavitary HDR
palladium-103	0.021–0.023 Mev (X-ray)	17 days	Permanent implants for prostate
ruthenium-106	3.5 MeV (beta particle)	366 days	Ophthalmic applications

Half-life and beta particles were explained in Section 6.5.6.

Figure 9.14 shows the set-up for prostate brachytherapy. The patient is anaesthetised and an ultrasound probe is placed in the rectum to allow imaging of the prostate. The tiny seeds of iodine-125 are then inserted in a carefully planned pattern.

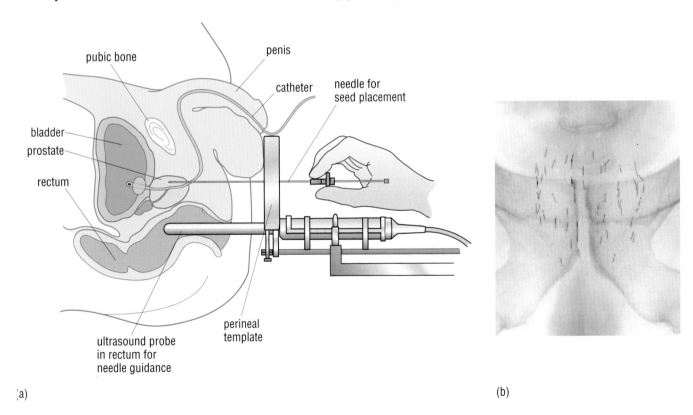

(a)

(b)

Figure 9.14 (a) The set-up for prostate brachytherapy. (b) X-ray of the pelvic area after insertion of the iodine-125 seeds. (Source: (b) Royal Berkshire Hospital)

Once the seeds have been placed in the prostate the patient can leave hospital. The seeds are left permanently in the patient and the radioactivity will gradually decay.

● Approximately how long will it take for the radioactivity of the iodine-125 to decay to one-quarter of its original value?

● Four months. The half-life of iodine-125 is 59.4 days (Table 9.2), which is about two months, so in that time the activity will have decayed to half. In a further two months it will have decayed to one-half of that, or one-quarter of the original activity.

Activity 9.3   Prostate radiotherapy

Allow about 25 minutes in total for this activity

Now watch the video sequence entitled *Prostate Radiotherapy*. In this sequence Paul Rogers summarises the two types of radiotherapy available for the treatment of prostate cancer and talks about the pros and cons of each of them.

Summarise the advantages and disadvantages of each of the two methods from the patient's point of view.

Comments on this activity are given in the Answer section at the end of this book.

Case study 9.1   Jôao has brachytherapy

As Jôao has complete health insurance, the waiting list for brachytherapy is short, and, following his ultrasound scan, the date for the treatment soon arrives. He goes into the hospital oncology department where he is given a general anaesthetic. The procedure takes about an hour; guided by the ultrasound images and other measurements of his prostate gland, about 100 radioactive metal 'seeds' are inserted into the tumour. The dose to the tumour is 160 Gy. When he wakes from the anaesthetic, he finds that he has been connected to a catheter to drain urine from his bladder. This is a temporary measure as the operation often causes short-term swelling of the prostate gland, which can prevent patients passing urine normally.

Patients having brachytherapy sometimes go home the same day, but as Jôao lives alone, he is kept in hospital overnight for observation. The next day, the catheter is removed and he is allowed to go home. He is warned that he will be slightly radioactive for a few days, and advised to stay away from pregnant women and small children. Jôao feels rather shaken after the anaesthesia, but this goes fairly quickly. The only side effect he notices is frequent urination.

9.4.3 Brachytherapy in the future

Brachytherapy has already established itself as an effective treatment, especially in prostate cancer, and its use is likely to grow. For interstitial brachytherapy other radionuclides, such as caesium-131 (half-life 9.7 days) may be introduced. The use of HDR brachytherapy is likely to expand because it is easier to deliver a larger dose to the tumour and a lower dose to the normal tissue than with teletherapy. Also the patient has fewer treatment sessions which is much more convenient.

HDR is now being used for prostate therapy (as an alternative to interstitial therapy) and a system has been developed for the breast. One company has developed a brachytherapy system which uses a very small low energy high dose rate X-ray source instead of radionuclides.

9.5 Unsealed source radiotherapy

In brachytherapy the sources are always sealed – that is to say, the radioactive material cannot escape from the sources and become dispersed around the body. If the radioactive material is not sealed, and is in a form that can be taken up by the body, then it will become distributed around the body. The chemicals used for unsealed source radiotherapy can be tailor-made to target the cancerous tissues – rather as in radionuclide imaging (Section 6.5.6) the radiopharmaceutical is tailored to reach the desired organ.

● Thinking about the range of the emissions, what kind of radioactive decay might be the best to use for this kind of therapy?

● A fairly short-range particle is the best – either alpha or beta particles.

Alpha particles have a very short range and are not widely used. Beta particles are the most widely used. Table 9.3 shows some of the most commonly used radionuclides (all of these are beta-emitting).

Table 9.3 Radionuclides used for unsealed source therapy.

Radionuclide	Half-life/days	Average beta particle energy/keV	Approximate maximum range in tissue/mm
iodine-131	8.0	0.191	4
phosphorus-32	14.3	0.935	8
samarium-153	2.0	0.221	3
strontium-89	50.5	0.583	7
yttrium-90	2.7	0.695	11

For the treatment to be effective the radiopharmaceutical (Section 6.5.6) needs to be taken up selectively by the tumour tissue. The first radionuclide to be used for this type of treatment was iodine-131 and it is still the most widely used. Thyroid hormones contain iodine and, therefore, iodine in the body is taken up almost exclusively by the thyroid gland. So, iodine can be administered orally to the patient and it then targets thyroid cells.

In all treatments of this type it is not enough just to know the half-life of the radionuclide (known as the physical half-life); it is also important to know how long it takes for that particular substance to be taken up, metabolised and excreted by the patient. This is known as the biological half-life. The effective half-life is a combination of the two – if either of them is very short, then the radioactivity will only remain in the body for a short time.

Activity 9.4   Unsealed source therapy

Allow about 20 minutes in total for this activity

In the treatment of thyroid cancer the usual procedure is to remove the thyroid gland surgically, and then to follow this up with iodine-131 treatment to remove any remaining gland and to treat any metastases elsewhere in the body. Now watch the video sequence entitled *Unsealed Source Therapy*. In this sequence Peter O'Sullivan, a medical physicist, shows you how the patient is kept in a separate room and how the radioactive iodine is administered. Note that he mentions the biological and physical half-lives mentioned above, and that he measures the patient's radioactivity using a Geiger counter.

As you watch the video consider the following questions.

(a)   Why does the patient need his/her own bathroom and toilet while receiving iodine-131 therapy?

(b)   The iodine-131 emits both beta and gamma radiation. The beta radiation is short-range and is used to kill thyroid cells; how can the gamma rays be used?

Comments on this activity are given in the Answer section at the end of this book.

Iodine-131 is also used in the treatment of thyrotoxicosis – a non-malignant condition in which the thyroid is overactive. A smaller dose of iodine-131 is used for this treatment.

This so-called 'targeted radiotherapy' is very successful in the radical treatment of thyroid cancer. Targeted radiotherapy can also be used for palliative treatment of bone metastases that have resulted from breast or prostate cancer. Samarium-153 and strontium-89 (see Table 9.3) can be used for this purpose, in each case chemically combined with other substances so that they are in a form that will be taken up by the targeted organ.

Case study 9.2   Julie is treated with radioactive iodine

After Julie's thyroid gland has been removed, she can be treated with radioactive iodine-131 which kills any remaining cancerous thyroid cells. Thyroid cells take up iodine selectively, so these are the only cells that are destroyed by this treatment; Julie can therefore expect few side effects.

Julie does need to take careful precautions before she can have this treatment. She is given two injections of a hormone called recombinant human thyroid-stimulating hormone (rhTSH), which enable her to carry on taking her hormone supplements. The rhTSH is injected into her buttocks, which she finds painful but is grateful for the opportunity to have this treatment. Before rhTSH was introduced, patients waiting for radioactive iodine treatment had to come off hormone supplements for a few weeks, and this caused extreme fatigue. She is also given a special diet that is low in iodine, which she has to be very careful to stick to. She is not allowed to eat fish and seafood, which she loves, and has to be very careful with milk and milk products.

When it is time for the treatment, Julie is admitted to hospital, where she is given a bed in a special shielded room on her own. The nurses run through the treatment plan with her and her partner so they know what to expect and then a medical physicist arrives to administer a capsule containing radioactive iodine. This has to be drunk with a glass of water and Julie is then checked with a Geiger counter. She will be quite radioactive during her treatment and for a few days afterwards, and she and her family will need to take safety precautions. She will stay in her isolation room until the radiation levels have reduced considerably, and she will be monitored for radioactivity throughout that time. Her partner and her parents will be allowed to visit for short periods only, and can come no closer than the end of the bed. She has an intercom that she can use to talk to other visitors. It is particularly important for her to have no contact with her pregnant sister and two-year-old niece until she has been given the all-clear.

During the treatment, Julie feels generally well; the only physical side effect she notices is a dry mouth, which is eased by sucking boiled sweets. Her main problem is the isolation; she has a TV in her room, and plenty of magazines and books to read, and appreciates the visitors that she is allowed, but time still seems to pass extremely slowly. She is very relieved when she is allowed home after five days.

9.6 Radiation protection

Teletherapy involves use of high-energy X-rays which, as you learnt in Section 5.5.1, are a type of electromagnetic radiation and have enough energy to cause ionisation. Brachytherapy and unsealed source therapy both involve the use of radioactive sources which, as described in Section 6.5.6, produce gamma rays (electromagnetic radiation again) and usually either alpha or beta particles. All three of these are also classified as ionising radiation. As you have seen, patient dose is carefully controlled to ensure that the tumour receives as large a dose as is needed and the normal tissue is spared as much as possible. However, it is also important to consider the protection of the staff, the patient's friends and family and the general public from these sources of ionising radiation. In all these cases the principle is that the dose should be

As Low As Reasonably Practicable (ALARP).

There are basically three methods of protection: these are shielding, distance and time.

Shielding

● What examples of shielding have you come across so far in this chapter, particularly in the video sequences?

● In the video sequence on teletherapy (Activity 9.1), you saw the bunker and the maze which together provide effective shielding for the staff when the linac X-ray beam is turned on.

Similarly, for HDR brachytherapy (Activity 9.2), the patient is in a bunker and all the staff leave the room before treatment starts.

For the unsealed source iodine therapy (Activity 9.4), the patient has to remain in a special room until the amount of radioactivity has dropped to an acceptable level.

You may also have noticed that the iodine capsule that was taken by the patient was brought to the room in a lead container. Lead has a high attenuation coefficient (Section 6.5.2), so is an excellent absorber of ionising radiation.

Time

When someone is exposed to a source of radiation the total amount of radiation received depends on the strength of the source, where the person is standing and the length of time for which they stay there. So the medical physicists in the hospital will always ensure that they handle sources for as short a time as possible, and visitors to the patient undergoing iodine therapy will be restricted as to the amount of time they can spend in the room.

Distance

If there were no shielding, one would have to be a very long way away from a linac to reduce the dose to an acceptable level; however, for the smaller sources such as brachytherapy seeds and the iodine capsule (and for the injections used in radionuclide imaging (Section 6.5.6)) keeping as far away from the source as possible is a useful method of reducing the amount of radiation received. If the distance from the source is doubled, then the amount of radiation received is reduced by a factor of 4; if the distance is tripled, the dose is reduced by a factor of 9, and so on. This is known as an inverse square law variation. This is why, when the patient receiving unsealed-source iodine therapy receives visitors they will only be allowed to sit at the opposite side of the room, or, when the prostate brachytherapy patient goes home, he will be advised to keep some distance away from pregnant women and small children.

All of these measures should ensure that no-one in the radiotherapy department – other than the patients – receives anything more than a very low dose of ionising radiation.

9.7 Radiotherapy around the world

Radiotherapy, like many other medical procedures, is expensive and complex; the provision of radiotherapy in any country is therefore affected by the funding available for health care. Radiotherapy in general (and teletherapy in particular) requires large expensive machines and support staff and is therefore often perceived as a particularly costly form of therapy. However, it is in fact very cost-effective: patients can attend as outpatients, and the machines, although expensive, last for a long time and treat large numbers of patients (a linac can cope with about 400 new patients a year). There are also considerable cost savings on pain-relief drugs and chemotherapy for patients undergoing palliative treatments.

Recent work on the role of radiotherapy in low- and middle-income countries (Barton et al., 2006) has looked at the gap between provision and need for linacs in poorer countries. Studies of the use of radiotherapy in Europe show that approximately 52% of all new cancer patients would be most effectively treated by radiotherapy (Delaney et al., 2005).

● Do you think this value would be larger or smaller in lower-income countries?

● Since many patients will present with cancers at a later stage than they might have done in a country with better health care and with cancer screening programmes, there is likely to be a greater need for radiotherapy as surgery may well not be possible and palliative treatment may be needed in many cases.

In fact, the authors of the study on low- and middle-income countries suggest that the percentage varies from region to region, depending on the prevalent cancers, but that the percentage of cases that need radiotherapy is at least 55%. Based on these figures they have estimated the number of teletherapy machines (either linacs or cobalt units) *needed* by each country and then compared it to the number *actually in use*. Their results are shown in Figure 9.15.

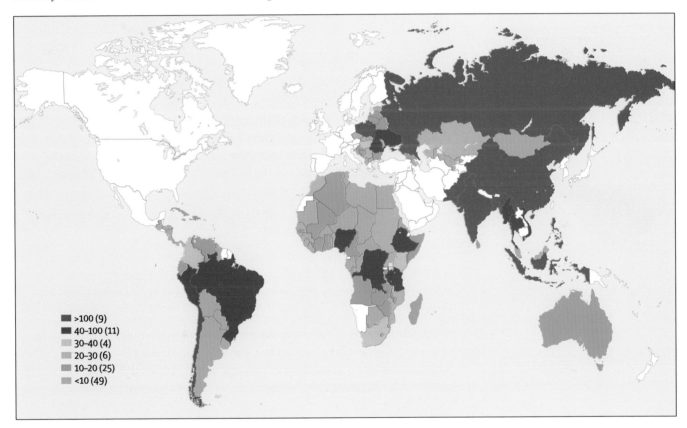

Figure 9.15   The difference between the demand and supply for teletherapy machines in Africa, Asia-Pacific, Eastern Europe, Central and South America, and Australia. The number of countries in each group is shown in brackets. (Source: Barton et al., 2006)

This figure shows that the vast majority of the world's population does not have access to adequate radiotherapy facilities. In fact, the situation in high-income countries is also not always as good as it might be; for example, in the UK it is estimated (NRAG, 2007) that there is a 63% gap between current treatment levels and the optimum treatment levels and that, in order to achieve the optimum levels, a 91% increase on current activity is needed by the year 2016.

9.8 Concluding remarks

In this chapter, we have only been able to give you a very broad outline of the different methods of radiotherapy available and the physics and radiobiology upon which they are based. However, we hope it has enabled you to understand that radiotherapy is an effective (and cost-effective) and widely used treatment for cancer. It can be used for both palliative and radical treatment but there is currently insufficient provision for radiotherapy in many countries of the world.

9.9 Summary of Chapter 9

9.1   There are two main types of radiotherapy – external and internal. External radiotherapy (teletherapy) consists of a beam of ionising radiation delivered from outside the body. Internal radiotherapy can be either brachytherapy, in which radioactive sources are placed close to or in the tumour, or unsealed source therapy.

9.2   Radiotherapy utilises the ability of ionising radiation to kill cells. A balance needs to be maintained between the control of the tumour and the possibility of normal tissue complications.

9.3   In most developed countries teletherapy is delivered by a high-energy X-ray beam from a linear accelerator (linac). The energy, dimensions and direction of each beam need to be very carefully planned to ensure that the best possible treatment is given.

9.4   Brachytherapy can be delivered by a variety of means: intracavitary, interstitial or mould. In each case the radionuclide used has to be carefully chosen to give the best treatment.

9.5   In unsealed source therapy the patient receives a tablet, an injection or a drink containing a radionuclide in a form that will be taken up by the tumour tissue. Patients remain radioactive until the radionuclide has decayed.

9.6   Because all forms of radiotherapy involve ionising radiation, care must be taken to minimise the dose to staff, patients' families and the general public. The three ways of reducing the dose due to ionising radiation are shielding, minimising exposure time and keeping as far away from the source as possible.

9.7   Radiotherapy is a successful means of treating cancer but is not available for all the patients for whom it is needed, especially in low-income countries.

Questions for Chapter 9

Question 9.1 (Learning outcomes 9.1, 9.2 and 9.4)

Why is teletherapy treatment delivered in fractions rather than as one large dose?

Question 9.2 (Learning outcome 9.7)

Figure 9.9 shows a treatment plan for prostate cancer with three beams. What might be advantages and disadvantages of using more than three beams?

Question 9.3 (Learning outcomes 9.1 and 9.5)

Figure 9.12b shows a cumulative DVH for both tumour and normal tissue. If the clinician had specified that less than 30% of this (unspecified) normal tissue must receive no more than 25% of the prescribed dose, would this condition have been satisfied?

Question 9.4 (Learning outcomes 9.6 and 9.8)

Table 9.4 lists three isotopes of iodine with their emissions and half-lives. Explain why each is most suitable for the use listed.

Table 9.4 Properties and medical use for three isotopes of iodine.

Isotope	Emitted radiation	Half-life	Usual use
iodine-123	gamma rays	13 hours	radionuclide imaging
iodine-125	X-rays	60 days	brachytherapy
iodine-131	beta particles and gamma rays	8 days	unsealed source therapy

Question 9.5 (Learning outcomes 9.6 and 9.8)

Modern airport scanners are designed to detect radioactivity at quite low levels so patients who are radioactive as a result of radiotherapy and who intend to travel after treatment will have to carry a letter from the hospital. Which of the methods of radiotherapy discussed in this chapter leave the patient radioactive after treatment?

References

Barton, M.B., Frommer, M. and Shafiq, J. (2006) 'Role of radiotherapy in cancer control in low-income and middle-income countries', *The Lancet Oncology*, vol. 7, pp. 584–95.

Delaney, G., Jacobs, S., Featherstone, C. and Barton, M.B. (2005) 'The role of radiotherapy in cancer treatment: estimating optimal utilization from a review of evidence-based clinical guidelines', *Cancer*, vol. 104, no. 6, pp. 1129–37.

Emami, B., Lyman, A., Brown, B., Coia, L., Goitein, M., Munzenrieder, J.E., Shank, B., Solin, L.J. and Wesson, M. (1991) 'Tolerance of normal tissue to therapeutic irradiation', *International Journal of Radiation Oncology, Biology and Physics*, vol. 21, pp. 109–22.

Munro, T.R. and Gilbert, C.W. (1961) 'The relationship between tumour lethal doses and the radiosensitivity of tumour cells', *British Journal of Radiology*, vol. 34, pp. 246–51.

NRAG (2007) Radiotherapy: developing a world class service for England, Report to Ministers from National Radiotherapy Advisory Group, 26 February 2007 [online], http://www.cancerimprovement.nhs.uk/documents/radiotherapy/NRAG_0507.pdf (Accessed June 2008).

Further reading

If you would like to read further about this topic, please refer to the following publication.

Living with Radiation (1998) National Radiological Protection Board, (5th edn).

CHEMOTHERAPY AND BIOLOGICAL THERAPY

10.1 Introduction

The word chemotherapy comes from two words 'chemical' and 'therapy'. It literally means 'drug treatment'. In fact, the term formerly encompassed the use of any drug to treat any disease; so even administering an aspirin was once regarded as chemotherapy. Nowadays, however, the term has a more restricted meaning which is the use of **cytotoxic** (cell-killing) drugs to destroy cancer cells. Currently, there are over 100 different anticancer drugs available and new ones are continually being developed.

Another therapeutic approach to cancer treatment uses biological molecules such as anticancer growth inhibitors or antibodies and is referred to as **biological therapy**. An alternative term is 'targeted therapy', which reflects the highly specific action of such therapeutic agents. Some biological drugs are developed from substances found naturally in the human immune system, in which case the treatment is called 'immunotherapy'. The drugs used in these newer therapies have been developed through a better understanding of tumour biology and are believed to kill cancer cells in a more specific way than is possible with traditional chemotherapeutic agents. Biological therapy is a more expensive treatment option than chemotherapy but is often more successful. (Various forms of biological therapy will be discussed in Section 10.6.)

The drugs used in chemotherapy and biological therapy enter the bloodstream and so reach tissues and/or organs in the body. Such generalised treatment is called **systemic therapy**. By contrast, surgery and radiotherapy are described as 'local treatments', since they usually only target the area where the tumour is located. Recall from Chapter 4 that cancer cells can break away from a tumour and may spread to nearby tissue or to other parts of the body through the bloodstream and via the lymphatic system, developing into secondary tumours (Section 4.4.1). In principle, anticancer drugs can also circulate in the bloodstream and reach cancer cells wherever they are in the body. Thus drugs administered systemically (e.g. orally or via injection) have the potential to completely eradicate cancerous cells from an individual. There are clear advantages to using systemic treatment in some types of cancer, especially in the advanced stages where tumour cells are more likely to have spread.

Anticancer drugs (both chemotherapy and biological therapy) can be used as a treatment on their own for cancers that are very sensitive to the drugs, but more often than not they are used in combination with surgery or radiotherapy. When administered prior to surgery and radiotherapy, the aim of an anticancer drug is to shrink the tumour so that either it becomes more manageable for surgery or so that a smaller area of the body requires radiotherapy. This is known as **neoadjuvant** treatment. Since the drug can restrict tumour growth, systemic treatment may be administered to patients for whom surgery or radiotherapy has been successful and there are no observable signs of the disease, but there is still a risk that cancer may spread in the future. As you saw in Chapter 7, chemotherapy or biological therapy used after surgery is known as adjuvant therapy. Anticancer drug treatment may also sometimes be administered concurrently with radiotherapy. This treatment regimen is known as 'chemo-radiation'. Such drug therapy can make radiotherapy more effective but it can also exacerbate the side effects caused to the patient.

● What are the major differences between radiotherapy and chemotherapy?

● As mentioned above, radiotherapy, in general, is a local treatment, affecting a small area of the body while chemotherapy is a systemic treatment, affecting the whole body; radiotherapy uses ionising radiation to treat cancer while chemotherapy uses toxic chemicals.

In this chapter we will discuss the use of the two types of anticancer drugs, namely chemotherapy and biological therapy. We will first introduce you to the basic concepts relating to each type of therapy, then illustrate the working principles underlying each of these two therapies, with examples, and then briefly discuss other issues related to the use of anticancer drugs in general. In order to illustrate the principles behind how these drugs work, we will show you some fairly complex chemical structures. You should not worry about the detailed structures and you will certainly not need to memorise them.

While studying this chapter you will come across a number of terms that you will be familiar with as well as some unfamiliar ones. We have summarised the important terms that will be used to describe the concepts in this chapter in Table 10.1 (overleaf) along with where they are defined in this book.

Table 10.1 Important terms and concepts used in Chapter 10.

Term	Definition / Explanation	Examples
Molecule	Two or more atoms held together by chemical bonds	Water (H_2O) and oxygen gas (O_2) (see Table 2.1)
Compound	A chemical substance that is composed of the atoms of two or more chemical elements	Water (H_2O) is a compound, but oxygen gas (O_2) is not (Chapter 2)
Base (in DNA)	A compound that pairs with other in DNA. There are two types of bases: purine and pyrimidine	Guanine and adenine are purine bases; cytosine and thymine are pyrimidine bases (Section 10.4)
Nucleotide	A compound that consists of a base (e.g. adenine), a sugar (e.g. ribose) and phosphate	The energy source: ATP (adenosine triphosphate) (Chapter 2)
DNA	The abbreviation for deoxyribonucleic acids. DNA is made of a large number of deoxynucleotides	DNA is the genetic material (Chapter 2)
Amino acid and protein	A compound that contains both an amine and an acidic group. Amino acids are the building blocks for proteins	Tyrosine in cell growth factors. Proteins are important macromolecules (Chapter 2)
Enzyme	A protein that binds to specific molecules, and transforms them into new substances. An enzyme functions as a catalyst and is not consumed during the process	Thymidylate synthase (TS) is the enzyme that converts uracil to thymine (Section 10.4)
Inhibitor	A compound that is able to block the action of an enzyme	Imatinib (Glivec®) can inhibit cancer growth (Section 10.7)
Drug	A compound that interacts with a biological system to produce a biological response	Imatinib is a drug (Section 10.7)
Generic name	The approved name for drug. A group of drugs that have similar actions often have similar sounding generic names	Imatinib, dasatinib and erlotinib are in one group of anticancer drugs (Table 10.4)
Brand name	The name chosen for a drug by the company that makes it. It is also called trade name. The name is often easier to say or spell than its generic name. Many drugs have more than one brand name	Imatinib is called Glivec® in Europe and Gleevec® in the USA (see the Tables 10.4 and 10.5 in the Appendix)

10.2 Chemotherapy drugs

Humans have been using drugs to treat diseases for a very long time, without any understanding of how they achieve their effects. Nowadays, the discovery and development of drugs is a cutting-edge science equipped with many sound theories and proven methodologies. However, in real life, the path towards discovering a new drug looks more like the process shown in Figure 10.1.

'That's Dr Arnold Moore. He's conducting an experiment to test the theory that most great scientific discoveries were hit on by accident.'

Figure 10.1 Research in progress … (Source: Sidney Hoff)

The beginnings of cancer chemotherapy can be traced back to the period of 1940–1950 when mustard gas (see Box 10.1), a chemical warfare agent used in World War I, was first observed to suppress bone marrow function and then discovered to be an effective treatment for lymphoma. This work was pioneering in that it led to the realisation that cancer could be treated by chemical agents.

Further studies showed that nitrogen mustards inhibit cell growth and replication by cross-linking DNA strands in the cell nucleus (Figure 10.3), thus blocking DNA replication. The principle underlying the activity of this type of drug on tumour cells (i.e. its mechanism of action) is referred to as

Box 10.1 Mustard gas and nitrogen mustards

Mustard gas is a sulfur-containing chemical and is one of a group of chemicals referred to as the sulfur mustards. Mustard gas is so named because its impure form is yellowish and smells rather like mustard. However, mustard gas is a synthetic chemical compound (i.e. it is manufactured in a factory) and does not come from the mustard plant. The chemical structure of mustard gas is shown in Figure 10.2a.

Nitrogen mustards have similar molecular structures to sulfur mustards, with the sulfur atom replaced by a nitrogen atom. Mustine (shown in Figure 10.2b) is a nitrogen mustard; it was the first drug used for cancer treatment, although it is now no longer in common use.

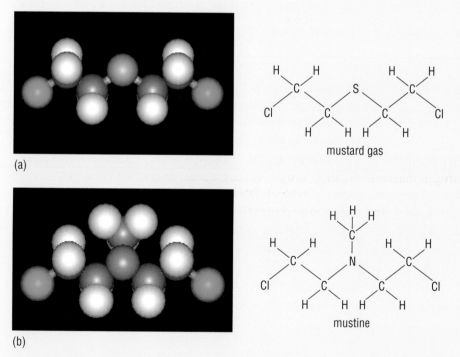

Figure 10.2 Molecular models and chemical structures of (a) mustard gas (a sulfur mustard) and (b) mustine (a nitrogen mustard).

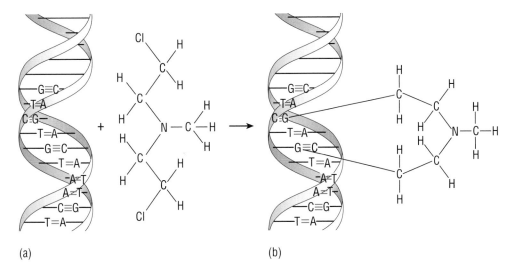

(a)   (b)

Figure 10.3   A nitrogen mustard cross-links two DNA strands.

alkylation and is explained in Section 10.3. Alkylation is still a major approach to cancer chemotherapy and is the basis of the activity of many drugs currently in use.

● Have a close look at the process of DNA replication shown in Figure 3.8. What would happen if the two strands of the DNA were linked?

● The process of DNA replication requires the double helix to unwind and reveal two strands. The linked double strands of DNA cannot unwind, thus the DNA replication would not proceed successfully.

Shortly after World War II, it was found that the vitamin folate (also known as folic acid) can speed up the proliferation of acute lymphoblastic leukaemia (ALL) cells in children. ALL is a cancer of immature lymphocytes. Thus antifolate compounds (i.e. compounds that compete with folate), for example methotrexate, were developed and found to be capable of blocking the function of enzymes that need folate in order to function. Folate-requiring enzymes are essential for DNA synthesis and cell proliferation. When administered to children with ALL, antifolate compounds induced remission and became the first drugs used for the treatment of this type of cancer. Remissions were brief, but the principle had been established. This is one of the first examples of rational drug design – in contrast with the accidental discovery of nitrogen mustards as cancer drugs. As the mechanism of action of antifolates as chemotherapeutic agents is to block DNA synthesis, i.e. to interfere with DNA metabolism, it is referred to as an **antimetabolite mechanism**. This is the second major approach to cancer chemotherapy and it is discussed in Section 10.4.

Enzymes were briefly mentioned in Section 2.6. In this chapter we will look in more detail about how specific enzymes are targeted by anticancer drugs.

● Alkylating drugs (e.g. mustine) and antimetabolites (e.g. methotrexate) have different mechanisms of action, but as chemotherapeutic agents what do they have in common?

● Both these chemotherapeutic agents target DNA synthesis.

You also learnt from Chapter 3 that cancer is the result of gene mutations at the molecular level. Thus using chemical agents to kill or remove cells that contain mutated DNA plays a crucial role in chemotherapy. As you have seen, this is achieved by targeting either the DNA molecule itself or the enzymes that are responsible for DNA replication. However, it is important to remember that, in general, the effects of chemotherapy drugs are not limited to cancer cells since the chemical compounds used to kill cancer cells by these two mechanisms can also damage normal cells. As a result, side effects are unavoidable (discussed briefly in Section 10.11.3). The next two sections explore in more detail the two main types of chemotherapeutic agents.

10.3 Alkylating drugs

Alkylation is a chemical term meaning the transfer of an alkyl group from one molecule to another. (An alkyl group consists of carbon and hydrogen atoms.) Alkylating drugs modify (i.e. alkylate) cellular DNA. In actively dividing cells such as tumour cells, this chemical modification of the DNA elicits (often futile) DNA repair responses. When DNA damage is beyond repair, it ultimately triggers apoptosis (Section 2.9.4), thereby inhibiting cell proliferation and tumour growth.

10.3.1 Nitrogen mustards

As mentioned in Section 10.2, nitrogen mustards were the first anticancer drugs discovered. You saw in Figure 10.3 that mustine reacts with the bases in the DNA molecule, primarily by cross-linking two DNA strands, so preventing DNA replication. Many other nitrogen mustards have now been developed and used as anticancer drugs (see Table 10.2 in the Appendix). Cyclophosphamide is currently probably the most commonly used one. It is inactive until metabolised (chemically converted) to its active form by enzymes in the liver. The drug is usually given orally or by intravenous injection (i.e. into a vein).

● Nitrogen mustards are powerful anticancer drugs, but most of them are also classified as human carcinogens. Why would they also promote the formation of tumours?

● Nitrogen mustards can be classed as carcinogens because they can modify DNA, which can result in gene mutations.

10.3.2 Temozolomide

Methyl ($-CH_3$) is the smallest alkyl group.

Hydrolysis is a chemical term and can be briefly defined as 'reaction of a chemical with water'.

Although nitrogen mustards are not ideal drugs, the DNA alkylation by the nitrogen mustards provides a theoretical basis to help scientists to search for improved chemotherapy drugs. One such drug is temozolomide (Figure 10.4). This drug is used as a treatment for several types of cancer, most notably for certain brain tumours. The mechanism of action for temozolomide is rather complicated but involves alkylation by an alkyl group called a methyl group. In simple terms, the drug is hydrolysed into small fragments and then metabolised to produce an active methyl group (the circled part of the molecule in Figure 10.4). This methyl group then reacts with (i.e. alkylates, in this case methylates) the DNA. The resultant methylated DNA can be partially repaired by DNA repair enzymes. However, any unrepaired DNA can introduce wrong bases into the DNA during replication, leading to gene mutations and, ultimately, to cell death.

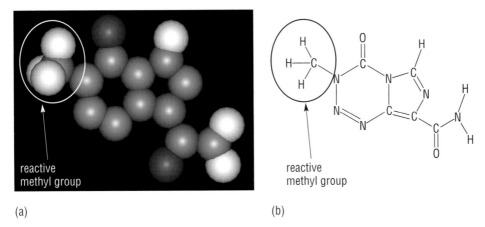

(a)   (b)

Figure 10.4 (a) Molecular model and (b) chemical structure of temozolomide. Its reactive methyl group is circled.

Since temozolomide (like cyclophosphamide mentioned above) requires chemical transformation before it can react with its molecular target, in this case DNA, it is called a **prodrug**. A prodrug is a chemical compound that needs to be chemically transformed inside the human body in order to become an effective drug. The rationale behind the use of a prodrug is to produce a more stable form of the drug with enhanced pharmacological properties (i.e. it has an increased rate of absorption through the gut, better distribution within the body, and a lower rate of metabolic degradation and excretion, allowing it to remain in the body for longer). If the active group in temozolomide (i.e. the methyl group) were available immediately, it would react with other molecules in the body before reaching the DNA inside the nuclei of the cells. But when it is within the structure of temozolomide, the methyl group is relatively stable, i.e. unreactive. When the drug is taken by mouth, it is gradually degraded to generate the active methyl group which then reacts with (alkylates) DNA – its intended target.

10.3.3 Alkylating-like (platinum-based) drugs

The creation of temozolomide was the result of many years of research and development, while the discovery of the use of the platinum-based compound cisplatin as an anticancer drug was accidental (for the detailed story, see Activity 10.1). Since its identification in 1969 and its clinical application in the early 1970s, cisplatin has continued to play a major role in chemotherapy. Although cisplatin and other platinum-based drugs do not contain alkylating groups, they act by a similar mechanism to the alkylating drugs and so are considered here. To understand this similarity in behaviour, you need first to look at the chemical structures of the two types of molecule. Cisplatin comprises a

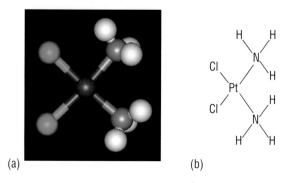

(a)   (b)

Figure 10.5 (a) Ball-and-stick model of cisplatin. The central atom is platinum; the green spheres are chlorine atoms; the pale blue, nitrogen; and white, hydrogen. Both chlorine (Cl) atoms are lost allowing the platinum (Pt) to form two bonds to nitrogen (N) atoms in bases that are in close proximity in DNA. (b) Chemical structure of cisplatin.

platinum atom at the centre joined to two ammonia (NH_3) groups and two chlorine atoms, to form a square structure as shown in Figure 10.5b. (Chlorine atoms are also referred to as chloro groups particularly when they are part of a larger molecule.)

● Compare the structure of cisplatin (Figure 10.5b) with that of mustine (Figure 10.2b). What can you predict about the mechanism of action of cisplatin?

● Both drugs contain two chloro groups that would allow it to react and link to bases in DNA strands. Thus, cisplatin can, in a similar way to mustine, link together two DNA strands and so stop DNA replication.

Indeed, cisplatin does have a similar mechanism of action to that of nitrogen mustards. However, the majority of DNA damage by cisplatin is the result of linking bases within the *same* DNA strand, and so it is termed an *intrastrand* link (see Figure 10.6b), in contrast with an *interstrand* link, which is formed between *different* DNA strands (see Figure 10.3b). This difference is due to the fact that the distance between the two chloro groups in cisplatin is shorter than in the nitrogen mustard and so cisplatin cannot usually link together two bases from two different DNA strands as do the nitrogen mustards. However, whether DNA is damaged by intrastrand or interstrand links it will induce DNA repair mechanisms, which in turn activate apoptosis when the DNA damage exceeds the capacity for repair.

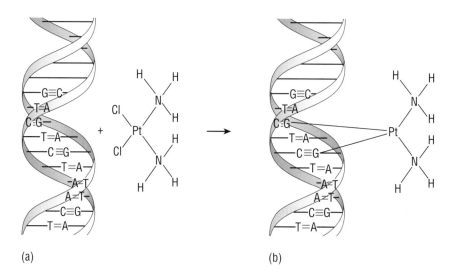

(a)   (b)

Figure 10.6 Cisplatin primarily forms intrastrand links in DNA.

● Do you think the action of cisplatin is specific (limited) to tumour cells?

● No. Because cisplatin is a non-specific alkylating drug, it will also affect other rapidly dividing cells in the human body, e.g. hair follicle cells, thus causing hair loss, and the epithelial cells lining the gut, resulting in vomiting, as well as producing other side effects.

The success of cisplatin has prompted intensive work to look for new platinum-based anticancer drugs. From over 3000 compounds tested, about 30 have entered clinical trials. Among them, two drugs (carboplatin and oxaliplatin) have already been marketed. Carboplatin has a similar mechanism of action to cisplatin, but has been shown to be markedly less toxic to the kidneys and nervous system and to cause less nausea and vomiting, while generally retaining equivalent antitumour activity. Oxaliplatin appears to have a different mechanism of action to that of cisplatin and carboplatin and the mechanism of resistance to oxaliplatin is therefore different too. For this reason, oxaliplatin is a useful alternative when cancer cells become resistant to cisplatin and carboplatin. (Further explanation of drug resistance is given in Section 10.11.4.)

Activity 10.1   The discovery of cisplatin

Allow about 30 minutes in total for this activity

In this activity you will watch short video sequence entitled *The Discovery of Cisplatin*.

You have seen in this section that although mustine, temozolomide and cisplatin have very different chemical structures, their mechanisms of action are similar. All three drugs link to bases in DNA, thus modifying its structure and preventing tumour cells from proliferating. Many other anticancer drugs use the same mechanism of action, and some of them are listed in Table 10.2 in the Appendix.

Activity 10.2   A common medicinal use for oxaliplatin

Allow about 15 minutes in total for this activity

In this activity you will use the internet to find a common medicinal use for the drug oxaliplatin.

10.4 Antimetabolite drugs

Antimetabolite drugs use synthetic compounds that compete with the molecules in cells that are necessary for DNA replication or interfere with other enzyme-catalysed reactions, thereby altering cell functions such as cell division, cell metabolism and protein synthesis. Methotrexate (which was mentioned in Section 10.2) is one such antimetabolite drug.

● Briefly describe what is meant by the concept of cell metabolism introduced in Section 2.6.

● All cells need to obtain from their environment the energy and materials required to synthesise the building blocks of macromolecules (e.g. DNA and proteins) in order to grow, reproduce and respond to the environment. These biological processes are carried out by enzymes in a highly integrated network of chemical reactions, which are collectively known as metabolism.

In Chapters 2 and 3, you learnt that DNA is made of long chains of deoxynucleotides each of which consists of a phosphate group, a base and a sugar (deoxyribose). As you also learnt in Section 3.1, four bases are used as DNA building blocks. These are: T (thymine) and C (cytosine), called pyrimidine bases; and G (guanine) and A (adenine), which are purine bases. In Figure 3.3, small squares are used to represent T and C, and rectangles are used for G and A. These simple shape presentations indicate that T and C are different from G and A. The main difference between the pyrimidine and the purine bases is more obvious from their chemical structures (Figure 10.7): pyrimidine bases (T and C) have one ring while purine bases (G and A) have two rings. There are also other subtle chemical differences between T and C and between G and A.

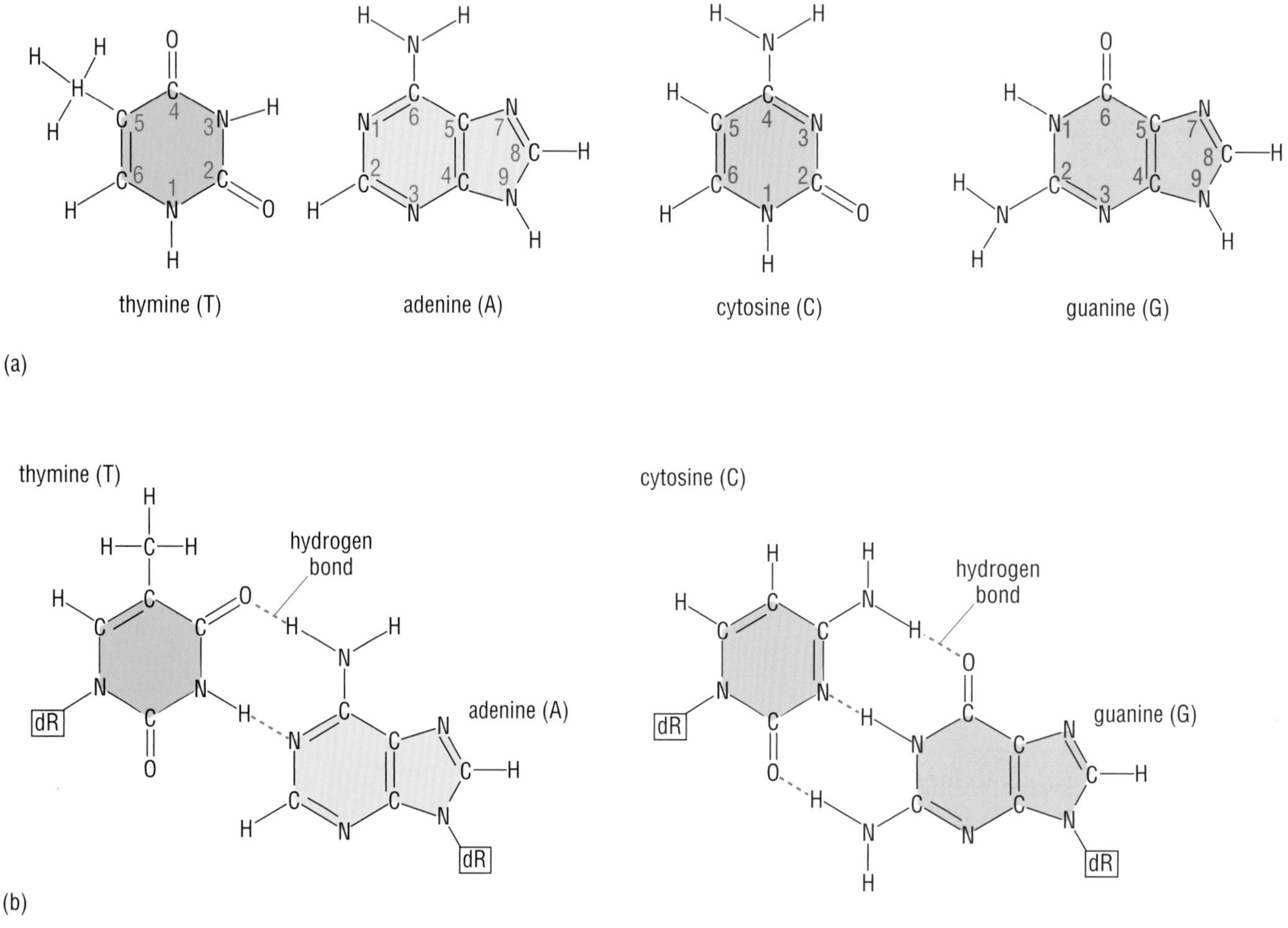

(a)

(b)

Figure 10.7 (a) Chemical structures of the four bases (two purines: G and A; and two pyrimidines: T and C) that make up DNA. (b) Base-pairing between A and T, and between G and C. dR represents deoxyribose.

The molecules that take part in metabolism, whether in DNA synthesis or in any of the other enzyme-catalysed chemical transformations occurring in living cells, are collectively termed **metabolites**. In the context of chemotherapy drugs, an antimetabolite is a chemical that somehow replaces a cell metabolite and thereby interferes with normal cellular functions (e.g. cell division and growth). In order to do this, an antimetabolite must have two distinct properties: (i) it must have a similar structure to a metabolite so that it can target the same chemical reactions, i.e. bind to the same enzyme; and (ii) its structure must however be different enough from the natural metabolite for it to block that particular chemical reaction (i.e. it inactivates the enzyme).

When antimetabolites are taken up as building blocks for DNA synthesis, they disrupt DNA replication and stop cell division. Because cancer cells divide at a higher rate than normal cells, and hence carry out more DNA synthesis, antimetabolites are particularly effective in triggering cell death in tumour cells. An example of an antimetabolite drug is 5-fluorouracil (5-FU). 5-FU acts in several ways, but principally it inhibits an enzyme called thymidylate synthase (TS for short). The biological role of TS is to convert the base uracil (U) into thymine (T). Thymine is then used to produce one of the four nucleotides necessary for DNA synthesis. The chemical structures of uracil, 5-FU and thymine are shown in Figure 10.8.

> Uracil is a base that is structurally similar to thymine. Thymine is synthesised from uracil in the cell.

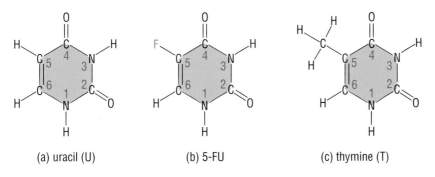

(a) uracil (U) (b) 5-FU (c) thymine (T)

Figure 10.8 Chemical structures of (a) uracil (U), (b) 5-fluorouracil (5-FU) and (c) thymine (T).

● Compare the chemical structure of 5-FU with those of uracil and thymine (Figure 10.8). What are the main differences?

● 5-FU has a similar structure to uracil and thymine. In fact, these three pyrimidines differ only in the atom or group attached at the 5-position of the ring: 5-FU has a fluorine (F) atom; uracil has a hydrogen (H) atom; and thymine has a methyl (CH_3) group.

In the cell, thymine is made from uracil in a three-step process catalysed by the TS enzyme (see Figure 10.9a). In the first step a methyl (CH_3) group is added to the 5-position in uracil and then the hydrogen atom at the 5-position is removed. Once the reaction has finished, the newly formed thymine (T) leaves the enzyme which is then available to catalyse the tranformation of further molecules of uracil. Because the size of the fluorine atom is similar to that of the hydrogen atom, 5-FU can be mistaken as uracil (U) by the

TS enzyme (Figure 10.9b). However, the bond (i.e. the link) between the fluorine atom and the carbon in the 5-position of 5-FU is very stable. Instead of moving out, the methylated 5-FU will remain attached to the TS enzyme (shown as step (ii) in Figure 10.9b). So at the end, the 5-FU is trapped within the TS enzyme preventing it from binding to further molecules of uracil. The enzyme is now blocked. As a result, no thymine is formed, so no DNA can be synthesised and no further cell division can take place.

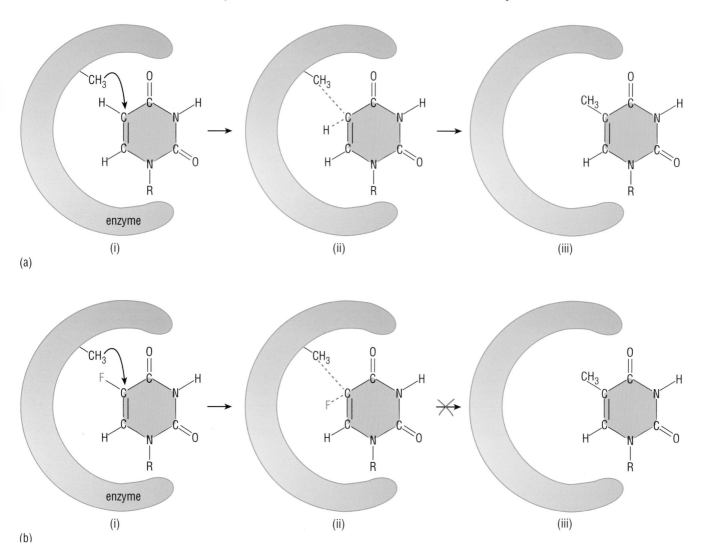

Figure 10.9   (a) The TS enzyme transforms uracil to thymine, but (b) the enzyme can be inhibited by 5-FU.

● Cisplatin and 5-FU are both chemotherapeutic agents; what are their similarities and differences in the context of their mechanisms of action?

● Both these anticancer drugs target DNA, but their mechanisms of action are different: cisplatin acts by cross-linking two DNA strands; 5-FU resembles thymine (T) and, as such, inhibits the activity of the TS enzyme, thus blocking DNA synthesis.

Since cisplatin and 5-FU have different mechanisms of action, using them together can be more effective than using each of them alone. 5-FU has been in use against cancers for about 40 years. If the drug is given to a patient for a long-term treatment, it is possible for the patient to develop drug resistance. Drug resistance is the process by which a drug can become less effective in treating a condition (Section 10.11.4). To overcome the problem of drug resistance in cancer treatment with 5-FU, raltitrexed is often used instead. Although raltitrexed also inhibits the TS enzyme, its mechanism of action is different from that of 5-FU. Raltitrexed allows uracil to bind to the TS enzyme but prevents the addition of a methyl (CH_3) group to the uracil (i.e. it inhibits step (ii) in Figure 10.9a); thus no thymine is made and so no DNA is synthesised. Other cancer drugs that work on the same principle are listed in Table 10.3 in the Appendix.

Raltitrexed is a folate antimetabolite (see Table 10.2 in the Appendix).

6-Thioguanine is another important antimetabolite drug and is discussed in Box 10.2.

Box 10.2 Thioguanine used for children's leukaemias

6-Thioguanine (G^S) is a modified guanine in which the oxygen (O) atom (at the 6-position) is replaced by a sulfur (S) atom (Figure 10.10a and b). Its primary medicinal use is for acute lymphoid leukaemia (ALL) and chronic myeloid leukaemia (CML).

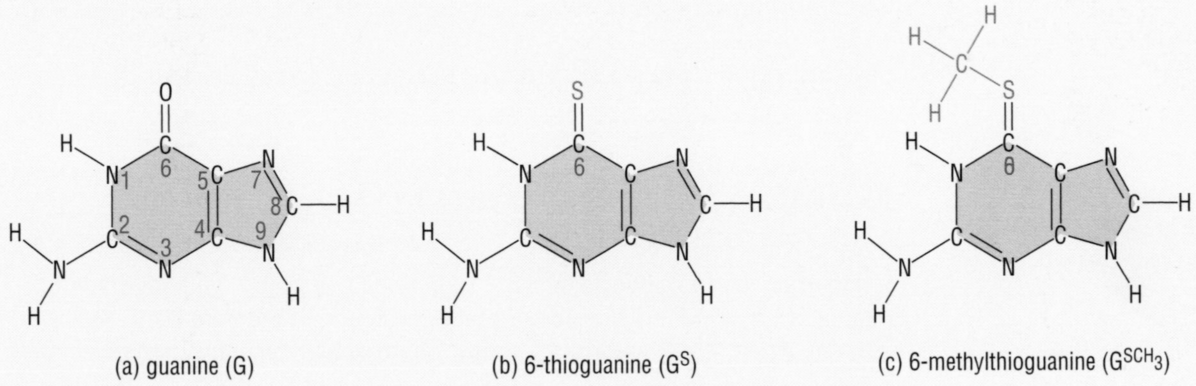

(a) guanine (G) (b) 6-thioguanine (G^S) (c) 6-methylthioguanine (G^{SCH_3})

Figure 10.10 Chemical structures of guanine and related modified guanines.

As a guanine-like compound, G^S can interfere the synthesis of guanine nucleotide. The sulfur atom is highly reactive and a methyl group can be added to G^S to form another modified guanine (G^{SCH_3}: Figure 10.10c). This modified guanine tends to pair with thymine (T) rather than cytosine (C), forming a faulty (mismatched) base pair. (You saw in Figure 10.7b that the standard (matched) DNA base pairs are G–C and A–T.) Mismatch repair enzymes work on the faulty base pair, leading to removal of the mispaired T rather than the trouble-making G^{SCH_3}. So as long as the faulty G^{SCH_3} remains, the DNA repair activity will not be successful. This so-called futile repair causes DNA strands to break down, which initiates cell apoptosis. Figure 10.11 illustrates the incorporation, methylation, formation of the mismatched base pair and its futile repair by the DNA repair enzymes.

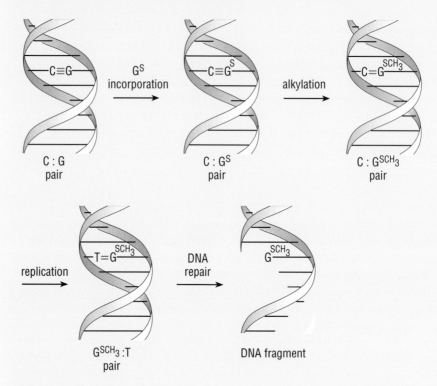

Figure 10.11   The mechanism of action for the drug thioguanine.

Case study 10.1 Trupti receives leukaemia treatment

Once Trupti has been settled on a ward at Great Ormond Street, she is started on the first induction phase of her chemotherapy. This involves intensive treatment designed to induce remission of the neoplasm. She has to stay in hospital throughout this phase, which lasts for just over four weeks, so doctors can keep an eye on her and treat any side effects of her medication. She is given specific drugs at specific times in a very complicated protocol. Some of the drugs are injected directly into her veins (e.g. the antimicrotubule agent vincristine, once a week), others into the muscle in her arm, and others by mouth. Half-way through this drug regime, the doctors find out that Trupti's ALL is not responding as well as they expected and they add another drug, daunorubicin, an antitumour antibiotic. This is more successful, and the number of leukaemia cells in Trupti's blood goes down very quickly. Another six-week phase called consolidation therapy aimed at destroying all remaining leukaemia cells starts. This regimen includes other different drugs such as the nitrogen mustard, cyclophosphamide, and the antimetabolites, 6-thioguanine and cytarabine.

During these difficult times, specialist children's nurses are always available to reassure and help Trupti. In particular, Trupti finds it very difficult to swallow the 6-thioguanine tablets. The tablets make her feel very poorly. She is always tired and sleeps a lot of the time, and often gets breathless or feels sick. The children's ward is a very pleasant place, and there are many toys which Trupti can play with whenever she feels well enough. Her family is encouraged to visit her whenever they are able to, and her parents stay overnight with her for the first few days. After that, they have to return to work, but still come with her brothers and sisters whenever they can. As she is so young, and often very ill, she is not given any lessons, but some of the older children on the ward go to classes in the hospital school.

After this period, the doctors take a further sample of Trupti's bone marrow to test it for any remaining leukaemia cells. Her parents are delighted to hear that they found none, and that their daughter's condition is officially in remission. Trupti, who is beginning to feel better, is more interested in when she can go home. Before she can, another chemotherapy drug – the folate-like drug methotrexate – is injected into her cerebrospinal fluid, close to her spine, on several occasions to prevent any remaining leukaemia cells spreading into the central nervous system. She receives these drugs under general anesthesia. 'Every time Trupti goes into the operating theatre, I fear the worst' says Mr Shah to his wife.

Trupti is doing very well, and she is allowed to go home before she starts the next, maintenance phase of her treatment, to make sure that the ALL does not come back. She is given lower doses of 6-thioguanine and methotrexate by mouth, and is taken to Great Ormond Street once a month for tests and an intravenous injection of vincristine. Once she has been established on this regimen, she goes back to school, initially for only half days as she still gets very tired. Her parents are told that she will have to stay on this regimen and have regular tests for at least two years.

10.5 Other types of chemotherapy drugs

There are many other anticancer chemotherapeutic agents with a variety of mechanisms of action. It is impossible to cover all types of chemotherapy drugs in the limited space of this chapter. Here we briefly discuss some of them.

10.5.1 Antitumour antibiotics

An antibiotic is a chemical produced by or derived from bacteria, fungi or other organisms that inhibits or stops the growth of other microbes, such as bacteria and fungi (e.g. penicillin, streptomycin). Thus an **antitumour antibiotic** is a drug derived from a microbe that inhibits or kills tumour cells. Antitumour antibiotics act by reacting with DNA (either binding to or breaking down DNA strands), thus interrupting cellular processes and inhibiting tumour growth. Doxorubicin, mitoxantrone and bleomycin are three drugs of this type.

10.5.2 Antimicrotubule agents

Microtubules are chains of protein molecules called tubulins that help maintain the shape of the cell and are hence considered to be one of the structural elements of the cell's internal 'skeleton'. Microtubules are continually formed by polymerisation (assembly) of tubulin molecules and dismantled again into free tubulin molecules within the cell (Figure 10.12). They play crucial roles in many cellular processes including chromosome duplication and segregation and the subsequent division of the cell into two daughter cells (Section 2.7.1). Since dividing cells (such as tumour cells) have higher rates of DNA replication, drugs that interfere with either the formation or the dismantling of microtubules can slow or stop cancer growth. Currently two types of natural substances (taxanes and vinca alkaloids) are used as antimicrotubule agents.

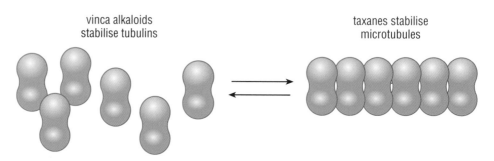

vinca alkaloids
stabilise tubulins

taxanes stabilise
microtubules

Figure 10.12   Microtubules, their roles and the action of inhibitors on their function.

Paclitaxel (trade name: Taxol®) is a naturally occurring taxane (it is found in the bark of a particular type of yew tree) and can stabilise tubulins in the already formed microtubules and so prevent the microtubules from depolymerising (dismantling) into tubulins. Thus tubulins cannot be reused to form the microtubules necessary for cell division. Taxane has been used to treat several cancers including ovarian, breast, lung, head and neck and bladder cancers.

A semisynthetic compound is a natural compound that is used after modification.

Docetaxel (trade name: Taxotere®) is a semisynthetic taxane and acts in the same way as Taxol. Taxotere is used for metastatic (spreading) breast cancer and non-small cell lung cancer (NSCLC).

Vinca alkaloids are derived from *Vinca rosea*, the Madagascan periwinkle (Figure 10.13). They are all nitrogen-containing alkaline organic compounds found naturally in plants. Vinca alkaloids have been historically used to treat numerous diseases and recently have been used for cancer treatments. The mechanism of action is similar to, but subtly different from, that of taxanes. Vinca alkaloids inhibit the assembly of microtubules by binding to tubulin monomers (single units) and stopping microtubule formation. By contrast, taxanes 'freeze' the structure of the microtubule by binding to tubulins in the assembled microtubules (Figure 10.12). The most commonly used vinca alkaloids are vinblastine (for solid tumours), vinorelbine (for breast cancer and NSCLC), vincristine (for acute leukaemia) and vindesine (for melanoma and lung cancers).

Figure 10.13   *Vinca rosea*, the Madagascan periwinkle. (Source: Ianni Dimitrov/Alamy)

10.6 Biological therapies

Conventional chemotherapy has been shown to be effective in curing some cancers and reducing rates of recurrence of others. However, conventional chemotherapy is far from ideal.

● What are the shortcomings of conventional chemotherapy?

● The primary mechanism of action for chemotherapeutic drugs is to damage DNA and initiate apoptosis. However it is not possible for any chemotherapeutic agent to target DNA in cancer cells without causing damage to DNA in normal cells too. The usefulness of chemotherapy is limited by the lack of sufficient selectivity.

Although chemotherapy, surgery and radiotherapy continue to be the main treatments, a number of new treatments have been developed and more selective drugs are gradually becoming available. These new drugs are aimed at specific cellular targets such as particular proteins known to be involved in important cellular processes. This type of drug development is based upon a better understanding of tumour biology. Thus the treatment of cancer with this type of new drug is collectively termed 'biological therapy'. Biological therapy can offer some promises that chemotherapy fails to deliver. In Sections 10.7 to 10.10, we will discuss some of most successful biological therapies, i.e. cancer growth inhibitors (Section 10.7), monoclonal antibodies (Section 10.8), hormone therapy (Section 10.9) and also some promising biological therapies including gene therapy (Section 10.10).

Since biological therapy is a new approach to cancer treatment, as yet there is no consensus on how best to define it. One definition is as follows: biological therapies are treatments that use natural substances or drugs that are made from natural substances. Another definition is based on the central role of the immune system: biological therapy is any type of treatment that stimulates or restores the ability of the immune system to fight infection and disease. Between them, these two definitions cover many types of, but not all, biological therapies. Here we use the term biological therapy for any cancer treatment, by means of therapeutic drugs, that does not fall into the category of 'classic' chemotherapy.

Note: If you are new to the study of science, you are advised to review the relevant sections of Chapter 2 before studying the rest of this chapter. Sections 2.9.1 and 2.9.2 are particularly useful.

10.7 Cancer growth inhibitors

As you learnt in Chapters 2 and 3, cancer is characterised by uncontrolled cell proliferation, resulting in the formation of tumours. Normally, cellular growth is precisely regulated by a myriad of growth-promoting and growth-inhibitory factors. Cancer can develop as a result of continuous growth-promoting signalling (see Section 2.9.1). In other words, a signal that instructs a cell to grow and divide becomes permanently switched-on (i.e. active) or a growth-inhibitory signal becomes permanently switched-off. Most therapies based on this tumour cell property have focused on attempts to inhibit growth-promoting signals, thus switching off the continuously active signal and thereby inhibiting tumour growth. Since such an inhibition is specific to a targeted growth factor with a role in a particular type of cancer, any drugs developed that are based on this approach need to be highly selective, affecting the cells of the tumour concerned, and not normal cells. One success story in this field is the development of imatinib.

10.7.1 Imatinib as a cancer growth inhibitor

Imatinib (Glivec® in Europe and Gleevec® in the USA) is an effective drug for a number of cancers, particularly for chronic myeloid leukaemia (CML).

The term myeloid is commonly used in the UK, whereas the term myelogenous is commonly used in the USA.

● You encountered the term 'chromosomal translocation' in Section 3.4.2. What is the Philadelphia chromosome?

● The shorter of the two products of chromosomal translocation between chromosome 9 and chromosome 22, i.e. the mutant chromosome 22, is called the Philadelphia chromosome. It is named after the city where it was first discovered.

● What is the *BCR–ABL* gene?

● The *ABL* gene is originally in chromosome 9. As a result of chromosomal translocation, the *ABL* gene becomes part of chromosome 22, adjacent to the *BCR* gene. A new gene is thus formed called *BCR–ABL* (see Figure 3.7).

CML patients have a large number of cells that originate in the bone marrow but are found in the blood containing the Philadelphia chromosome. As you know from Chapter 3, genes code for proteins and the gene product of *ABL* is an enzyme whose biological role is to activate signalling proteins that control cell division. The ABL protein in normal cells is only active when cells are stimulated by interactions between a growth factor and its receptor in the cell membrane. The effect of the chromosome translocation in CML is to bring the *BCR* and *ABL* genes together resulting in a fused *BCR–ABL* gene (Figure 3.7). The fused BCR–ABL protein is a permanently active enzyme. In other words, the enzyme is always in the 'switch-on' form, thereby signalling the cell to continually divide. The understanding of the role of the mutant *BCR–ABL* gene in CML has prompted scientists to search for inhibitors that can 'switch-off' the BCR–ABL enzyme. Imatinib was identified as a potent inhibitor and proved to be the first drug of this kind.

Many cellular enzymes, including the ABL protein, function by adding a phosphate group to themselves. The source of these phosphate groups is the molecule that functions as an energy store in cells, i.e. ATP (Section 2.6). Imatinib acts by blocking the site where ATP binds to the ABL protein, thus inhibiting its activity. Although there are a large number of enzymes in the body that use ATP, their structures and ATP binding sites (the place for interaction between ATP and protein) are not exactly the same. Imatinib is highly specific for the ATP binding site of the ABL protein. This high specificity means that imatinib acts selectively on tumour cells whose *ABL* gene is mutated.

10.7.2 Other growth inhibitors

Imatinib is the first member of a new class of agents that act by inhibiting particular enzymes instead of non-specifically inhibiting the proliferation of rapidly dividing cells. The success achieved with imatinib has allowed scientists to develop many other inhibitors, some of which are listed in Table 10.4 in the Appendix.

Since these biotherapeutic cancer growth inhibitors are much more selective than classic chemotherapeutic drugs, such treatment is also called targeted therapy. **Targeted therapy** is a type of cancer treatment that blocks the growth of cancer cells by interfering with specific (targeted) molecules that are essential for tumour growth, rather than by simply acting on all rapidly dividing cells. Targeted cancer therapies are more effective than conventional treatments (chemotherapy) and are believed to be the therapy of the future. However, at the time of writing (early 2008), these drugs are expensive, leading to public debate as to who (the patient or the State) should cover the cost of treatment.

Although the targeted therapies discussed above are based on the use of small molecules, larger molecules can also be used for targeted therapy. This is the case of the use of monoclonal antibodies, a special type of antibody, discussed in the next section.

10.8 Immunotherapy

The immune system is a complex mechanism by which an organism protects itself from pathogenic agents (Section 4.5). This function is mediated by a variety of cell types, examples of which are T lymphocytes (T cells) and B lymphocytes (B cells). Each T cell and B cell can recognise and become activated by an **antigen**. An antigen is any molecule that the immune system recognises as foreign. In response to this activation, the cell divides and produces many identical copies of itself. Each progeny cell recognises the same antigen as the original T cell or B cell. Within this process the T and B cells have different roles. The main role of B cells is to make its particular antibody that is directed against its specific antigen, while that of T cells is to identify and kill cells that contain the antigen. An improved understanding of the immune system has led to the development of various therapies based on this system that can prevent or even kill cancers.

10.8.1 Monoclonal antibody therapy

Recall from Section 4.5 that antibodies are proteins produced by B cells to neutralise foreign agents, also known as pathogens (e.g. bacteria, viruses, fungi) that invade the body. **Monoclonal antibodies (MABs)** are the antibodies produced by a single B cell and all its progeny (a 'clone' of B cells; refer back to Section 3.5 for a definition of a clone of cells), so MABs are identical and are highly specific for a particular antigen (Section 3.5). MAB therapy is a cancer treatment that uses MABs to target cancer cells specifically.

● What is the meaning of the term 'clone'? (You may need to refer back to Section 3.5.5.)

● A clone of cells is formed by a cell and all its progeny which contain the same genetic information.

The immune system responds to pathogens on the basis of discrimination between self and non-self. If a molecule is recognised as foreign (i.e. non-self), an antibody will be produced to counteract (bind to) that foreign molecule (the antigen). The antigen–antibody complex is then destroyed and disposed of (Section 4.5). Tumour cells are not specifically targeted by the immune system since they are the patient's own cells. However, tumour cells are highly abnormal and many display unusual proteins on their surfaces. If the tumour cell surface proteins are sufficiently abnormal, they may be antigenic, i.e. they may be recognised as non-self by the cells of the immune system and will be destroyed. However, more commonly, the structure of tumour-specific proteins is not sufficiently abnormal to induce an immune response. They are proteins that are either inappropriate for the cell type, or expressed at unusually high or low levels, or normally present only during early development. Therefore these proteins are not seen as foreign to the body. This is the case for some tumour cells which can display high levels of cell surface receptors that are rare or absent on the surface of healthy cells but nevertheless are able to proliferate unimpeded.

A lot of research has focused on developing methods to create MABs specific to the receptors found on the surface of various types of cancer cells, with the aim being to disrupt cell activity. One such method involves the injection of human cancer cells into mice. This procedure does not give the mice cancer. Rather, the mouse's immune system recognises the injected cells as non-self and makes antibodies against them. Then the mouse antibody-producing B cells, also known as plasma cells, are isolated and fused with laboratory-grown tumour cells (specifically myeloma cells which are tumour cells derived from B cells, which themselves do not produce antibodies) to create 'hybrid' cells called hybridomas. A single hybridoma is then allowed to multiply in culture, so producing a large population of cells each of which produces an identical (i.e. monoclonal) antibody. In this way, large quantities of MABs can be obtained. The procedure is summarised in Figure 10.14.

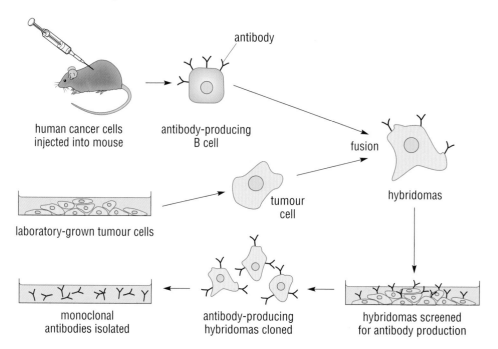

Figure 10.14   The production of MABs.

● What is a disadvantage of this method to create antibodies for use in cancer therapy?

● The human immune system will recognise the mouse MABs as foreign and will try to neutralise them. Thus the mouse MABs become useless.

To avoid an immune response to injected mouse MABs, new versions of 'humanised' MABs are being created by using a technique that manipulates the DNA of the hybridoma (i.e. fused) cells to create MABs that are similar those found in humans. Humanised MABs are now used as anticancer drugs and act by binding only to tumour cell receptors and inhibiting their growth-promoting activity thus rendering them insensitive to growth-promoting signals. Clearly such drugs would be highly effective and selective. Trastuzumab (also known as Herceptin®) is a well-known example of an MAB used to treat metastatic breast cancer (see Box 10.3). More recently, MABs have been chemically linked to anticancer substances (such as radioactive materials, toxins), thus targeting the substance directly to the specific tumour.

Currently, more than 20 MABs have been approved by the FDA (the US Food and Drug Administration), and hundreds more are undergoing clinical trials. Examples are given in Table 10.5 in the Appendix.

Box 10.3 Herceptin®, its uses and side effects

Herceptin® (trastuzumab) is a 'humanised' MAB that recognises a specific sequence of amino acids in the HER2 receptor (i.e. its antigen) (Section 2.9.2). Activation of the HER2 receptor signals the cells to divide. Herceptin is used only for breast cancers that are HER2-positive, i.e. those that overproduce HER2 (Section 2.9.2). (Approximately 25% to 30% of all breast cancers are HER2-positive.) These tumours tend to grow faster in response to the growth factor that binds HER2.

Herceptin works by attaching itself to the HER2 receptors on the surface of the HER2-positive cancer cells and blocking the growth-promoting signal. As a result, Herceptin slows or even stops tumour cell proliferation. The drug is given by intravenous infusion (a continuous administration of a solution containing the drug into venous blood). This is because Herceptin cannot be taken orally since it is a protein and would be readily destroyed by proteases (enzymes that digest proteins) in the gastrointestinal tract. Fever, chills and toxicity to heart muscle are some common side effects during the first treatment with Herceptin.

The reason why Herceptin is toxic to heart muscle in some patients is not fully understood. One hypothesis is that heart muscle cells also express the HER2 receptor and so the intracellular signalling in response to HER2 activation – which is essential for the contractile function of the cells – is blocked by Herceptin. Therefore, the patient's heart function needs to be checked before she is allowed to receive Herceptin, and then again at intervals while she is receiving the drug. This can be done using radionuclide imaging (Section 6.5.6). The usual measure of heart function is the 'left ventricular ejection fraction' which is a measure of the percentage of the blood in the left ventricle that is pumped out round the body at each stroke. The complex series of radionuclide images in Figure 10.15 allows the ejection fraction to be calculated. In this case the pretreatment value is 65%, which is a good level. (A video version of the images in this figure is available on the course website.)

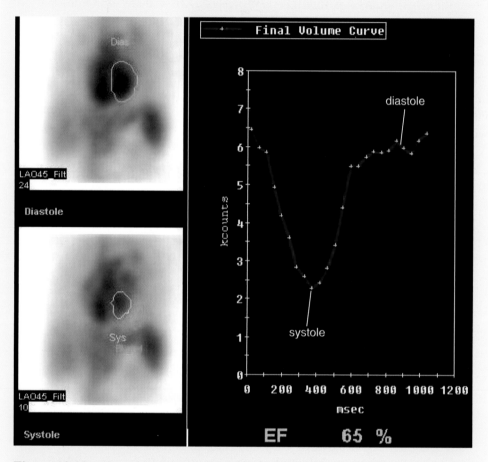

Figure 10.15 Heart images from a patient who has been prescribed Herceptin. A radiopharmaceutical is injected into the bloodstream so that the blood in the heart chambers can be imaged. At top left is the image obtained when the left ventricle is at its largest (diastole) and at bottom left, the image obtained when the left ventricle is at its smallest (systole). The blue and yellow coloured lines outline the left ventricle in diastole and systole respectively and the green line outlines the background area. By counting the gamma rays received from these regions and subtracting the background count, the ejection fraction can be calculated as 65%. If the information is recorded over the whole heartbeat the volume of the heart at any point in the cycle can be plotted as a graph (right-hand side). (Source: University Hospitals Coventry and Warwickshire NHS Trust)

10.8.2 Cancer vaccine therapy

A **vaccine** is a treatment designed to stimulate the immune system to fight against specific targets (i.e. antigens). You may in the past have had a flu (influenza) vaccine at some stage. The flu vaccine contains copies of inactivated (killed) flu virus. Antigens on the inactivated virus in the vaccine can still stimulate the immune system to produce cells that can fight against the active flu virus. Because the flu virus changes from year to year, a new flu vaccine is needed every year. Your immune system, however, still protects you against last year's flu type. This type of vaccine is called a preventive vaccine.

As with MAB therapy, cancer vaccine therapy takes advantage of the immune system to fight or prevent cancer. Cancer vaccines represent an emerging type of biological therapy that is still mostly experimental. However, two vaccines have been approved to help prevent cancer, particularly for cancers associated with viral infections. One is designed to prevent cervical cancer by impeding infection with the human papilloma virus (HPV); the other is to prevent liver cancer and works by fighting against the hepatitis B virus.

Cancer vaccines are intended either to prevent the development of cancer (as in the two examples just mentioned) or to treat existing cancer. Cancer preventive vaccines are given to healthy people and are designed to target infectious agents that can cause cancer. On the other hand, cancer vaccines used for therapy must not only provoke an immune response; they must also stimulate the immune system strongly enough to overcome its usual tolerance of cancer cells. As discussed earlier, since cancer cells differ from normal cells in only small, subtle ways the immune system largely tolerates cancer cells rather than attacks them.

Cancer vaccine therapy is becoming more and more promising. Equipped with a better understanding of how cancer cells avoid detection by the immune system, scientists have developed new strategies for stimulating a more powerful anticancer immune response to make tumour antigens more visible to the immune system. Animal model studies have shown that cancer vaccines capable of stimulating the immune system can help cancers recede. In humans, however, the situation is more complicated. A lot of work and many challenges remain for scientists to demonstrate clearly that cancer vaccines can be effective. It is also possible that vaccines could prove more effective when combined with other therapies and that multiple vaccinations may be necessary for a benefit to be seen. It may take years, but the potential is great (see Chapter 12).

In addition to MAB therapy and cancer vaccine therapy, there are other therapies that are also based on the immune system. For instance, cytokines are now used as therapeutic drugs. As an example, interleukin-2 has been used for the treatment of malignant melanoma and renal cell cancer. Interferons (mentioned in Case study 7.3) are another class of cytokines that can help the immune system to destroy tumour cells.

Case study 10.2   Terri's cancer vaccine therapy

As soon as Terri has completely recovered from what was actually quite a minor operation, she goes to the Sidney Melanoma Unit to start her cancer vaccine therapy. Amongst much paperwork and information, she is told that she could either be given a placebo or the cancer vaccine since the clinical trial is randomised. This bit of information takes her aback because she always thought that she would be given the 'real' thing. After a moment of hesitation and some soul searching, she signs the informed consent form.

Her treatment involves first taking a blood sample to isolate her immune cells which are then grown in the laboratory for 7 days. The immune cells are then added synthetic protein preparations originating from melanoma cells of other patients to activate them against Terri's tumour. Terri's activated immune cells would then be injected into her lymph nodes in the right groin at weekly intervals for the first four injections, then less regularly for a total of three years. The placebo vaccine would involve injection of non-activated immune cells. At each of these visits she does not feel any side effects apart from a burning sensation on the injection site but a thought is nagging in her head: has she been given the placebo vaccine or the treatment with melanoma-activated immune cells?

Terri returns to the hospital regularly for checks, first every three months, then every 6 months then at longer intervals after her treatment ends. She initially feels extremely anxious, will her melanoma come back? She gradually gets used to the feeling of not knowing what to expect, although at times she feels depressed; it is over a year, for instance, before she can contemplate a night at the opera. But, five years on, she is still melanoma-free. She knows that there is still a chance that her cancer will come back, but a diminishing one.

10.9 Hormone therapy

Hormones are molecules that occur naturally in the body and are produced and regulated by the endocrine system (Section 4.6.2). These molecules play important roles in various biological processes including metabolism, growth, development and puberty. Most, but not all, endocrine glands work under the influence of a single master gland, the pituitary gland (which is situated at the base of the brain). In this way the actions of individual glands can be coordinated to achieve homeostasis (Section 4.7). The female hormones oestrogen and progesterone are produced by the ovaries following puberty and up to menopause. After the menopause, the ovaries stop producing these hormones but they are still produced, though in much smaller amounts, by the adrenal glands. In general, hormones do not affect cancer cells; however, in breast cancer and other endocrine-related cancers (such as ovarian cancer, thyroid cancer, testicular cancer, prostate cancer and adrenal cancer) the situation is different. The female hormones can affect the growth of the breast cancer cells containing hormone receptors. (Hormone receptors are proteins that allow oestrogen or progesterone to fit in like a lock and key; see Section 2.9.1 and Figure 2.9.) This means that any drugs or treatments that block the effects of either of these hormones, or reduce their levels, can be used as a treatment for these types of breast cancer. Such drugs currently in use include the following:

- *Tamoxifen* (trade name: Nolvedex®) effectively blocks the oestrogen receptor. It is primarily used to treat breast cancer in post-menopausal patients or those with oestrogen receptor-positive tumours. It is also used as a preventive treatment for breast cancer in high-risk patients.

- *Anastrozole* (trade name: Arimidex®) blocks oestrogen synthesis. So this drug is only suitable for post-menopausal patients.

- *Goserelin acetate* (trade name: Zoladex®) works by blocking a hormone produced in the pituitary gland of the brain that stimulates the ovaries to synthesise and release oestrogen. Zoladex can be described as a pituitary downregulator.

Treatments that block the effects of male hormones such as testosterone are used to alleviate prostate cancer – these treatments can also be regarded as hormone therapy. They are pituitary downregulators such as *leuprorelin* (trade name: Prostap®) and *Goserelin acetate* (Zoladex®; also used for breast cancer – see above). The other drugs used to treat prostate cancer are those with structures similar to testosterone. They can block the receptors on the surface of the cancerous prostate cells and thus prevent testosterone from attaching to its receptor. Without testosterone, the cancer cells either grow more slowly, or stop growing altogether.

10.10 Gene therapy

The history of medicine has been marked by monumental innovations (e.g. surgery, immunisation and the use of antibiotics) that have changed the world. Gene therapy has not done that yet, but it is often reported to be one of the most hopeful achievements in medicine. So what exactly is gene therapy? How can gene therapy be used for cancer treatment?

Just looking at the two words coupled in the phrase 'gene therapy' raises an important ambiguity.

● From what you have learnt (or heard) so far, what might gene therapy mean?

● It could mean treatment that involves correcting genes that are involved in causing an illness in an individual. Or it could mean using genes to treat an illness caused in some other way.

It turns out that both interpretations are right. Most of the public debate has been about the correcting or repairing genes, but most applications have focused on the use of 'designer' DNA to tackle diseases. **Gene therapy** is the genetic modification of cells to prevent, alleviate or cure diseases. It does not prevent the passing on of inherited diseases. This is a separate area of research referred to as germline cell genetic therapy, and is not relevant to the present discussion. Approximately half of all current gene therapy research is on cancer.

At the time of writing (early 2008), gene therapy remains an experimental treatment (i.e. its use is restricted to clinical trials) that involves introducing genetic material into a patient's cells to fight disease. The introduced DNA in gene therapy is intended to target oncogenes (Section 3.5.4) so that it can disable them, or to restore the activity of tumour-suppressor genes or genes for DNA repair proteins in order to stop the tumour growing. Various gene therapy treatments are currently undergoing clinical trials for many different types of cancer and for other diseases too. Gene therapy is not currently available outside clinical trials, but is predicted to have a bright future in cancer treatment.

10.11 Other issues related with anticancer drugs

So far we have discussed anticancer drugs as if they were readily delivered in close proximity and in the optimum amounts to the tumour cell so that they can exert their action. But this is far from the case, for tumour cells usually grow in inaccessible places (with the exception of skin cancers and some tumours accessible from body orifices, e.g. colon carcinoma). First, the drug must reach its target, i.e. the tumour cell, and the easiest way to do this is by being transported via the blood which disseminates it throughout the body. The method used to get a particular drug into the bloodstream (i.e. the route of administration) – whether orally, directly via injection, etc. – is determined by its chemical characteristics. Second, the amount of drug, the dose, must be sufficient to allow the drug to access the tumour in sufficient quantities to be effective, but not so high that the patient experiences too many side effects. This section deal with these pragmatic considerations relating to drug administration.

10.11.1 Drug delivery

Drug delivery is the term that refers to the delivery of therapeutic agents (drugs) to the body tissues. The common delivery routes (also known as routes of administration) are listed below:

- oral route (given by mouth)
- sublingual route (under the tongue)
- rectal route (inserted into the rectum)
- application to other epithelial surface (e.g. skin and nasal mucosa)
- inhalation (through lungs)
- injection and infusion: intravenous (into vein); intramuscular; intrathecal (into the spinal canal) and subcutaneous (under the skin).

The preferred method of delivery is the oral route. It is non-invasive and easy for the patient. Using this route, the drug goes via the mouth through the stomach and is then absorbed into the bloodstream from the small intestine. Many drugs, in particular those in biological therapies, however, cannot be delivered orally because such drugs are susceptible to degradation by digestion. For example, the stomach is an acidic environment which would destroy drugs that are proteins (e.g. MABs) or nucleic acids (i.e. gene therapy drugs) if they were administered this way. Furthermore, the gut produces digestive enzymes which can break down biological drug molecules, just as they do our normal food. Therefore, most of chemotherapeutic drugs are delivered via intravenous injection because this is the fastest and most certain route for drug administration. The drug will first reach the heart and lungs, then circulate around the body eventually reaching its target.

10.11.2 Drug dose

Drug dose is the amount of therapeutic agent, e.g. an anticancer drug, that is administered to the patient. Administration of the right dose is an important issue: if the dose is too low, it will be ineffective against the tumour and could increase the likelihood of drug resistance (discussed in Section 10.11.4), while at excessive doses the toxicity (side effects: see Section 10.11.3 below) will be intolerable to the patient without improving the efficacy of the drug. This has led to the formation of detailed 'dosing schemes' in most hospitals, which give guidance on the correct dose balancing efficacy against toxicity; this approach is used in the treatment of many other diseases. In most cases, the dose is adjusted for the patient's body surface area (BSA), as this is a measure that correlates well with blood volume.

Case study 10.3 Lin's palliative chemotherapy is targeted to his liver

As Lin Ming is one of the 50% urban Chinese who have health insurance (provided by Lin's factory), he is quickly hospitalised at the provincial hospital. For five days, he receives further medical examinations, including blood tests, ultrasound sonography and angiography (a test to determine the blood circulation going in and out of organs). The doctor discusses with Lin and his wife about a special drug treatment named transcatheter arterial chemoembolization (TACE). In TACE, a tube called a catheter would be put into Lin's femoral artery (the artery in the leg) and threaded along until it reached the hepatic artery so that drugs can be delivered at high doses directly into the liver. The doctor would check that the catheter was in the right place in the liver and a combination of drugs (cisplatin, doxorubicin, and mitomycin C) would be injected into the tube with gel foam particles which would block the blood supply of the tumour. The aim of TACE is to induce tumour cell death while preserving as much functional liver tissue as possible, and so to prolong life, although this is kept from Lin Ming. After the procedure, Lin Ming develops fever and abdominal pain together with nausea and vomiting as a result of his already decreased liver function being further damaged. In Lin's case, TACE is repeated every 6 weeks.

When Lin is finally told by his wife that he has liver cancer, he appears quite calm on the surface. He considers himself to be a quite traditional person and although he accepts being treated with Western drugs, he also asks for Chinese medicines which he believes will protect his liver. For a few weeks, Lin takes pills of traditional medicines for activating the blood to resolve stasis and the *qi* and *yin* tonic herbs, consisting of ginseng, astragalus, codonopsis, lycium fruit, adenophora and many others.

10.11.3 Side effects

Since chemotherapeutic drugs are cytotoxic substances, chemotherapy will cause certain side effects, most notably feeling sick or tired, hair loss, nausea and vomiting, among others. Biological therapy is generally more selective, so the side effects are less severe. Some side effects are usually unavoidable.

This is because anticancer drugs (both chemotherapy and biological therapies) act not only on cancer cells, but also, inevitably, on normal cells. Cancer drugs primarily target cells that divide and proliferate continuously and quickly, but other growing cells such as those in the bone marrow are also affected.

● Why are hair loss, sores in the mouth and throat, dry skin, nausea, vomiting and diarrhoea often associated with cancer treatments?

● The hair follicles, the skin, and the lining of the mouth and the gastrointestinal tract (stomach and intestines) all comprise continuously dividing and growing cells, which are damaged by anticancer drugs.

● Why are many side effects related to bone marrow?

● Bone marrow is the inner part of some bones which produces blood cells (red blood cells, white blood cells, and platelets). When red blood cells are depleted, the amount of oxygen delivered to the tissues may be insufficient; thus patients could feel short of breath, weak and tired (fatigue). Reduced quantities of white blood cells can weaken the ability to fight infections. When the blood platelet count is low, any cuts will take a longer time to heal.

10.11.4 Drug resistance

Anticancer drugs, if used repeatedly, can become less effective, or even ineffective, in killing cancer cells. This phenomenon is called **drug resistance**. It is more obvious in chemotherapy than in biological therapy due mainly to the fact that the latter is still relatively new. So here we focus on the resistance to chemotherapy; however, the principles are likely to be applicable to biological therapy too.

The resistance that cancer cells display to cytotoxic drugs can be primary (existing when the drug is first given) or acquired (developing during treatment with the drug). Primary resistance to a drug is low in general. More crucial is the acquired resistance, which may be due to either adaptation or mutation of the tumour cells, resulting in newer cells that are less affected or unaffected by the drugs. Some resistance mechanisms are listed below.

• Rapid repair of drug-induced damage. For instance, alkylating drugs (e.g. temozolomide, Section 10.3) cause alkylation of DNA bases and the resultant modified bases can be repaired by certain DNA repair enzymes.

• Insufficient activation of the drug (e.g. 5-fluorouracil, Section 10.4). Drugs of this type require certain metabolic transformations (i.e. activation) before they can be used as DNA building blocks. When newer cells acquire mutations that render them no longer capable of activating the drug it becomes ineffective for the cancer treatment.

• Decreased accumulation of drugs in cells. This is due to the increased production of a drug-transport protein (the protein that can take drugs out of cells). The transport protein functions as a 'vacuum cleaner', picking up certain drugs (e.g. doxorubicin) as they enter through the cell membrane and expelling them to the outside.

10.11.5 Combination chemotherapy

So, how is the problem of resistance to anticancer drugs addressed? A smart solution would be to carry on using a particular drug but in combination with other drug(s) rather than individually. This is the same type of strategy as used in antibiotic therapy for tuberculosis, which uses combinations of drugs, each having a different mechanism of action. Tumour cells could conceivably mutate to become resistant to a single drug, but by using different drugs *concurrently* it would be more difficult for the tumour to develop resistance to the combination. A combination of prednisone, oncovin (vincristine), methotrexate, and 6-mercaptopurine (together referred to as the POMP regimen) has been successfully used for acute lymphoblastic leukaemia in children. Each of the component anticancer drugs used has a different mechanism of action. Thus it is much harder for cancer cells to develop full resistance to all four drugs in a short timespan. Currently, many successful cancer chemotherapy regimens employ a combination of drugs given simultaneously.

- Could chemotherapy combined with radiotherapy offer some advantages against resistant tumours over chemotherapy or radiotherapy alone?

- Yes. Radiotherapy has a different mechanism of action to chemotherapy. So a tumour that has become resistant to radiotherapy may remain sensitive to chemotherapy. Furthermore, chemotherapy is a systemic treatment whereas radiotherapy (and surgery) is mainly limited to the area that is treated. In fact chemotherapy is frequently used in combination with radiotherapy (or/and surgery).

- Do you think biological therapy can be used to combine with radiotherapy or surgery or even with chemotherapy? Explain your answer.

- Biological therapy can be used in combination with the other therapies (radiotherapy or surgery or chemotherapy), or even with a different biological therapy, in order to obtain a better result. As long as each therapy has a different mechanism of action, then combination therapy can alleviate the problem of drug resistance.

Case study 10.4 Trupti's leukaemia relapse

All goes well for a year. Trupti continues with her combination therapy and has been hospitalised on two occasions, to be given even more potent combinations of chemotherapeutic drugs. Her energy levels gradually return to something near normal. At one monthly appointment, however, Mr and Mrs Shah receive the news that they have been dreading: Trupti's leukaemia has returned, and her best chance of a complete recovery is now with very high dose chemotherapy and a bone marrow (or stem cell) transplant. Trupti's parents and her three older siblings were given a simple blood test to see if their blood types were compatible with Trupti's, and her oldest brother, now fourteen, proved to be a good match.

Trupti goes back into Great Ormond Street Hospital and is put back on very high dose combination chemotherapy by infusion through a central line into her chest. This makes her feel very tired and sick, and her hair begins to fall out. 'It breaks my heart to see Trupti with no hair but at least she's not feeling self-conscious, as many kids in the ward look the same' says Mrs Shah. When the doctors believe that all of Trupti's bone marrow cells (including the cancer cells) have been destroyed, and she is ready for the transplant, her brother is injected with a growth factor to help his bone marrow produce more stem cells. He then comes into hospital for a day, where these stem cells are 'harvested' from his blood. This procedure is not painful, but it is unpleasant, and like any teenage lad he finds staying quite still for as long as four hours very tedious.

Once Trupti has completed her high dose chemotherapy, and the donor cells are ready, the transplant can go ahead. By that time, Trupti is a very sick little girl, and her parents are desperately worried. They have also been rather worried about their eldest son, although they were reassured that the donation procedure holds no danger: their principal emotion is pride in what he is doing for his little sister. When all is ready, Trupti is moved from the main ward into a single room to protect her from infection, and her brother's harvested stem cells are infused into her bloodstream through the same central line that delivered her chemotherapy. Her brother's stem cells diffuse into her blood stream and then into her bone marrow, where they can start multiplying. She, also, is given growth factors to stimulate this process. She stays in isolation, protected from any external infection, for about four weeks, and in hospital for another month. Although there are no signs of leukaemia, she is not well enough to return to school for another term.

A year later, she is still well. She is catching up well at school, and is back to her old, lively, mischievous self. No-one is happier to see her running about and playing with her school friends than the brother whose gift of stem cells enabled her to get well.

10.12 Concluding remarks

In this chapter, chemotherapy and biological therapy and their working principles have been discussed. There are a number of chemotherapy drugs available for various cancers. Chemotherapy drugs are cytotoxic molecules. They are effective in killing rapidly dividing cancer cells, but also cause side effects. Biological therapy is a collective term for many newly developed cancer treatments. Some of them are now well established, and many more are in the clinic trial stage (40 new drugs in final stages of development and 500 in earlier stages at the time of writing in early 2008). Together with surgery and radiotherapy, chemotherapy and biological therapy offer great hopes to prevent cancer occurring, stop cancer spreading, or even cure cancers. As with other cancer treatments, both chemotherapy and biological therapy will inevitably inflict some damage to normal cells, especially those that are proliferating, resulting in a myriad of side effects. Therefore the costs need to be considered, not only in economic terms, but also in terms of the quality of life. This is especially true in the case of elderly patients. The next chapter will discuss these issues in detail.

10.13 Summary of Chapter 10

10.1   Chemotherapy is the treatment of cancer with drugs, often small molecules. There are two major types of chemotherapeutic agents: (1) DNA-alkylating (and alkylating-like) drugs, most of which (e.g. nitrogen mustards and cisplatin) form chemical links to DNA strands, resulting in defective replication and triggering apoptosis; (2) antimetabolite drugs, which block or subvert DNA synthesis (e.g. methotrexate interferes with the synthesis of purine and thymine nucleotides and 5-FU inhibits thymine nucleotide synthesis).

10.2   Biological therapy is the treatment of cancer with drugs that are often biological molecules. Biological therapies include targeted therapy (with growth inhibitors), immunotherapy (MAB and cancer vaccine therapy), hormone therapy and gene therapy. The therapies that use growth inhibitors and MABs have been extensively used to treat various cancers with excellent results. Cancer vaccine therapy and gene therapy are still being developed and both have a promising future.

10.3   Drug delivery and drug dose are important practical issues in the treatment of cancer. Different methods of delivery or doses can have huge effects on the patient.

10.4   Side effects (e.g. fatigue, hair loss, nausea and vomiting) can occur with chemotherapy and to lesser extent with biological therapy, due to the toxicity of the drugs to normal cells in the body. Some side effects are usually unavoidable.

10.5   Drug resistance is the phenomenon in which cancer drugs become less effective or ineffective in killing cancer cells.

10.6   Combination therapy is a treatment using two or more different drugs or therapies which often produces a better result. Combination chemotherapy can also prevent or delay the onset of drug resistance.

Questions for Chapter 10

Question 10.1 (Learning outcomes 10.1 and 10.4)

Which of the three cancer treatments listed below is a systemic therapy and why?

(i)   Removal of the tumour by surgery.

(ii)   Radiation of the area of the tumour.

(iii)   Taking a tablet containing temozolomide.

Question 10.2 (Learning outcomes 10.2 and 10.3)

Nedaplatin is a platinum-based drug under clinic trial (together with other drugs) in patients with oesophageal cancer. State which of the following is the most likely mechanism of action for nedaplatin and briefly explain your choice.

(i) Alkylating-like; (ii) antimetabolite; (iii) antimicrotubule.

Question 10.3 (Learning outcome 10.5)

Briefly explain why hair loss is a common side effect of chemotherapy treatment.

Question 10.4 (Learning outcomes 10.2 and 10.6)

Briefly explain why Herceptin has been successful in the treatment of some, but not all, breast cancers.

Further reading

Boulikas, T., Alevizopoulos, N., Ladopoulou, A., Belimezi, M., Pantos, A., Christofis, P. and Roberts, M. (2007) 'Anticancer therapeutics' in *The Cancer Clock*, Missailidis, S. (ed.), Chichester, John Wiley & Sons.

Carter, P. (2001) 'Improving the efficacy of antibody-based cancer therapies', *Nature Reviews Cancer*, vol. 1, pp. 118–29.

Karran, P. and Attard, N. (2008) 'Thiopurines, in current medical practice: molecular mechanisms and contributions to the therapy-related cancer', *Nature Reviews Cancer*, vol. 8, pp. 24–36.

Kelland, L. (2007) 'The resurgence of platinum-based cancer chemotherapy', *Nature Reviews Cancer*, vol. 7, pp. 573–84.

LIVING WITH CANCER

11.1 Introduction

At this point in the course you should have a good understanding of the biological and medical aspects of cancers, the risk factors that make them more likely to develop and how these may be modified, the general features of cancer diagnosis by MDTs, and the most common treatments aimed at eradicating malignant disease or slowing its progression. You also know some of the ways in which the side effects of surgery, radiotherapy and chemotherapy may be controlled. This chapter considers the impact that living with a cancer can have on the quality of life of those affected and how the most common adverse consequences may be alleviated. You will learn about the medical follow-up that generally occurs after cancer treatment in countries like the UK, where there are extensive cancer services, and the palliative care and support available if the cancer leads to terminal illness.

Throughout the chapter, bear in mind that the experiences of one person with cancer and another – even though both may have the same type and stage of disease – may be strikingly different depending on a range of factors, such as their personality, coping style, family and social support networks, income, occupation and the availability of medical and nursing care in the country in which they live. We look first at the psychological adjustment to living with cancer and then at the management of the physical symptoms and the side effects of treatment.

11.2 Psychological adjustment to living with cancer

In Section 7.2, you met examples of varying reactions to the initial diagnosis of cancer and learned that it can have a profound adverse effect on the quality of life of some individuals, whereas others take it in their stride and get on with life as normally as possible. There has been much research into whether particular coping styles are associated with better long-term psychological health, and typical findings are illustrated by one of many studies of women with breast cancer (Stanton et al., 2002). Those who reacted to their diagnosis by avoidance or denial were found to have more psychological difficulties one year after diagnosis compared to women who acknowledged their illness and were open about it with others. Psychological effects such as these can persist and may also influence physical well-being. In another study, women who actively expressed their emotions about having cancer required fewer medical appointments during the follow-up period and reported better physical health and quality of life than those who repressed their feelings (Stanton et al., 2000).

However, although outcomes of this general type are commonly reported, there are some conflicting results. For example, a study looking at denial as a reaction to a cancer diagnosis showed that it could improve the quality of life in some individuals, whilst adversely affecting it in others (Vos and de Haes, 2006). Note that, to date, there is no conclusive evidence that psychological adjustment or coping style can influence how long a person with cancer survives.

11.2.1 Coping with depression and anxiety

Depression and anxiety can often feature in learning to live with a cancer, at least intermittently and particularly in the first years after diagnosis. In one study, the lifetime risk of suffering a major depressive disorder was estimated to be as high as 60% of people with cancer, compared to a risk for all women of 20–25% and for men of 7–12% (Newport and Nemeroff, 1998).

- What do you understand by the term 'depression'?

- You may have mentioned feeling sad or low in mood. If you already know something about how the nervous system works, you may have said that depression can involve an imbalance of the neurotransmitters (chemicals) that signal between nerve cells in the brain.

The WHO defines **depression** as:

> … a common mental disorder that is characterized by sadness, loss of interest or pleasure, feelings of guilt or low self-worth, disturbed sleep or appetite, low energy and poor concentration. These problems can become chronic or recurrent, substantially impairing an individual's ability to cope with daily life.

(WHO, 2008)

Depression is a debilitating illness that can erode a person's ability to cope with the challenges of undergoing cancer treatment and the inevitable uncertainty about the outcome. **Anxiety** is characterised by symptoms such as rapid breathing, a pounding heartbeat, nausea, fear, increased alertness and an inability to relax or concentrate, and it could be seen as a normal initial reaction to a cancer diagnosis. For most people with cancer, anxiety is transient, but in some the symptoms become prolonged or recur frequently, causing serious interference with their daily lives.

A reason for emphasising the potential impact of these psychological symptoms on quality of life is that depression and anxiety are often undiagnosed in people with cancer, or treated too late.

● Can you suggest some reasons why?

● You may have noted that the physical symptoms of depression and anxiety, such as fatigue, sleep disturbance and loss of appetite, may be confused with the effects of the cancer or its treatment. The medical team may be focused on a person's physical symptoms and forget to ask about their psychological state. Someone with cancer may expect to feel low in mood or anxious, and may assume that these feelings are 'normal' and not worth mentioning to the medical team, or conversely be reluctant to admit to depression.

Difficulties such as these in diagnosing depression or anxiety among people with cancer (and others) can be addressed by using specially designed questionnaires, such as the one in Figure 11.1 (overleaf). The results can indicate whether treatment with antidepressant drugs and/or psychological therapies is advisable, but these interventions can have problems of their own. For example, the prescription of antidepressants may be limited by adverse side effects and possible interactions with other drugs already being taken to treat cancer symptoms. Group psychotherapy or one-to-one counselling may benefit at least some people with cancer whose psychological symptoms were undermining their quality of life (Sheard and Maguire, 1999), but very few receive these treatments.

● Can you think of reasons why people with cancer may not receive psychological therapy?

● You may have suggested some of the following (there are others):

In countries with a national health service, there may be a long waiting list to see a therapist. In low- and middle-income countries, psychological therapies may not exist at all or only for the very rich.

It is expensive to pay for private sessions of any psychological therapy and many people could not afford the cost.

An individual may be reluctant to see a therapist, fearing this would label them as 'mentally ill'.

A reticent person might find it intrusive or threatening to share their thoughts and feelings with a stranger.

Equally, a person may be in denial about being depressed, or may not have any confidence that psychotherapy could help.

PATIENT HEALTH QUESTIONNAIRE (PHQ-9)

NAME: _____ DATE: _____

Over the *last 2 weeks,* how often have you been
bothered by any of the following problems?
(use "✓" to indicate your answer)

	Not at all	Several days	More than half the days	Nearly every day
1. Little interest or pleasure in doing things	0	1	2	3
2. Feeling down, depressed, or hopeless	0	1	2	3
3. Trouble falling or staying asleep, or sleeping too much	0	1	2	3
4. Feeling tired or having little energy	0	1	2	3
5. Poor appetite or overeating	0	1	2	3
6. Feeling bad about yourself—or that you are a failure or have let yourself or your family down	0	1	2	3
7. Trouble concentrating on things, such as reading the newspaper or watching television	0	1	2	3
8. Moving or speaking so slowly that other people could have noticed. Or the opposite—being so fidgety or restless that you have been moving around a lot more than usual	0	1	2	3
9. Thoughts that you would be better off dead, or of hurting yourself in some way	0	1	2	3

add columns: _____ + _____ + _____

(Healthcare professional: For interpretation of TOTAL, TOTAL: _____
please refer to accompanying scoring card.)

Figure 11.1 An extract from the Patient Health Questionnaire (PHQ-9) designed to reveal underlying depression or anxiety. (Source: Pfizer Inc.)

10. If you checked off *any* problems, how *difficult* have these problems made it for you to do your work, take care of things at home, or get along with other people?	Not difficult at all _____
	Somewhat difficult _____
	Very difficult _____
	Extremely difficult _____

More attention has been paid to addressing the adverse effects on quality of life resulting from the physical symptoms of different cancers and the unpleasant side effects that cancer treatments can produce.

11.3 Managing cancer symptoms and side effects

If a person with cancer experiences particular symptoms and side effects, careful interventions are necessary to avoid the risk of treating one problem (e.g. pain) but making another (e.g. constipation) worse. Managing the complex cluster of health problems that may affect people with widespread cancer or repeated treatments for recurrent disease is a delicate balancing act. It can take time to find the best compromise, but most symptoms can usually be alleviated if not completely controlled. Here the focus is on the most common problems – pain, breathlessness, nausea and vomiting, and constipation – but you should keep in mind that some people with cancer never experience any of these, and most of those who do are affected for relatively short periods.

11.3.1 Pain control

Whilst not all people with cancer will experience pain, it is generally reported as the most feared of all symptoms and the one with the greatest impact on quality of life if it cannot be adequately controlled. Pain may be caused by the cancer itself or as a side effect of treatment, as you learned in Section 8.5, where the control of pain following cancer surgery was discussed. In addition to surgery, pain may arise from metastases in the bones (as shown in Figure 6.23b), distension or distortion of internal organs affected by cancer, the infiltration of peripheral nerves by a tumour, or pressure exerted by a tumour growing in a confined space, e.g. in the brain (Figure 11.2).

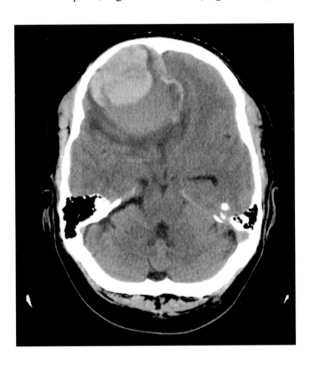

Figure 11.2 CT scan showing a tumour at the front of the brain pressing against the membranes lining the skull. The image is an axial cross-section through the head above the level of the eyes and shows the bone around the outside as white with the brain in shades of grey. The tumour is situated at the front left of the brain and the pressure it exerts pushes the membranes close up against the inner surface of the skull. (Source: University Hospitals Coventry and Warwickshire NHS Trust)

One of the difficulties in managing pain is in assessing how much pain a person is experiencing in order to prescribe appropriate treatment and evaluate its effectiveness.

● Why can it be difficult to estimate a person's pain level accurately?

● Pain is subjective, accessible only to the person who experiences it. How one person describes their pain may not be meaningful to someone else. Tolerance for pain varies over time, depending on what else is going on, the person's state of mind, and so on. It is particularly difficult to estimate pain in children, or in people who are confused or distressed or unable to speak the same language as the doctor.

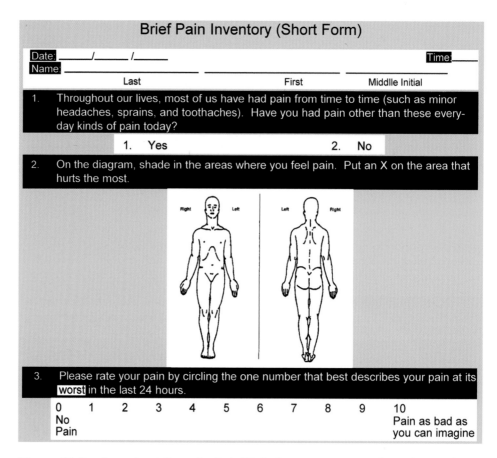

Brief Pain Inventory (Short Form)

Date: _____/_____/_____   Time:_____

Name: _____   _____   _____
                    Last   First   Middlle Initial

1. Throughout our lives, most of us have had pain from time to time (such as minor headaches, sprains, and toothaches). Have you had pain other than these every-day kinds of pain today?

         1.   Yes   2.   No

2. On the diagram, shade in the areas where you feel pain. Put an X on the area that hurts the most.

3. Please rate your pain by circling the one number that best describes your pain at its worst in the last 24 hours.

       0   1   2   3   4   5   6   7   8   9   10
       No   Pain as bad as
       Pain   you can imagine

Figure 11.3   An extract from the Brief Pain Inventory, a questionnaire used to help estimate the extent of pain, for example as experienced by a person with advanced cancer or pain following cancer surgery. (Source: Charles Cleeland, 1991)

Various pain rating scales can be useful in overcoming these difficulties; for example, a person may be asked to rate their pain on a scale from 0 to 10, where 0 is no pain and 10 is the worst pain imaginable (Figure 11.3).

In recent years, significant progress has been made in diagnosing the cause of cancer pain and alleviating it by prescribing appropriate analgesic (pain-killing) medication.

●   What type of drug was referred to in Section 8.5.6 for treating moderate to severe post-operative pain? How does it exert its effect?

●   Opioids are a widely used class of painkillers which work by blocking the transmission of nerve impulses to the brain that generate the sensation of pain.

Section 8.5.6 also referred to painkillers such as paracetamol (known as acetaminophen in most countries outside the UK) and non-steroidal anti-inflammatory drugs (NSAIDs) such as ibuprofen, both of which may treat relatively mild or short-acting pain. Other interventions include prescribing steroids to reduce the swelling around a tumour, thereby alleviating pain caused by the pressure the tumour exerts on neighbouring organs and tissues. Radiotherapy can also be used to reduce the size of a tumour that is causing pain (this is palliative radiotherapy, described in Section 7.4.2). Certain antidepressants or anti-epileptic drugs may reduce nerve pain, and local anaesthetics or steroids may be injected into the area of a nerve that does not respond to other analgesics. A combination of different interventions may be needed to control a person's pain, particularly in advanced cancer, a point we return to later when we discuss palliative care.

The WHO estimates that globally up to 4 million people experience cancer pain on a daily basis, the majority in countries where the treatment of pain is rudimentary and there is little access to pain specialists. In countries like the UK, where pain control services are well developed, the WHO's guidelines using the 'three-step ladder' are generally followed (Gupta et al., 2007), starting at step 1 and only moving up the ladder if pain control isn't achieved at the lower level:

Step 1: Paracetamol and other non-opioid drugs, mainly NSAIDs, adjusted individually for each patient, since some respond better to certain drugs than to others.

Step 2: Weak opioids, usually combined with step 1 drugs.

Step 3: Strong opioids (e.g. morphine), usually combined with step 1 or 2 drugs, and always prescribed with laxatives and stool softeners.

As the use of strong opioids illustrates, every treatment has side effects and pain control is no exception. Opioids cause constipation unless laxatives are started at the same time. They can also induce nausea and vomiting in less than a third of people, which generally resolves within two weeks of starting the drug; however, sometimes anti-sickness medication is required. The third side effect of opioids is drowsiness, which affects less than 20% of people prescribed these drugs; the symptom usually resolves within a week (Tookman and Kurowska, 2000).

Even paracetamol (acetaminophen), which is well tolerated by most people, may not be safe to take by someone with cancer in the liver because it may not be adequately broken down in this organ and could build up to dangerous levels. NSAIDs such as ibuprofen can increase the sensitivity of the stomach lining to stomach acid, triggering side effects such as nausea, vomiting, gastritis (inflammation of the stomach), indigestion and stomach ulcers. These examples illustrate the care that must be taken to treat pain without causing or exacerbating other health problems.

11.3.2 Breathlessness

Being unable to 'get your breath' is a distressing symptom that can lead to feelings of panic, as well as severely restricting the activities that a breathless person can manage. This can have a major effect on their quality of life, and their ability to work or to remain independent.

The medical term for breathlessness is dyspnoea (pronounced 'disp-nee-ah').

● What types of cancer or cancer treatments might lead to persistent breathlessness? (Think back to earlier chapters, particularly Chapter 4.)

● Cancer in the lungs can reduce the amount of oxygen that the lungs can absorb; so too can surgery to remove a lung cancer. Anaemia (lack of red blood cells) due to certain types of cancer (e.g. in the bone marrow), or after radiotherapy or chemotherapy, reduces the amount of oxygen carried in the blood so the person has to breathe faster to obtain an adequate supply. A chest infection, radiotherapy to the chest and some types of chemotherapy can cause inflammation of the lungs, leading to a build-up of fluid and difficulty in breathing. Fluid in the abdomen (ascites) can press against the diaphragm, compressing the lungs and reducing their ability to inflate. Cancer treatments can also reduce the production of white blood cells, making chest infections more likely.

The treatment for persistent breathlessness varies with the cause, as you might expect; for example:

• Anaemia may be treated with iron tablets or a blood transfusion.

• A chest infection will normally be treated with antibiotics.

• Excessive fluid in the lungs or the abdomen can be treated by draining it away.

• Oxygen can be given to a breathless person to increase the amount of oxygen carried in the blood (Figure 11.4).

• Opioids can help reduce the sensation of breathlessness, which can be helpful if the underlying cause cannot be treated.

Figure 11.4 A portable oxygen cylinder can enrich the oxygen supply to a person with lung damage (in this case, due to chronic obstructive pulmonary disease, COPD), relieving breathlessness and enabling greater mobility and autonomy. (Source: Owen Horn, Open University)

11.3.3 Nausea and vomiting

In some types of cancer, nausea and vomiting may be caused by the disease itself; for example, when a tumour in the gut blocks the passage of the bowel contents, or when a brain tumour causes an increase in pressure within the skull which triggers vomiting.

● What treatments might also lead to these symptoms?

● Various chemotherapy drugs and radiotherapy to the abdomen commonly cause nausea and vomiting (Chapters 9 and 10). Painkillers such as opioids and ibuprofen can have the same effects.

Drugs that treat sickness are called **anti-emetics** and they have two main modes of action. They either act on the areas of the brain that trigger nausea and vomiting, or they encourage the stomach to empty more rapidly. If a person is having chemotherapy, an anti-emetic will normally be prescribed in anticipation of the fact that nausea and vomiting are likely to occur. However, these drugs can also cause constipation.

11.3.4 Constipation

Anti-emetics and opioid drugs commonly cause constipation, but this problem can also be due to the cancer itself; for example, a cancer in the abdomen may block the bowel, or it may press on the spinal cord and interfere with the transmission of nerve signals that trigger the muscular movements of the bowel that push the contents along. Constipation can also be due to a diet low in fibre, a poor fluid intake or a lack of exercise – all of which may be difficult to achieve for a person living with a cancer, or with the side effects of treatment, that make bulky foods difficult to digest or unpalatable and exercise uncomfortable or exhausting.

Changing the drug regimen, intervening to reduce a blockage in the bowel or increasing fluid intake and fibre in the diet, may alleviate constipation, but treatment with laxatives is often required. They work by stimulating the contractions of the bowel or by increasing the bulk and softness of the stools, making them easier to expel.

● What side effects might laxatives cause?

● Increasing bowel contractions can cause abdominal cramps, and increasing the bulk of stools can cause bloating and distension. Taking too much laxative can cause diarrhoea.

This is another example of how carefully 'tailored' any intervention must be to address each individual's symptoms with the aim of achieving the best possible quality of life with the least possible adverse outcomes.

11.3.5 Difficulties in taking medication

Common practical problems in taking prescribed medication are often overlooked; for example, people with poor manual dexterity may find it difficult to open blister packs of tablets or medicine bottles, and some people can't remember to take medicines regularly. They may be helped by putting their medication in a prominent place, setting an alarm to go off when a dose is due, or using a dosette box (Figure 11.5a).

(a)

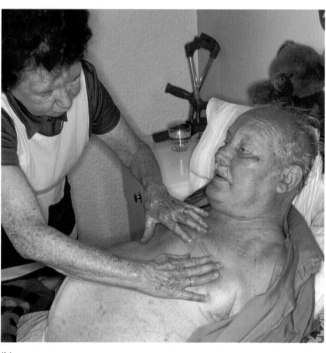

(b)

Figure 11.5 (a) A dosette box with compartments for each day of the week. (b) A medication patch stuck onto the body can deliver painkillers absorbed through the skin; the dosage is more consistent over time than taking the analgesic by mouth. (Sources: (a) Image Source/Rex Features; (b) Science Photo Library)

Certain cancers can cause difficulty with swallowing, which makes it hard to take tablets or capsules. Some drugs have to be taken with food, but if a person has lost their appetite they may miss some doses or take them on an empty stomach, which reduces their efficacy or increases the risk of side effects. Alternative routes of administration, such as injections or medication patches (Figure 11.5b), may help overcome these problems.

You should now be able to see why the use of multiple medications (or **polypharmacy**) is common in people with cancer who are undergoing major treatments, or for the management of a range of symptoms. Polypharmacy can be a problem because different drugs may interact with each other and increase the severity of side effects; for example, an opioid taken for pain relief can interact with a sleeping drug to cause profound drowsiness. Often one drug needs to be taken to counteract the unwanted effects of another, but this can cause additional problems.

● Can you suggest an example involving opioids?

● Opioids can cause nausea which can be treated with an anti-emetic; both cause constipation, which is prevented by prescribing a laxative. Thus three different medications may be needed simply to control pain and the side effects of the analgesic.

11.3.6 Sources of help and support

Most people who are learning to live with cancer are able to rely on the emotional and practical assistance of friends and family. Some offer help with practical tasks, such as childcare or shopping, or give emotional support by listening if the person with cancer needs to talk about it. But supportive reactions aren't universal and some relatives and friends find it too upsetting to deal with, or they lack knowledge about cancer and avoid the subject. As you might expect, a supportive social network tends to reduce the risk of disabling depression and anxiety in people with cancer (Edwards and Clarke, 2004). Cancer, like any major illness, can be particularly hard to bear for people who live alone.

Another major source of support comes from family doctors (known as 'general practitioners' or GPs in the UK) and other healthcare professionals such as nurses working in the community. The knowledge that anxieties about cancer can be discussed with familiar members of a local health team can be very reassuring. The hospital where specialist cancer treatments are given is also likely to offer support in the form of specialist nurses, counsellors and volunteers, and so do cancer charities such as Macmillan Cancer Support, Marie Curie Cancer Care (Figure 11.6) and Hospice Care in the UK.

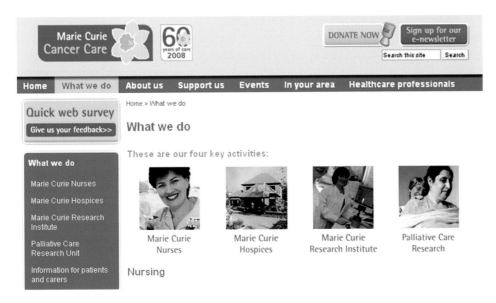

Figure 11.6   A web page from the UK-based Marie Curie Cancer Care charity. (Source: Marie Curie Cancer Care)

Figure 11.7 Miriame, her brother and his two sons; families in poor countries often bear the cost of looking after someone with cancer. (Photo: WHO/Marko Kokic)

However, professional help and support is at best patchy and at worst non-existent in many parts of the world, particularly where rural populations may be hundreds of miles from the nearest doctor, or the only cancer services available are in fee-paying private hospitals and clinics that poor people like Miriame (Figure 11.7) cannot afford:

> Two years ago, Miriame Nnamusoke was diagnosed with cervical cancer. … Miriame's illnesses forced her to stop working as a farmer in her small village of Natete, Uganda. She was sent to a private hospital, which soon depleted her life savings. … The financial burden fell not only on Miriame, but on her whole family. With all their savings exhausted, Miriame's daughter was forced to leave her education behind and become her mother's full-time caregiver. They moved in with Miriame's brother in Kampala and are now totally dependent on him for financial support, while he himself struggles to raise his two young boys.
>
> (WHO, 2006)

Families the world over are often the main source of care and support for people coping with a major illness, and sometimes they become involved in decisions about changes in lifestyle that have far-reaching consequences for themselves, as the next section illustrates.

11.4 Effects on lifestyle

For some people, being diagnosed with cancer can encourage a more positive approach to life, helping them feel more in control at a time when the disease presents many uncertainties. It may prompt them to re-evaluate aspects of their lifestyle that may have increased their risk of developing cancer (Chapter 5), or that could improve their quality of life in its aftermath. The term **lifestyle** can be defined as 'the way of life that is typical of a person, group or culture'. Some people coming to terms with cancer decide to change their lifestyle by altering their diet, or the amount they exercise, their pace of work, how they spend their leisure time; or they may give up or cut down on tobacco and alcohol. Anneke and her husband gave up smoking in Case study 6.6. Dave's family also get involved in the lifestyle changes that he decides to make (Case study 11.1).

Case study 11.1 Dave and his family change their lifestyle

The year following Dave's surgery is a particularly difficult one for him and his family. He finds it very hard to come to terms with the colostomy bag and limitations on what he can and can't eat, but he is more concerned about the financial difficulties resulting from his illness. With limited health insurance, he has to dig into what savings he has to pay for essential medicines. He gets very tired and is no longer able to work long hours in the diner; he has to accept that getting more rest is an essential change to his former lifestyle. His eldest son – the first member of the Bayler family to get to graduate school – puts his plans on hold, comes home and takes over running the diner. Dave's extended family, church community and local friends continue to rally round, offering whatever support they can, and, a year after the chemotherapy ends, his financial position is much eased by a legacy from his wife's uncle.

As Dave begins to feel better, and particularly once his serious money worries have eased, he begins to think hard about his previous lifestyle. With his family happy to take over running the diner, he is able to relax more and he begins to exercise. He starts very gently as he was unfit before he became ill, and he became weaker during his treatment, but he perseveres, and his family, who have been frightened by his illness, join in. They all make an effort to change their diet, eating more fruit and vegetables and far less red meat.

11.4.1 Normal food and special diets

Most forms of cancer don't require the affected person to eat a special diet; the same principles of healthy eating apply to a person with cancer as to everyone else. However, in certain circumstances a special diet is necessary; for example, people with a colostomy like Dave are advised that foods like beans and cauliflower should only be eaten in moderation because they cause 'wind', and fruits like apples and tomatoes should be peeled because the skins are hard to digest.

If you are interested, there is a link to information about what constitutes a healthy balanced diet on the course website.

- Can you think of any other examples of dietary changes that may help people with other types of cancer? (*Hint*: look back at Section 8.4.)

- You saw in Section 8.4 that an obstruction may occur with oesophageal cancer, which may be helped by eating soft foods.

Poor appetite and weight loss as a result of cancer or its treatment can be counteracted by a diet high in calories. Other examples include increased fluid intake and eating bland foods to avoid further irritation to a sore mouth caused by radiotherapy or chemotherapy; reducing nausea by taking small amounts of food frequently, avoiding strongly flavoured foods and drinking ginger tea; increasing dietary fibre to relieve constipation, and eating foods such as bananas, boiled rice and porridge to control diarrhoea, which can occur after surgery for bowel cancer. There are many more examples of ways in which diet can help improve cancer symptoms and treatment side effects; if you are interested, more information can be found via links from the course website.

11.4.2 Alcohol

For most people who enjoy alcohol in moderation, there is no reason to stop drinking it because of a diagnosis of cancer. However, drinking alcohol can cause some problems in people with particular types of cancer; for example, Dave had to reduce his alcohol intake to an occasional beer after his colostomy. Certain types of chemotherapy and other medications (such as opioid painkillers) can interact with alcohol and cause unpleasant side effects. Cancer and its treatment can affect the liver, so a person may be less able to process alcohol efficiently within the body, thus enhancing its effects and reducing the liver's ability to function. Alcohol may exacerbate symptoms such as nausea. And for anyone who is finding it hard to cope with the stress of living with cancer, there is also a risk of drinking excessively to try to relax, with all the attendant immediate and longer-term risks to health such as falls and liver disease.

11.4.3 Exercise

● Can you think of reasons why a person with cancer may be less likely to exercise?

● Some treatments for cancer may reduce a person's ability to exercise, for example by causing fatigue, anaemia and shortness of breath. Or they may be unable to undertake exercise during cancer treatment and then find it difficult to start exercising again.

Exercise can have various benefits for a person with cancer (Figure 11.8), such as reducing stress, anxiety and depression, and building stamina. It can also improve bone density and prevent osteoporosis, which may be important in women with breast and some other cancers who cannot take hormone replacement therapy during the menopause.

However, exercise may also pose some risks. Symptoms such as breathlessness and fatigue may be exacerbated and the risk of fracture may be increased in people with bone cancer. For these reasons, a person returning to exercise after treatment for cancer should discuss it with a healthcare professional, and do as Dave did (Case study 11.1) – start gradually.

Figure 11.8 Gentle exercise can be beneficial in reducing stress and returning to a more active life after treatment for a major illness. (Source: Stock Connection Blue/Alamy)

11.4.4 Smoking

You learned in Section 5.3 that tobacco smoke contains carcinogens, and that stopping smoking is one of the most important things a person can do to reduce their cancer risk. But is there any benefit to giving up smoking if a person already has cancer?

Smoking reduces the amount of oxygen that the blood can carry and can cause shortness of breath; it also increases the risk, duration and severity of chest infections. These symptoms are more likely to occur in a person with cancer (Section 11.3), so smoking may reduce their quality of life. It also reduces appetite, which may make it harder to make lifestyle changes that could boost well-being, such as eating more nourishing food.

However, giving up smoking is not easy: most people find it very difficult to stop. As smoking is often used to relieve stress, it may be more difficult to achieve if a person with cancer is feeling anxious about their diagnosis and treatment.

Someone with incurable cancer may decide that there is little purpose to stopping, and continue smoking rather than go through the stress of giving it up in whatever time they have remaining.

11.5 Returning to normal life

Changing aspects of lifestyle may be part of the process of returning to normal life after cancer treatment. This transition is both helped and hindered by the schedule of routine medical check-ups.

11.5.1 Medical check-ups

In most countries, a person who has been treated for cancer will normally attend follow-up appointments with cancer specialists, but the frequency and the services offered vary with local circumstances. In high-income countries like the UK, appointments usually happen every few months in the first year after treatment has concluded (Figure 11.9), or more often if symptoms cannot be resolved. The frequency then reduces to an annual check-up, until five years after diagnosis when the follow-up may cease or return visits may be scheduled at longer intervals.

Figure 11.9   A patient may feel anxious during a follow-up appointment. (Source: Larry Williams/CORBIS)

● What do you think is the purpose of follow-up appointments?

● The main aim is to detect any recurrence of cancer, but there are other functions: for example, a person who has had an operation may be seen by a surgeon to ensure that healing is progressing normally; physical or psychological problems caused by the cancer or its treatment can be reviewed and medication adjusted.

There are several other benefits, for example, assistance with managing a return to work, advice on recommencing sexual activity, and so on. Dave lives in the USA, where cancer services are among the best in the world and his follow-up includes genetic testing for other family members (Case study 11.2).

> **Case study 11.2   Dave returns to normal life, but faces another dilemma**
>
> For years after his treatment, Dave has to have regular checks to make sure that his cancer has not returned. These gradually get less frequent until, after five years, the appointment is annual. Dave cannot be certain that his cancer will never return, but he is becoming more confident. And he is feeling much fitter and has started coaching Little League baseball for the first time.
>
> Dave has learned more about genetics than he ever thought he would need to. He realises that his children may have inherited his cancer-risk gene variant and encourages the older two to spend some of their great-uncle's

legacy on genetic testing. They are asked to prepare a family history, marking each relative who has contracted cancer, what type it was and how old they were when they were diagnosed or died. Then each has a sample of DNA taken for the test. His son is given the all-clear, but his daughter is told that she has inherited the *hMLH1* cancer-risk gene. She will be offered a colonoscopy to detect early signs of bowel cancer, initially every two years. But she has just got engaged and worries about what she should tell her fiancé and what risk any future children would face. Dave's concern about his daughter is frequently on his mind, but he tries to stay positive and remind everyone in the family that early detection means he now lives a normal life despite the colostomy.

The actions taken at follow-up appointments, even in well-resourced cancer services, vary depending on the type and stage of cancer, the treatment received and who the appointment is with. But every attendee will be asked about their recent 'history' to reveal symptoms that may relate to the cancer or its treatment, for example, pain, weight loss or increased fatigue. A physical examination will be performed, such as palpating (feeling with the fingers) the site of the primary cancer, or a surgical wound site, to look for signs of a recurrence; or feeling for an enlarged liver or lymph nodes, which may indicate that the disease is returning. These manual techniques may be supplemented by CT or ultrasound scans (Section 6.5).

Blood tests may be ordered, revealing the proportion of different types of blood cell and whether abnormal cells are present, and liver or kidney function tests may be undertaken to indicate whether the cancer may have recurred.

● Can you think of another test that could reveal a cancer recurrence? (Think back to Chapter 6.)

● Some cancers can be monitored by looking at the levels of tumour markers in the blood, i.e. unique molecules found only in the structure of cancer cells (Section 6.4).

Specialist clinics deal with a specific aspect of cancer or its treatment; for example follow-up clinics for women after mastectomy, lymphoedema clinics, and stoma clinics for people like Dave with a stoma (normally a colostomy). Various studies have been carried out to assess the usefulness of follow-up appointments. In the UK, several studies have found that reassurance is considered the most important and useful aspect (Papagrigoriadis and Heyman, 2003). The advantages of regular medical check-ups are obvious, but there are also drawbacks.

Lymphoedema is the swelling resulting from fluids building up in the tissues, instead of draining away via the lymphatic system, which normally returns it to the bloodstream (as described in Section 4.4.2).

● Why might a follow-up appointment adversely affect a person's quality of life? Are any other problems likely to be associated with it?

● Some individuals become anxious leading up to their appointment because follow-up focuses their attention on the cancer and the possibility that it may recur. Other problems include the inconvenience or difficulty of getting to a clinic at the stated time, and financial drawbacks in terms of travel costs or taking time off work.

Several research studies have questioned whether routine appointments are effective at detecting recurrent cancers. A study of women treated for breast cancer in the UK (Morris et al., 1992), another of lung cancer patients in the USA (Walsh et al., 1995), and a third study of stomach cancer treated by surgery in Germany (Böhner et al., 2000) all concluded that routine follow-up wasn't effective at detecting recurrence, was unnecessary and wasn't cost-effective. However, there are several other benefits, including symptom control and psychological aftercare.

In many low- and middle-income countries, medical check-ups after cancer treatment are scarce, and many people don't receive any routine follow-up. Even if medical checks don't increase the *quantity* of life remaining, they may improve the *quality* of life for those with symptoms that can be alleviated.

11.5.2 Returning to work

Most working people who are diagnosed with cancer take time off work while they are receiving and recovering from treatment. The length of time varies with the type of cancer, the treatment and the kind of work a person does. Returning to work after treatment can be an important milestone in recommencing a normal life (Figure 11.10), as Julie found (Case study 11.3 overleaf).

Figure 11.10 Recovery from cancer treatment can enable returning to physically demanding jobs. (Source: Scott Camazine/Alamy)

Case study 11.3   Julie goes back to work

After radioactive iodine treatment, Julie gradually begins to feel better, although she is still tired and rather low in spirits. She has been off work since before her first operation, and really misses the stimulation of her job and particularly the company of her colleagues. She is delighted when, a few weeks after she finishes the iodine treatment, her boss offers her part-time work. She finds that going back to work, even for only two days a week initially, is a big step towards returning to normality.

After the iodine treatment, her thyroid hormone therapy is changed from liothyronine sodium to thyroxine (the active ingredient is levothyroxine sodium). She has to take it every day for the rest of her life to replace the hormones her thyroid gland would have produced. She also has regular scans to check that the cancer has not returned, sometimes with a much lower dose of the radioactive iodine than she had before. This is much less unpleasant and time-consuming than the initial iodine-131 treatment; the worst part is the injections of thyroid-stimulating hormone that enable her to carry on taking thyroxine during the iodine-131 procedure.

Five years after treatment Julie is still well and the check-ups reduced to once a year. She is finally able to put her cancer and its treatment behind her; she thinks of herself as cured. She is still with her partner, and has been back working full-time for three years. The old Julie might have had difficulty remembering to take a daily tablet, but she has worked it successfully into her routine. She is still running and has a place in next year's London Marathon – she will be running to raise money for Cancer Research UK.

● What difficulties might be faced on returning to work following treatment for cancer?

● Fatigue or other symptoms may interfere with the ability to work. If someone has been away from work for a while, it may be difficult to catch up on recent developments or changes in procedures. There may also be difficulties in relationships with colleagues, who may not know how to react to someone who has recently had cancer.

Where cancer services exist, most people will discuss a return to work with their oncologist or family doctor; large companies may require returning employees to see an occupational health specialist for practical advice. Macmillan Cancer Support (2007) gives the following guidelines:

* A gradual and flexible return to work, building up at a pace you can handle.
* Informal visits to the workplace before your actual return date.
* A catch-up meeting on your first day back.
* Regular reviews with your manager.
* Realistic goals.
* Sensible working hours and regular breaks.

Unfortunately, whilst many employers are supportive and helpful, others may be reluctant to negotiate a gradual return to work, possibly fearing this places an unfair burden on others. In the UK, the Disability Discrimination Act (HMSO, 2005) states that it is against the law for anyone to be discriminated against as a result of their illness. Whilst most work-related problems are resolved by discussion and negotiation with managers and human resources departments (e.g. taking time-off to attend medical appointments), occasionally legal action is necessary to challenge discrimination against a person with cancer. The provisions of the Act can be used to support someone who needs to reduce their hours or work more flexible hours. It is important that people with cancer and employers are aware of this legislation and how it applies to the workplace.

11.5.3 Maintaining relationships

In many cases, relationships with family are unaffected or even improved by living with cancer (as Dave found: Case study 11.1). It may help bring people closer together and help them to realise what is important in life (Figure 11.11). Friends and relatives can be a great source of support, encouragement and practical help to a person with cancer, but relationships with family and friends can also be adversely affected.

Figure 11.11   Facing a serious challenge such as major illness can bring families closer together. (Source: Sally and Richard Greenhill)

● How might relationships within a family be put under strain by a diagnosis of cancer?

● The cancer may affect the person's ability to carry out their usual domestic roles (e.g. cleaning, gardening, cooking, childcare, or looking after other dependents such as an elderly relative) and other family members may have to carry a greater load. If paid work is affected, reducing the person's ability to contribute financially towards the household, this may place greater strain on relationships. Stress, anxiety and depression are common symptoms among people with cancer, at least for a time (see Section 11.2.1), and this can alter the dynamics of relationships.

Relationships with friends and work colleagues may be affected in a similar way. Some friends may stay away and others may not know how to talk about cancer. Talking through any changes in roles, especially if there is resentment about these changes, can help resolve difficulties and prevent stress from building up. Jôao finds that talking to a counsellor helps him cope with the follow-up after his prostate cancer treatment and aids his return to normal life (Case study 11.4).

> ### Case study 11.4   Jôao's recovery from cancer
>
> Jôao is asked to return to the hospital oncology clinic as an outpatient for regular checks after his brachytherapy. These involve the same PSA test that diagnosed his cancer, as well as other tests, and also give him a chance to discuss any problems that might indicate either side effects or the cancer returning. At the second of these appointments, he is told that his PSA level has returned to normal, no cancer cells can be found, and his cancer can be considered to be in remission. The doctors will, however, continue to monitor him for any sign that the cancer has returned or spread.
>
> Jôao's PSA levels stay low, and his life gradually returns to something like normal. He still gets more tired more often than he used to, but he is not sure whether that is simply because he is growing older: he is now in his late seventies. He also finds that he gets anxious more often, particularly before his regular screening tests. Rather surprisingly, he has found talking to a counsellor very helpful, and he continues to book – and is happy to pay for – regular appointments with him. He is delighted when his son arranges to spend a month-long vacation with him, and they enjoy spending time together.

11.5.4 Becoming a cancer survivor

Throughout this book we have been careful to refer to 'people with cancer' and wherever possible avoid 'cancer patients', on the grounds that the latter term gives a predominant status to the disease and its treatment, obscuring everything else about the individual in question. In recent years, a new terminology has come into use – that of the **cancer survivor**. The UK Department of Health defines this as

> … someone who has completed treatment and has no apparent evidence of active disease, or is living with progressive disease and may be receiving treatment but is not in the terminal phase of illness, or someone who has had cancer in the past.

(*Cancer Reform Strategy*, Department of Health, 2007, p. 80)

● Why might it be helpful to refer to someone as a cancer survivor?

● One obvious advantage is that it provides a much more positive language for referring to a person who has had cancer. It also encourages healthcare professionals to acknowledge that cancer survivors have physical, psychological and other needs that require long-term plans, which may have to be maintained for many years after diagnosis and treatment.

Notice that the definition of a cancer survivor does not equate 'surviving' with 'being cured'. This is an important distinction because routine follow-up of someone who has been treated for cancer, apparently successfully, may cease after five years, and discharge from the annual hospital check-up is often assumed to be evidence of a cure. In reality it simply signifies that there is unlikely to be any advantage from attending further check-ups, since the costs to the health service and the individual who has to attend the clinic outweigh the diminishing possibility that a recurrence might be detected a little earlier if the follow-ups had continued. Five-year relative survival and five-year disease-free survival are the most common statistics for evaluating the effectiveness of cancer treatments (Section 1.2.4). It is certainly true that for cancers with generally good treatment outcomes, the risk of a recurrence diminishes as the time since diagnosis increases, but even in the most treatable cancers, recurrences can still occur more than five years after the original diagnosis. Doctors will often refer to 'complete remission' rather than cure, signifying that although there is no sign of cancer in the body, they cannot be 100% certain that it will not recur in the future.

It is worth bearing in mind that for those cancers where early detection and treatment have generally good outcomes in high-income countries, the percentage of 'survivors' is much lower elsewhere in the world, as Table 11.1 reveals. By contrast, survival is similar all over the world for cancers such as those of the lung, liver and oesophagus, in which a relatively low proportion (under 20%) survive for five years after diagnosis even with the best available treatment.

Table 11.1 Comparison of percentage five-year relative survival in high-income versus low- and middle-income countries for certain cancers. (Data from Parkin et al., 2005)

Cancer type	5-year relative survival in high-income countries/%	5-year relative survival in low- and middle-income countries/%
prostate	76	45
breast	73	57
uterine cervix	61	41
colon or rectum	55	39
leukaemia	40	19

11.5.5 Living with uncertainty

Living with cancer must always mean living with the threat of death even, I imagine, if you manage to increase the distance between you and the diagnosis to the five years which counts as a cure.

(Diamond, 1998, p. 255)

John Diamond's comment above encapsulates both the uncertainty involved in living with cancer and the misconception that surviving for five years 'counts as a cure'. Many cancer survivors worry about recurrence, even if assured that their treatment has been successful.

● Suggest two contrasting ways in which a person may react to never knowing for certain that their cancer will not recur.

● Some individuals may become depressed or anxious, or become overly concerned about their health, going frequently to consult their doctor with symptoms they fear might signify a recurrence. Alternatively, a person may react by living life to the full, having recognised that there are no guarantees and the most should be made of every day. Others may decide to improve their lifestyle or change their priorities, for example by cutting down on their working hours and spending more time doing the things they love.

In Section 11.2.3, you learned about sources of psychological support for people with cancer; these may also be helpful in learning to live with uncertainty (as Jôao did: Case study 11.4). The majority of cancer survivors don't seek professional help, but gradually come to terms with their new status and readjust to living a normal life.

Activity 11.1   Meeting the needs of cancer survivors

Allow about 10 minutes in total for this activity

Drawing on what you have learned in Section 11.5, complete Table 11.2 by giving an example of a way in which each example of a need may be met. To get you started, the top row has been filled in. You can compare your suggestions with those given in the Answers section at the end of this book.

Table 11.2 Ways in which the needs of cancer survivors may be met.

Type of need	Example	A way in which this need may be met
Physical	Breathlessness as a result of surgery for lung cancer	Regular review by doctors/nurses who specialise in this area and can offer advice, treatment and follow-up, e.g. draining any fluids that build up in the lungs, prescribing antibiotics to prevent chest infections, or opioids to reduce the sensation of breathlessness
Physical	Colostomy following surgery for bowel cancer	
Psychological	Altered body image due to cancer surgery leads to depression	
Social	Concerns about work colleagues avoiding contact after returning from cancer treatment	
Financial	Inability to work full-time in previous occupation leads to financial difficulties	
Information	Lack of knowledge about the possibility of recurrence of cancer	

Not all people with cancer survive, but they don't all die of cancer. In the final section of this chapter, you will learn about what happens when a person's cancer cannot be cured and they enter the terminal phase of life, but first consider what happened to Jôao (Case study 11.5) before you move on.

Case study 11.5 Jôao dies

Two years after diagnosis, the news is still good: Jôao's PSA levels are still low, and his cancer is still in remission. But six months later he is dead: not from the cancer, but quickly and relatively painlessly from a heart attack. He was 79 years old. He had survived beyond the average age for Brazilian males and, thanks to prompt and first-class treatment and access to psychological support, he lived with his prostate cancer and had a good quality of life until the end.

11.6 Facing the end of life

We begin by returning to Anneke's story (Case study 11.6).

Case study 11.6 Anneke's cancer returns

For about a year after her first operation, Anneke's life returns to something very like normal. She is able to do most of the voluntary work she used to do, and to see almost as much of her beloved grandchildren, although she still gets tired and finally has to admit that her cycling days are over. She also continues to visit the hospital regularly for extensive checks.

But then, at a routine check-up, Anneke is told that an X-ray has revealed another suspicious shadow in her lung. She is asked to provide a sputum sample and come back the following week for more detailed tests. Feeling extremely worried, even though she is in no pain and physically no less able than she has been for some months, she asks her husband to come with her to the next appointment. And the news is what she has half expected: her cancer has returned and there is now no prospect of curing it. Anneke and her husband have to face up to the news that her health will deteriorate and she probably has less than a year to live. The doctor who tells them this is very caring, and gives them time and space to try to come to terms with it in their own way.

11.6.1 Receiving news of terminal illness

Much has been written on the subject of how doctors should tell a person with cancer that the disease has advanced to a stage where it will lead to death in a relatively short but unpredictable period. Breaking such frightening news should be done sensitively, honestly, without time pressure or interruptions, and with reassurance and support that everything will be done to alleviate pain and reduce discomfort to the minimum possible, while respecting the person's privacy and dignity and enabling as much contact with friends and family as the person desires.

The news that the disease is entering the terminal phase may come as a terrible shock, but some people (like Anneke) will have suspected this and be prepared to accept it, at least to some extent. Reactions inevitably fluctuate over time and commonly include periods of depression and fear about dying; sometimes feelings of guilt or worthlessness are experienced and withdrawal from other people may occur. Conversely, the knowledge that time is short can bring families and friends closer together, old issues are resolved, business is put in order and some good times are shared. People who are facing death may be most anxious and troubled about how those close to them will cope. There may be denial ('It can't be true, I don't accept it.') or anger ('Why me?'), sometimes directed at others in the person's immediate circle, including healthcare professionals, or at institutions the person blames for their cancer (e.g. tobacco companies), or at God or fate.

Bargaining or goal-setting often occurs as the person attempts to make a deal about how long they have left, for example: 'I'll die happy if only I can live long enough to have one more family Christmas'. Joking about death and dying is surprisingly common among terminally ill people, and a kind of euphoria may be experienced at times as each remaining day is seen as precious and simple pleasures become intensified because they can no longer be taken for granted. Some people achieve a tranquil acceptance of the inevitability of their impending death, and some remain distressed about it to the end.

There are as many ways of approaching death from cancer as there are individuals, but recognising some of the common reactions to terminal illness can help those caring for a dying person to understand their behaviour and emotional responses. It also focuses attention on their psychological needs as well as their physical state. This holistic approach to the end of life is encompassed by the medical specialty called palliative care, which grew out of the hospice movement of the 1960s.

11.6.2 History of palliative care

> **Palliative care**, as the World Health Organization has recognized, is the active, total care of patients whose disease no longer responds to curative treatment, and for whom the goal must be the best quality of life for them and their families.
>
> (Samson Katz and Komaromy, 2004, p. 10)

Although palliative care is a relatively recent discipline, hospices have existed for many centuries. Originally a hospice was a place of shelter for travellers and hospices were often found on pilgrimage and commerce routes. During Medieval times, houses devoted to the care of those with leprosy were founded throughout Europe, with hospices also established to care for elderly or insane people. **Hospices** as places dedicated exclusively to the care of dying people began in the 1840s and until the mid-20th century most of them were run by religious orders.

Figure 11.12 Dame Cicely Saunders who founded the hospice movement for people dying from cancer. (Source: St Christopher's Hospice)

The modern hospice movement was started by Cicely Saunders (Figure 11.12), who opened the St Christopher's Hospice in London in 1967. She was originally a nurse, who later trained as a doctor and worked with people with advanced cancer, pioneering the use of various drugs to treat symptoms in those who were terminally ill. Over the next few decades, more hospices were opened in the UK and elsewhere and the range of services offered to terminally ill people expanded. Whilst palliative care in the UK is free to individuals and their families, most hospices are charities and raise at least some of their income through fundraising. Hospices exist in many other countries, but in some (e.g. in China) the care they give must be paid for by the individual or their family.

11.6.3 The aims of modern palliative care

Today much terminal care is delivered by palliative care specialists based in hospices and hospitals, often working in the community with patients and families in their own homes, or in residential or nursing homes, backed up by non-specialists such as family doctors and community nurses. The most important carer for a terminally ill person may well be a close relative, so the needs of family members are an essential part of the work of a palliative care team. Palliative care now encompasses the total care of a person with an incurable illness and their family, tailored to the specific needs of the individual (Case study 11.7).

> ### Case study 11.7 Anneke worries about facing death
>
> For the next few months, Anneke feels something of a fraud. She is still feeling relatively well, if increasingly tired. She sometimes finds it difficult to believe that she is terminally ill, and then catches herself wondering whether she will see any of her grandchildren's next birthdays. These conflicting emotions are troubling, but she finds it helpful to talk to a counsellor recommended by some friends at church. When she first starts getting severe pain in her back her doctor prescribes steroids, which help a lot, but which make her face puffy. Anneke and her husband's major concern is what kind of medical and psychological support they can expect as her health worsens. Their doctor decides it is time to refer them to the palliative care team.

● What do you think someone in Anneke's situation is most likely to be anxious about?

● Common anxieties are about experiencing unpleasant symptoms, such as pain or vomiting, as health deteriorates, or losing the ability to look after oneself and becoming dependent on others. There is likely to be grief and perhaps anger at leaving family and friends prematurely, without being able to achieve dearly held goals such as seeing a grandchild married. There may be anxieties about practical concerns like putting household affairs in order and making a will.

All these concerns, and many others, fall within the remit of palliative care. The definition refers to the 'active, total care' of people who are facing death, ensuring the best possible quality of life for them and their families. This requires a holistic approach to the dying person and their carers, as summarised in Box 11.1 (overleaf).

Box 11.1 Aims of palliative care

- To provide symptom control and pain relief for the dying person, avoiding unnecessary treatment.

- To create a support system for dying people, providing social, emotional, spiritual and practical care in an individualised way, and enabling them to exert control, independence and choice, live as actively as possible and participate in decisions relating to managing their problems.

- To provide support for the dying person's family and friends during the illness and after death.

- To establish a team including the dying person and his/her family, with good communication between members.

- To provide support and expert advice to those caring for dying people (such as the hospital oncology team, family doctor, district nurse, psychologist, ministers of religion, etc.) irrespective of the place of care.

In summary, the overall aim of palliative care is not to prolong life but to make life as comfortable as possible for a dying person, enabling them to be as pain-free, dignified and lucid as possible during the terminal phase of their illness, as Lin's story illustrates (Case study 11.8). In Activity 11.2 you will research the skills required in a palliative care team for yourself.

Case study 11.8 Lin's palliative care

Lin is still in hospital, but his condition is worsening so quickly that he can no longer avoid the recognition that his illness is going to end his life. For a time he experiences the common reactions of shock, anger and depression, but with the help of the palliative care team and his relatives, he begins to accept the reality of his situation. Although Lin's factory (and the health insurance it provides) has been supporting him financially through his illness, his family is facing monetary problems and so, after consulting the doctors, a decision is made to move him back home and to continue his treatment there. Once Lin is at home, family members look after him while his wife is at work, and community nurses visit every day to treat his pain with regular injections. Occasionally he has to return to hospital for a blood transfusion. His workmates and friends visit him sometimes and give Lin and his family as much support as they can afford. Lin has come to accept the inevitability of his death, but he worries about his family's future.

Activity 11.2 The palliative care team

Allow about 30 minutes in total for this activity

In Section 7.3, you learned about the various members of the MDT involved in treating a person with cancer. In this activity, you will learn about the palliative care MDT by using the internet.

11.6.4 Symptoms in the terminal phase of illness

A dying person may experience various physical symptoms, most of which you have already learned about in Section 11.3. The most common are pain, breathlessness, nausea and vomiting, constipation or diarrhoea, **anorexia** (loss of appetite), weakness, anaemia, drowsiness and depression – but note that it would be very unusual for someone to experience all of these symptoms, and they are generally well-controlled where good palliative care services exist (as in countries such as the Netherlands: Case study 11.9).

Case study 11.9   Anneke's health deteriorates

As the months pass, Anneke's condition has visibly worsened. She has a very poor appetite and has lost weight and looks much older than her age, particularly as she now walks with a stick. She is getting more and more breathless and finds even the smallest tasks too much effort; she regularly sleeps in the afternoons. Her doctor arranges for her to attend the local hospice as a day patient, where the palliative care team help her to manage her symptoms, and arrange various complementary therapies for her, such as aromatherapy massage. As her health deteriorates, arrangements are made for regular visits from her family doctor and community nurses at home.

Pain in terminal cancer can be caused by much the same conditions as described earlier, but it may be more severe if it involves the bones, lungs, abdominal or pelvic organs, for example, due to pressure on pain-sensitive structures such as the pleura (the lining of the lung cavity), or stretching of the capsule that surrounds the liver. Cancer can infiltrate or compress a nerve, which can result in pain along the nerve track. In palliative care, the painkillers you learned about in Section 11.3 are prescribed using the three-step ladder. Opioid analgesics, which may be given by mouth initially, may be given as an injection if the dying person loses consciousness, normally via a device called a syringe driver (Figure 11.13) which delivers a constant infusion of painkiller. Syringe drivers may also be set up to enable a conscious person to 'top up' their own analgesia by increasing the dose. Steroids or palliative radiotherapy may treat pain by reducing the size of a tumour and antidepressant drugs may alleviate nerve pain. Practical interventions such as using a wheelchair may help if walking is painful, and massage can relieve muscle spasms.

Eighty per cent of dying people experience weakness (Samson Katz and Komaromy, 2004) due to a variety of causes, including anaemia, compression of the spinal cord or metastases in the brain. It may also be caused by poor nutrition as a person with terminal cancer may lose interest in food; a dietician may suggest easily digestible and nutritious foods with a high calorie content. Physiotherapy may help mobilisation and an occupational therapist can provide various aids and adaptations

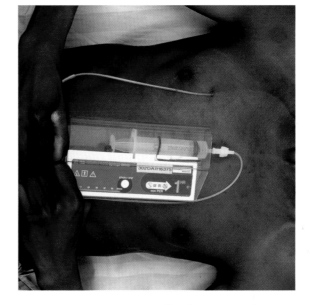

Figure 11.13   An example of a syringe driver delivering medication via an intravenous tube connected to a vein in this person's chest. (Source: Alex Bartel/Science Photo Library)

to a person's environment to make life easier, for example, a perching stool to sit on while washing, or a stair lift to improve mobility around the home (Figure 11.14). Anaemia may be treated by blood transfusions, whilst spinal cord compression or brain metastases may respond to steroids or radiotherapy to relieve the pressure.

Anorexia is another common problem in terminal illness and is experienced by around 60% of people with advanced cancer (Tookman and Kurowska, 2000). There may be a treatable cause, such as oral thrush, a fungal infection in the mouth which often emerges as a dying person's immune system loses its effectiveness. The side effects of medication such as nausea can reduce appetite, as too can depression or anxiety, all of which may respond to the treatments outlined earlier in this chapter. Food may be made more palatable and attractive by giving smaller portions more frequently than normal and by encouraging eating for pleasure rather than to build strength. Steroids can stimulate appetite, if only transiently, but anorexia may persist despite all these interventions. Often, a dying person's loss of appetite is more of a problem for family and carers, who may feel that not getting the person to eat is neglectful. In reality, a person who knows they are dying may have made a choice not to eat, particularly if food causes discomfort; in this situation, carers may need reassuring that the dying person should be allowed to make this choice.

Figure 11.14   A stair lift can prolong the period in which a person disabled by age or illness can remain in their own home. (Source: Paul Doyle/Alamy)

11.6.5 A good death?

Many people who are terminally ill hope for a good death and may have clear ideas about what they mean by this. However, the concept of a 'good death' varies according to individual and family preferences and religious and cultural contexts, as Activity 11.3 is intended to reveal.

Activity 11.3   Reflections on a good death

Allow about 10 minutes in total for this activity

Spend a few minutes thinking about the characteristics of what you would consider a good death: for example, where would it ideally take place, who should be present and how alert or otherwise should the dying person be in the hours leading up to their death? If it seems appropriate to you to do so, you may also choose to ask a friend or relative what they feel might constitute a good death. You may be surprised at how much their views differ from your own. (Comments on this activity are given in the Answers section at the end of this book.)

Another term that may be used is an 'appropriate death', which has four aims, as described by Weisman (1972):

1 Reducing, but not necessarily eliminating, conflict.

2 Making dying people's dying compatible with their own views of themselves and their achievements.

3 Preserving or restoring relationships as much as possible.

4 Fulfilling some of the dying person's expressed aims.

When reading the final case study in this book, you may like to keep in mind your ideas about a good death and the aims of an appropriate death, as you consider how far Anneke's death fulfils these aspirations.

Case study 11.10 Anneke dies

Anneke is now very seriously ill. She is bed-bound and spends many hours asleep. Steroids and codeine are no longer enough to control her pain, so she is given morphine tablets. She has oxygen to help her breathing, most often through a tube under her nose, but sometimes if she is very breathless, she needs an oxygen mask. Sometimes she seems to enjoy a little food, but often she won't eat anything at all. Unless she is too tired, she encourages family and friends to come as often as possible and gets particular pleasure from watching her grandchildren playing round her bed; she takes comfort in seeing that they are too young to understand how ill she is. Many friends visit, and others phone, but her family find it hard to tell someone who has made a real effort to come that Anneke can only see them for a few minutes. She still talks coherently when she is awake and is involved in family discussions and even games.

Her daughters have kept in close touch with their brother since Anneke became seriously ill. One day, after a particularly bad episode in which she struggles for breath even with the oxygen mask on, they ask him to come home. Two days later, he is beside his mother's bedside. After another 48 hours there is another change. She gradually sinks into a deeper sleep, and when she is awake she appears confused, sometimes mistaking who is in the room with her, or talking to people who are not there. She has stopped eating and is now unable to drink, and her skin feels cold. She can no longer take painkillers by mouth, so she is given diamorphine through a syringe driver, which delivers the drug constantly at a controlled rate. At times she appears distressed and agitated and is given an extra dose of diamorphine to ensure that she is not in any pain.

Twenty-four hours later, Anneke's breathing begins to change, becoming more laboured. Her husband becomes concerned that her chest sounds rattly and congested, but the family doctor tells him that this is normal when someone is nearing death and that Anneke is not in distress. He encourages Anneke's husband to call the family together, believing her death to be near. When, a few hours later, her breathing slows further and peacefully stops, her husband and three children are with her.

11.7 Concluding remarks

Taboos about even saying the word 'cancer', which pervaded the subject in the past, have gradually been broken down in favour of greater openness, and this has improved the quality of life for cancer survivors like Dave and Julie, and the quality of dying for people like Lin and Anneke. The positive message of this chapter is that living normally with cancer has become a commonplace and far more manageable prospect than it once was. The message of the next and final chapter is that the chances of surviving cancer are increasing all the time, as research into prevention, early diagnosis and treatment advances.

11.8 Summary of Chapter 11

11.1 Cancer and its treatment can cause a variety of symptoms and side effects, including depression and anxiety, pain, nausea and vomiting, constipation or diarrhoea, breathlessness, drowsiness, weakness, anorexia and anaemia. These symptoms become more common and more severe if the disease becomes terminal.

11.2 Various drugs and other medical interventions, together with adaptations to the environment and changes in lifestyle, can usually control or alleviate these symptoms sufficiently to enable a good quality of life for people living with cancer, unless it becomes advanced.

11.3 Medical interventions to alleviate the symptoms of cancer must be carefully balanced and tailored to an individual's needs, to minimise the risk of side effects causing additional health problems that also need treating.

11.4 The sources of help available to a person returning to as normal a life as possible after cancer treatment include follow-up clinics, community health services, and the care and support of family, friends and work colleagues.

11.5 When cancer survivors return to a normal life, they have to live with the uncertainty about whether the disease could recur in the future, as well as the practical and emotional challenges it poses, for example to their working lives and relationships.

11.6 The main aim of palliative care is the active, total care of people who are facing death, ensuring the best possible quality of life for them and their families.

Questions for Chapter 11

Question 11.1 (Learning outcomes 11.1 and 11.4)

What is meant by the term 'polypharmacy' and what problems does it pose for healthcare professionals treating cancer symptoms or side effects? Illustrate your answer with an example.

Question 11.2 (Learning outcome 11.2)

Imagine that the staff in a hospital want to estimate how much pain a person with cancer is experiencing, so they use the pain scale shown in Figure 11.15. With what types of patient would a scale like this be particularly appropriate to use and why?

Figure 11.15 The Wong-Baker 'faces' pain scale. (Source: Hockenberry et al., 2005)

Question 11.3 (Learning outcomes 11.2 and 11.3)

There is some evidence that antidepressant drugs are not prescribed as often to people with advanced cancer as you would expect from surveys that show depression to be a relatively common symptom in this group of patients (Ly et al., 2002). Can you suggest some reasons why these drugs may be underused?

Question 11.4 (Learning outcome 11.3)

Think back to what you have learned about cancer therapies in this chapter and earlier parts of the course. Complete Table 11.3 by entering possible treatments for nausea and vomiting with different causes as given in the left-hand column.

Table 11.3 Causes of nausea and vomiting and possible treatments.

Cause of nausea and vomiting	Possible treatment
Painkillers such as ibuprofen	
Cancer in the brain	
Bowel obstruction	
Constipation	

Question 11.5 (Learning outcomes 11.5 and 11.6)

Identify the sources of support among the members of a typical palliative care team in the UK for a person with terminal cancer who is distressed about the possibility that their family may not be able to manage financially after their death.

Question 11.6 (Learning outcome 11.7)

Read the following extract from a 'blog' (web log) posted on a cancer support website. What features of bob jk's account illustrate the symptoms and the challenges of terminal cancer that you have read about in Chapter 11?

> A bit better day today. Really tired but not so uncomfortable. I have spent a good part of the day sunning myself as we have the cruise in little over two weeks time and I don't want to get thrown in the water by the crew thinking I'm a great white whale. As the weather was so glorious we had a bar-b-q and all the boys plus katie came over so it was really good. Tom did the cooking as my get up and go had got up and gone. We then went over to Lindas brother's house to look at two new additions to the family, we spent a couple of hours cooing and gurgling and even brooding until they started crying, then we came to our senses and handed the little ones back. Somehow when your life has been mapped out for you and you know you are not going to live to a ripe old age it makes it even more touching to see newborns. You hope their lives will be happy and long.

> (bob jk, 2008)

References

bob jk (2008) [online], Post 309 posted on 29 June 2008 at 22:06:46. http://share.macmillan.org.uk/Share/Forums/?topic=1003477&page=30&goto#307 (Accessed July 2008).

Böhner, H., Zimmer, T., Hopfenmüller, W., Berger, G. and Buhr, H.J. (2000) 'Detection and prognosis of recurrent gastric cancer – is routine follow-up after gastrectomy worthwhile?', *Hepatogastroenterology*, vol. 47(35), pp. 1489–94.

Cleeland, C.S. (1991) [online], http://www.ohsu.edu/ahec/pain/paininventory.pdf (Accessed July 2008).

Department of Health (2007) *Cancer Reform Strategy*, London [online], http://www.dh.gov.uk/en/Publicationsandstatistics/Publications/PublicationsPolicyAndGuidance/DH_081006 (Accessed July 2008).

Diamond, J. (1998) *C: Because Cowards Get Cancer Too*, London, Vermilion.

Edwards, B. and Clarke, V. (2004) 'The psychological impact of a cancer diagnosis on families: the influence of family functioning and patients' illness characteristics on depression and anxiety' *Psycho-Oncology*, vol. 13, pp. 562–76.

Her Majesty's Stationary Office (2005) *Disability Discrimination Act 2005 (c.13)*, HMSO, London [online], http://www.opsi.gov.uk/acts/acts2005/ ukpga_20050013_en_1 (Accessed July 2008).

Gupta, N., Patel, F.D., Kapoor, R. and Sharma, S.C. (2007) 'Pain management in cancer', *Internet Journal of Pain, Symptom Control and Palliative Care*, vol. 5(1), p. 3. [online], http://www.ispub.com/ostia/index. php?xmlFilePath=journals/ijpsp/vol5n1/cancer.xml (Accessed July 2008).

Hockenberry, M.J., Wilson, D. and Winkelstein, M.L. (2005) *Wong's Essentials of Pediatric Nursing*, 7th edn, London, Moseby.

Ly, K.L., Chidgey, J., Addington-Hall, J. and Hotopf, M. (2002) 'Depression in palliative care: a systematic review. Part 2. Treatment', *Palliative Medicine*, vol. 16(4), pp. 279–84.

MacMillan Cancer Support (2007) *Working through Cancer: A guide for employees*, London, MacMillan Cancer Support [online], http://www.macmillan. org.uk/Documents/Support_Material/Get_support/Working_through_cancer/ Employee_booklet.pdf (Accessed July 2008).

Morris, S., Corder, A.P. and Taylor, I. (1992) 'What are the benefits of routine breast cancer follow-up?', *Postgraduate Medical Journal*, vol. 68, pp. 904–7.

Marie Curie Cancer Care (2008) [online], http://www.mariecurie.org.uk/ (Accessed July 2008).

Newport, D.J. and Nemeroff, C.B. (1998) 'Assessment and treatment of depression in the cancer patient', *Journal of Psychosomatic Research*, vol. 45(3), pp. 215–37.

Papagrigoriadis, S. and Heyman, B. (2003) 'Patients' views on follow-up of colorectal cancer: implications for risk communication and decision making' *Postgraduate Medical Journal*, vol. 79, pp. 403–7.

Parkin, D.M., Bray, F., Ferlay, J. and Pisani, P. (2005) 'Global cancer statistics, 2002', *CA – A Cancer Journal for Clinicians*, vol. 55, pp.74–108 [online], http://caonline.amcancersoc.org/cgi/content/abstract/55/2/74?etoc (Accessed July 2008).

Samson Katz, J. and Komaromy, C. (2004) K260 Death and Dying, *Workbook 2: Caring for Dying People*, Milton Keynes, The Open University.

Sheard, T. and Maguire, P. (1999) 'The effect of psychological interventions on anxiety and depression in cancer patients: results of two meta-analyses', *British Journal of Cancer*, vol. 80(11), pp. 1770–80.

Stanton, A.L., Danoff-Burg, S., Cameron, C.L., Bishop, M., Collins, C.A., Kirk, S.B., Sworowski, L.A. and Twillman, R. (2000) 'Emotionally expressive coping predicts psychological and physical adjustment to breast cancer', *Journal of Consulting and Clinical Psychology*, vol. 68(5), pp. 875–82.

Stanton, A.L., Danoff-Burg, S. and Huggins, M.E. (2002) 'The first year after breast cancer diagnosis: hope and coping strategies as predictors of adjustment', *Psycho-Oncology*, vol. 11, pp. 93–112.

Tookman, A. and Kurowska, A. (2000) K260 Death and Dying, *Palliative Care Handbook*, Milton Keynes, The Open University.

Vos, M.S. and de Haes, J.C.J.M. (2006) 'Denial in cancer patients, an explorative review', *Psycho-Oncology*, vol. 16, pp. 12–25.

Walsh, G.L., O'Connor, M., Willis, K.M., Milas, M., Wong, R.S., Nesbitt, J.C., Putnam, J.B., Lee, J.J. and Roth, J.A. (1995) 'Is follow-up of lung cancer patients after resection medically indicated and cost-effective?', *The Annals of Thoracic Surgery*, vol. 60, pp. 1563–72.

Weisman, A. (1972) *On Dying and Denying*, Behavioural Publications, New York.

WHO (2006) Face to face with chronic disease: Cancer, *Miriame's story* [online], http://www.who.int/features/2006/cancer/en/index.html (Accessed July 2008).

WHO (2008) Health topics: Depression [online] http://www.who.int/topics/depression/en/ (Accessed July 2008).

CHAPTER 12

CANCERS IN THE FUTURE

12.1 Introduction

Having almost completed this course, you should have a working knowledge of many aspects of cancers from a contemporary point of view: the current global incidence of cancers; our current understanding of the cellular and molecular biology underlying the formation of cancers and how they cause disease in the human body; the environmental and lifestyle factors we now associate with increased risk of cancers; an overview of the modern techniques used to diagnose cancers, and of the most advanced therapies used to treat cancers from both a curative and a palliative perspective; and, finally, an indication of the emotional and psychological impact that these disorders have on people directly affected by cancers, and on those around them. Many questions concerning the direction these important issues may take in the future remain unanswered and the challenges that we face in the context of cancers are largely unknown. For example, you already know that the incidence of cancer is predicted to go on rising all over the world, but by how much and where will the burden fall most heavily? Will the incidence of cancer deaths remain unequally distributed in global terms? Or, will cancers come to be perceived as being no different from other long-term conditions, in much the same way as, for example, diabetes is at present? Although it is impossible to predict accurately how cancers will be dealt with in the future, in this last chapter, we will revisit each one of the cancer topics covered in this course and attempt to evaluate possible future trends based on current scientific knowledge.

12.2 Cancers: a worsening global health problem?

Making projections of the incidence of cancers at the global level is complicated, as demographic changes will invariably influence cancer mortality and incidence in the future. You should first consider the effect of the estimated changes in the world population on cancer mortality and incidence. Figure 12.1a gives the projections in the number of cancer deaths in the world for the years 2015 and 2030 compared to those reported in 2002, together with estimates of the world population size for the same years (Figure 12.1b). Note that both population size and the number of cancer deaths in the world will gradually increase in the years 2015 and 2030 compared to 2002.

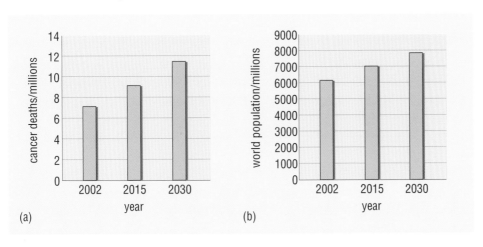

Figure 12.1 Estimated number of deaths (a) and population size (b) in the world in 2015 and 2030 compared to those reported in 2002. (Source: replotted with data from Mathers and Loncar, 2006)

317

It would be logical to suppose that an increase in the world population directly results in an increase in the number of cancer deaths. However, it is not a simple case that a larger population means that more people die of cancer. The same consideration may be applied to cancer incidence, which is projected to increase by one-quarter in each of the next two decades. Indeed, the reported 11 million new cancer cases in 2002 have been estimated to increase to 16.5 and 27 million by 2020 and 2050, respectively (Bray and Møller, 2006). Yet, as you have already seen in Chapter 1 for testicular cancer (see Figure 1.6), it is possible for the incidence of a particular cancer to increase, whilst the mortality rate decreases, mostly due to effective treatments becoming available. Thus, although both mortality and incidence are projected to rise, they will not do so at the same rate nor entirely for the same reasons. Indeed, cancer mortality rates may decrease relative to the population size due to better screening, diagnostic and therapeutic approaches. By contrast, it is possible that cancer incidence rates will increase faster than population numbers rise due to changing population dynamics and to increases in exposure to risk factors.

What other factors may affect cancer incidence rates in the world? First you should consider the relative wealth of a region. As population size is estimated to increase faster in low- and middle-income countries than in high-income countries, it is not surprising that the global burden of cancer cases will shift more to low- and middle-income countries in future years (Figure 12.2).

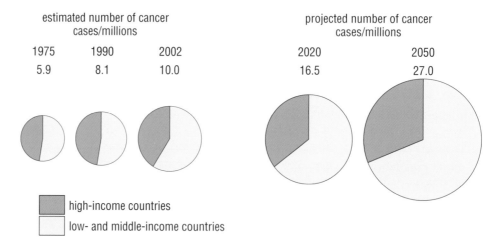

estimated number of cancer cases/millions

1975	1990	2002
5.9	8.1	10.0

projected number of cancer cases/millions

2020	2050
16.5	27.0

high-income countries

low- and middle-income countries

Figure 12.2   Reported (1975, 1990, 2002) and projected (2020, 2050) incidence of cancer cases in high-income and low- and middle-income countries. (Source: Bray and Møller, 2006, Figure 4b)

The shift observed in Figure 12.2 is not an indication that cancer is not increasing in the high-income countries; just that low- and middle-income countries are projected to have a larger proportion of the global incidence than before. Thus, from an almost equal share in 1990, a larger proportion of people who develop cancer will be resident in low- and middle-income countries by 2020, reaching 61% by 2050. Population factors that may influence this change include relative wealth, as well as age distribution (Section 1.2.2).

Another factor you should consider here is age distribution. In 2000, 6.9% of people worldwide were older than 65, but it is estimated that 16.4% of the world population will be 65 and over by 2050. Recall from Section 1.2.2 that the risk of developing cancer rises with age. Thus, an 'ageing' population may account for the sharp rise in the estimated number of cancer cases and deaths in the future. The effect of an increased ageing population on cancer incidence is shown in Figure 12.3: by 2050 more than three in five cancer cases will occur among those older than 65, compared with about two in five in 2002.

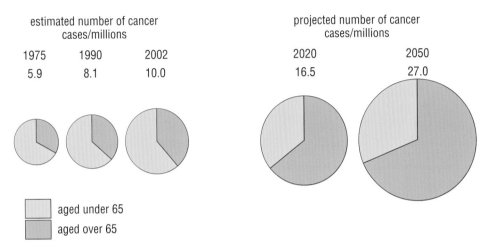

Figure 12.3 Reported (1975, 1990, 2002) and projected (2020, 2050) incidence of cancer cases (in millions) in people younger and older than 65. (Source: Bray and Møller, 2006, Figure 4a)

Finally, note that the picture becomes even more complicated due to the fact that populations in different parts of the world are 'ageing' at different rates, are subject to different rates of economic growth, are exposed to different risk factors, and have access to different treatments and prevention campaigns. In addition, these projections are usually calculated assuming that the current risk of developing cancers is maintained over time. But cultural, economic and social factors in the future may change the nature and/or extent of the risk factors to which humans are currently subject. If this is the case and the sources of risk increase (as they currently appear to be doing) the number of cancer cases and deaths will certainly be larger than those projected.

12.3 The biology of cancer

It is not all bad news. Even though humanity may face a greater global challenge in the context of cancer, we have recently advanced by leaps and bounds in our scientific knowledge of cancers. This has been mainly due to the realisation that cancers are genetic diseases and to the completion of the sequencing of the whole human genome at the turn of the century.

Over 300 genes have been identified as proto-oncogenes or tumour-suppressor genes (see Section 3.5.4) to date and the list is likely to grow, due to research initiatives such as The Cancer Genome Atlas launched in the USA. This rapidly developing area of research is known as oncogenomics and aims to establish the repertoire of gene and chromosomal mutations in different cancer types. To do so, the investigators use molecular techniques such as cheap and fast DNA

DNA sequencing refers to the identification of the order of bases in a stretch of DNA.

DNA microarrays are small laboratory 'tools' used for rapid surveys of the expression of thousands of genes and/or their mutations simultaneously.

sequencing methods, and DNA microarrays that analyse thousands of genes in a tumour sample at the same time (Figure 12.4).

Similarly, other recent molecular techniques quickly analyse the protein expression in a tumour sample (an area of research called oncoproteomics). These recent techniques will allow scientists to answer important questions in tumour biology, which are presently unknown.

- Out of all the mutations accumulated by a particular tumour type, which are the most important to initiate and maintain disease?
- What is the genetic profile that determines invasion of surrounding tissue or metastases into a specific organ or tissue by a particular type of cancer? And why are other tissues not invaded?
- What extracellular and intracellular signals are essential for the survival of a particular cancer type?
- How do cancers resist destruction by the body's defences, and how do they obtain the nutrients and oxygen to sustain their growth?

Another expanding area of research in tumour biology is the application of modern molecular techniques to the understanding of the relationship between the tumour and its environment. This is based in the realisation that tumours are not isolated biological entities and that they rely on communication with normal cells to proliferate and survive. A number of such interactions between tumour and normal cells have already provided the basis for efficient targeted therapies. These include the use, by tumour cells, of growth-inducing signals released by normal cells to promote proliferation (Sections 2.9.2 and 10.7), or the release of angiogenic growth factors by tumour cells to promote the growth of new blood vessels into the tumour (Sections 4.3), or the interactions between cells of the immune system and tumour cells (Sections 4.4.2 and 10.8).

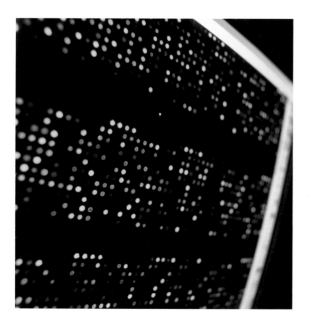

Figure 12.4 Computer display of a section of a genome produced by DNA microarray technology. The pattern of coloured dots indicates the presence of specific DNA target sequences in the sample. Microarrays can be used to study gene expression or detect mutations. (Source: TEK Image/Science Photo Library)

The most exciting consequence of the molecular and cellular understanding and characterisation of tumours is the possibility of 'personalising' diagnosis and treatment to the particular relationship between an individual and the cancer in their body. By analysing the molecular 'signature' of tumour and normal cells, scientists will be able to answer questions specifically tailored to that particular cancer and its prognosis:

- How aggressive is the tumour?
- Will it metastasise and, if so, to which organ?
- How should a particular person with cancer be treated and how is he/she responding to that treatment?

These aspects will be further discussed in the following sections.

12.4 Cancer prevention

The best therapy against cancer is prevention. Our increasing knowledge of the causes of cancer, the links between cancer and diet, smoking or alcohol (as exemplified by the 2007 WCRF/AICR report on 'Food, Nutrition, Physical Activity and the Prevention of Cancer'), environmental and socioeconomic factors, inflammation and infection, can offer the potential to delay, postpone indefinitely or completely avoid the onset of the disease. Indeed, the WHO launched in 2005 a 'Global Action Against Cancer' initiative (WHO, 2005) to decrease the current incidence of cancer by over 40% by 2015, using preventive measures in three key areas: diet and exercise, tobacco use and infection.

The link between the consumption of red meat and the occurrence of colorectal cancer has now been established (Section 5.5.5). It has also been documented that women in Japan suffer very little from breast cancer, but when they move to the USA the breast cancer incidence in the group increases dramatically (Section 5.6). As such links are becoming better established, both on the harmful effects of certain dietary products and on the positive effects of others (such as fruit and vegetables that are rich in antioxidants), diet can be used as a considerable force in preventing cancer. Thus, with improved diet, our chances of avoiding the disease are greatly improved. Although not covered in this course, many studies have shown that lack of exercise is a risk factor for cancers. Hence, cancer prevention strategies may include increasing the 'fitness' of the general population.

The link between tobacco smoking and cancer is now very well-established and a reduction in smoking through public education would lead to a reduction in incidence rates of lung and other cancers. Despite this, tobacco use in low-income countries is on the increase (Figure 12.5) and preventive campaigns are aimed at decreasing this trend.

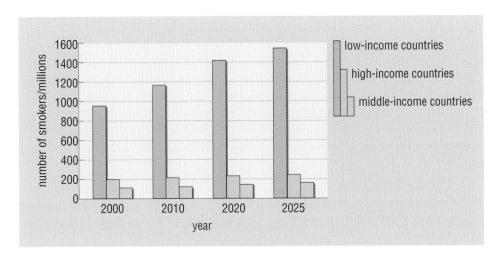

Figure 12.5 Projected numbers of smokers in low-, middle- and high-income countries. (Source: WHO (2005) and World Bank, 2002)

The link between infection and cancer has also led to better screening levels, such as those attained with the use of the Pap smear test (Section 6.6) for cervical cancer, and ultimately the prevention of the disease. Human papilloma virus (HPV) is sexually transmitted with a prevalence of about 7% in high-income countries and 15% in low-income countries and has been clearly associated with cervical cancer. Supported by the success of the screening programme, a vaccine for the prevention of HPV infection has been developed and approved for use in the UK and by the FDA (the US Food and Drug Administration) for use in the USA. There is now the hope that HPV vaccination may provide an opportunity to profoundly affect cervical cancer incidence worldwide. Thus, with appropriate preventive changes in lifestyle and better screening techniques and treatment options becoming available, cervical cancer should become a preventable disease.

12.5 Early detection and diagnosis

At the present time, a number of cancers are still diagnosed too late for treatment to be successful. A key aim of future screening and diagnostic developments will be to make an earlier diagnosis; this in turn will lead to more successful treatments and better survival rates.

With the knowledge of the detailed sequence of the human genome acquired in recent years, an important advance in cancer diagnosis will be the ability to identify genetically individuals who are most at risk of developing a particular type of cancer. This is with the aim of implementing preventive measures to avoid the onset of disease in susceptible individuals (i.e. increased monitoring or lifestyle changes). In addition, the boom of genomics and proteomics will allow a number of new tumour markers (DNA, RNA and/or proteins; Section 6.4) to be identified and characterised once the whole repertoire of cancer-critical genes and their mutated forms are known.

Note that proteomics and genomics study the protein and gene profiles in the human body whereas oncoproteomics and oncogenomics investigate protein and gene profiles specifically related to cancers.

This should enable the development of more accurate blood and urine tests to identify tumour markers and thus facilitate the early diagnosis of tumours through screening. Importantly, the power of these newer molecular techniques is likely to be extended by the early identification of 'patterns' of molecules (rather than a single tumour marker) characteristic of a particular cancer.

As far as imaging is concerned, there is no doubt that there will be continual improvements in both the length of time needed to image the patient and in the level of fine detail that can be achieved in all types of imaging, and probably the trend towards 3D reconstructions will continue. Multi-modality combined techniques such as SPECT/CT, PET/CT (Section 6.5.6) and maybe PET/MRI seem likely to play an important role because of their ability to give both functional and anatomical information simultaneously. The ever-increasing speed and storage capacity of computer systems will continue to be an essential factor in these developments.

As discussed in Chapter 6, we may see new imaging techniques coming into regular use, especially if they do not involve harmful ionising radiation. Ultrasound elastography and optical tomography (Figure 12.6) are both promising techniques which highlight the differences in the properties (elasticity and blood flow, respectively) of tumour tissues and normal tissues. 'Biological imaging', where receptors or antibodies specific to a particular cancer can be imaged in some way, is already at the research stage and may be available before very long.

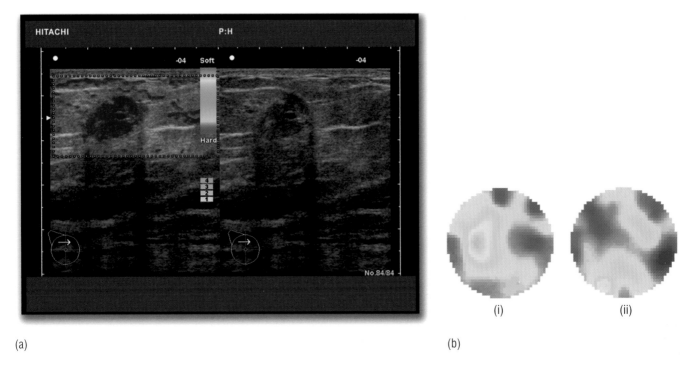

(a)   (b)

Figure 12.6   (a) Elastography image of the breast. This is a standard 2D ultrasound scan (on the right) overlaid with information about the elasticity of the tissue in the left-hand image. The invasive carcinoma shows up as blue because the tumour tissue is stiffer than the normal tissue. (b) Optical tomography images of (i) the right breast and (ii) the left breast of a woman with a tumour located in the right breast. (Source: (a) Hitachi Medical Systems Europe; (b) Professor Jem Hebden, University College, London)

Pathologists have long relied on the appearance of tumour cells under the microscope in order to be able to grade cancers with the aim of implementing diagnosis and treatment guidelines. As indicated earlier in the chapter, oncology is likely to enter a new era in which molecular and cellular information is obtained from several different sources – from tumour tissue, from healthy cells and/or tissues that are known to influence tumour behaviour, from other body tissues, and from molecular imaging studies (e.g. the study of tumour metabolic activity) – and applied to an individual with cancer. This knowledge is likely to be able to help healthcare professionals in the early detection and diagnosis of cancers with increasing precision.

As discussed in Section 6.7, successful screening depends on there being both a suitable test and the economic conditions to introduce it. There seems no doubt that higher-income countries will continue to introduce more screening where it has been shown to be effective. This may be either on a population basis in those countries where there are government-supported health services, or as an 'on demand' service in other countries. The issue of 'on demand' screening for the well-off is a contentious one; for example, whole body CT scans are being widely offered but will not detect all cancers (e.g. more detailed CT colonography is needed to detect colon cancer) so they may be just giving the 'worried well' a dose of ionising radiation!

12.6 Advances in cancer treatments

You have already seen that preventive methods, such as improved vaccinations and screening techniques or changes in lifestyle, can significantly reduce cancer incidence. However, cancer rates are still going to rise (Section 12.2). Thus, there is clearly a need for improved therapeutic approaches to make these cancers treatable or controllable long-term conditions, instead of life-threatening or debilitating diseases. There is continual effort to develop novel therapeutic approaches, based on improvements in surgery, chemotherapy and radiotherapy. These may attempt to improve on previous surgical techniques, find new ways to target cancer cells, deliver radiation more specifically and use different kinds of radiation with improved properties, or generate novel molecular therapies that are targeting new markers identified from large-scale proteomic studies.

Ideally, all therapeutic approaches aim to improve therapeutic efficiency, reduce side effects, and make treatments more specific, better tolerated and accessible to larger parts of the world. With this in mind, different therapeutic approaches have moved ahead in different ways, but aiming at the same outcome, as you will briefly see in this section.

A continuing trend in cancer surgery is an improvement in precision: a process that has been aided by combining surgery with the use of sophisticated imaging techniques that allow tumours to be visualised in 3D, making it possible to remove cancers in locations where up to now this would have been impossible and, importantly, to remove tumours with little or no damage to the surrounding healthy tissue. Currently, surgical techniques in cancer are undergoing a further revolution in precision with the introduction of endoscopic robotic techniques. This approach also allows surgeons to operate from a remote location and, when combined with modern telecommunications, the expertise of the surgeon can be extended to anywhere in the world with the technology; helping people who otherwise would go untreated. As mentioned at the end of Section 8.3, surgery is not simply a process of 'cutting' the cancer out but is a gateway to a growing band of techniques; one area of growth is surgery combined with photodynamic therapy. Here, light-sensitive but otherwise inactive cytotoxic drugs are given to the patient and a surgical probe is then used to apply light that activates the drugs locally, at the site of the cancer.

In the field of radiotherapy, future developments will concentrate on improving the ability to get the radiation dose to where it is needed and to spare normal tissues as much as possible. In teletherapy, this may be achieved by devices such as the gamma knife or by image-guided radiotherapy (IGRT). Proton and other heavy-ion therapies, also discussed in Chapter 9, have much to commend them; whether or not they are widely introduced may depend on economic factors more than on their proven efficacy. Furthermore, the use of neutrons in boron neutron capture therapy (BNCT) may also find a place in the radiotherapy of the future, especially for some difficult-to-treat brain tumours.

Brachytherapy (Section 9.4) is currently developing fast and being used for more sites around the body. It has a promising future, not least because of its cost-effectiveness. It is likely that the next few years may see the use of new radionuclides for brachytherapy. One manufacturer has developed a system that uses very small X-ray sources – it will be interesting to see how this develops.

Research on new ways of targeting cancers with radiopharmaceuticals is likely to result in the wider use of unsealed source radiotherapy (Section 9.5), with the possibility that treatment may be individually tailored to the patient's cancer. Such molecular targeted radiotherapy approaches are now evolving into using targeted therapeutics to deliver radiotherapy specifically to the tumour site where a seed can not be introduced. With the use of appropriate targeting agents, such as antibodies and other novel targeting molecules, a new generation of targeted radiopharmaceuticals has emerged, with conjugated (i.e. linked) antibodies, such as Zevalin®, already in the market, and others following up in clinical development. Overall the future of radiotherapy promises to be very interesting.

Chemotherapy and biological therapy approaches are also trying to address similar points of improved efficacy and reduced side effects. To achieve these targets, various approaches have been adopted and are promising to deliver the chemotherapeutic and biological agents of the future.

The biggest boom in anticancer therapeutic development has been in the area of biological therapy. Antibodies and nucleic-acid-based therapeutics have been obtaining approval faster than ever before, and dozens of these reagents are now in clinical trials. The attempt to generate molecules that are more specific and thus have a better therapeutic outlook is ultimately leading towards personalised medicines. Such advanced medicines are specifically selected based on individuals' genetic profiles. As not all individuals are the same, not all cancers are the same and new drugs are being developed in conjunction with associated diagnostic genetic tests to identify the individuals where such drugs would be effective. The promise is to deliver more specific drugs, targeted to specific groups of people, with the knowledge and certainty that these drugs will be effective against their cancers, offering higher efficacy and reduced side effects.

Another approach taken to reduce side effects and improve the efficacy of cancer chemotherapy is focused on delivering or activating known potent chemotherapy agents to the cancer site specifically. Small molecular therapeutics, such as cisplatin (Section 10.3.3), have been at the forefront of cancer therapy for many years. Many variations and optimisations have been made to the original cisplatin molecule, resulting in several second- and third-generation compounds. Yet, these compounds have only marginally improved on the original molecule. One approach to improve such potent cytotoxic compounds is to deliver them specifically to the cancer site or activate them in the vicinity of tumour cells, thus allowing them to exert their action at the site of need, increasing their potency and minimising their side effects.

A final approach in targeting cancer is through the use of the immune system to eliminate any cells that express tumour-related proteins or antigens, in what are known as cancer vaccines (Section 10.8.2). Though vaccines have reached the market against cancer-related viruses, such as the HPV vaccine mentioned earlier, no vaccine has yet been successful directly against cancer cells; however, 105 different cancer vaccines were in the pipeline in 2008, of which 14 were in late-phase clinical development.

Overall, significant progress has been made in the treatment and management of malignant diseases and, whilst a number of cancers are already treatable, the future of cancer medicine may lie not in a complete remission of all of them, but rather in curing some and making others manageable long-term conditions, and to offer previously untreatable patients the opportunity to live out their lives in reasonable comfort.

12.7 Quality of life for people with cancer

The potential advances in treatment, outlined in the previous section, offer hope for significant future improvements in the quality as well as the 'quantity' of life remaining for people with cancer. In particular, there is growing understanding among healthcare professionals of how to manage cancer pain, and the medical specialty of palliative care is increasingly available in hospitals and hospices in high-income countries and is being actively promoted in other parts of the world (WHO, 2007). The reluctance that many doctors once felt about prescribing strong opioids such as morphine for people with otherwise intractable cancer pain has diminished, though has not yet disappeared. Progress is also being made in counteracting side effects such as nausea during chemotherapy and radiotherapy.

Perhaps the most significant developments that will affect the quality of life of people with cancer in the future stem from the gradual recognition, in most cultures, that the 'taboos' formerly associated with a cancer diagnosis are losing their power. Doctors in high-income societies now rarely use euphemistic language to disguise the fact that a person has cancer, and in future it may come to be seen as no different from other long-term conditions that have never generated the fear and anxiety formerly attached to cancers. As it becomes more widely understood that many cancers are curable or manageable, and have a better prognosis than some other conditions that increase with age (e.g. dementia), the mental health of people with cancer can be expected to improve. Living with cancer then becomes similar to living with, say, diabetes or heart disease. Increasing openness among healthcare professionals in discussing cancer treatments with patients and their families has tended to shift the balance of decision-making more in their direction, encouraging participation in choices about treatment options rather than 'doctor knows best'. For example, patient-controlled analgesia is increasingly available and gives decision-making power to the person with pain about when analgesia is needed.

However, these advances are not happening everywhere; for example, only about a third of US hospitals have palliative care teams and in poorer countries huge investments in equipment and the training of cancer specialists are required if even the most basic level of cancer care is to become accessible to the majority of the population. The WHO's 2005 Global Cancer Control Strategy includes a series of six modules in the *Guide for Effective Programmes* (WHO, 2006) which aim to strengthen and accelerate the translation of knowledge about cancer prevention and treatment from those countries where scientific evidence has led to the identification of best practices, to those whose services are inadequate. A feature of the plan is to find ways to offer sufficient incentives in terms of pay and conditions to keep or attract cancer specialists in low- and middle-income countries, and to stem the flow of specialists emigrating to better-paid jobs in high-income countries.

12.8 Concluding remarks

In this final chapter of the book, we have attempted to discuss the future global trends in the fight against cancer. We have based our discussion roughly on the strategies supported by the WHO's 'Global Action Against Cancer' (WHO, 2005), which centre on four main areas:

- Prevent what's preventable, i.e. prevent about 40% of cancers occurring by avoiding and reducing exposure to risk factors (prevention strategies)
- Cure what's curable, i.e. ~ 40% by early detection, diagnostic and treatment strategies
- Relieve pain and improve quality of life (palliative care strategies)
- Improvement of cancer services and government directives on cancer treatment.

It is certainly difficult, if not impossible, to predict the progress in cancer diagnosis and treatment that should be anticipated over the next 10–50 years because cancers present such complex biological and medical problems. Tackling cancers globally depends not only on the advancement of medical science, but also on far-reaching changes in the cultural and socioeconomic contexts in which science and medicine operates. Although there is still a great deal of progress to be made, there are many reasons to be optimistic about the way humans will deal with cancers in the future.

Activity 12.1 Beyond SK123: researching new cancer topics

Allow about 60 minutes in total for this activity

In this activity you will use the internet to research a particular topic related to understanding cancers.

References

Bray, F. and Møller, B. (2006) 'Predicting the future burden of cancer', *Nature Reviews Cancer*, vol. 6, no. 1, pp. 63–74; [online], http://dx.doi.org/doi:10.1038/nrc1781 (Accessed July 2008).

Mathers, C.D. and Loncar, D. (2006) 'Projections of global mortality and burden of disease from 2002 to 2030', *PLoS Medecine*, vol. 3, no. 11, e442 [online], http://dx.doi.org/doi:10.1371/journal.pmed.0030442 (Accessed July 2008).

WCRF/AICR (2007) Second Expert Report on *Food, Nutrition, Physical Activity, and the Prevention of Cancer: a Global Perspective*, Washington DC: World Cancer Research Fund/American Institute for Cancer Research [online], http://www.aicr.org/site/PageServer?pagename=res_report_second (Accessed July 2008).

WHO (2005) *Global Action Against Cancer* [online], http://www.who.int/cancer/media/en/GlobalActionCancerEnglfull.pdf (Accessed July 2008).

WHO (2006) *Cancer Control: Knowledge into Action, WHO Guide for Effective Programmes*, World Health Organization, Geneva [online], http://www.who.int/cancer/modules/en/index.html (Accessed July 2008).

WHO (2007) *Palliative Care* module in *Cancer Control: Knowledge into Action, WHO Guide for Effective Programmes*, World Health Organization, Geneva [online], http://www.who.int/cancer/media/FINAL-PalliativeCareModule.pdf (Accessed July 2008).

ANSWERS TO QUESTIONS

Question 1.1

The prevalence rate will rise, i.e. the number of men living with the disease will increase due to improvements in treatment. As incidence rises, an increasing number of new cases of testicular cancer will be diagnosed; in calculating the prevalence, the new cases are added to the already existing cases diagnosed in the past among men who are still alive, because the mortality rate has fallen so low.

Question 1.2

Compared with Europe, the fact that Africa records a smaller percentage of cancer deaths relative to the size of its population is mainly due to its relatively 'young' age-structure containing fewer older people who are most at risk of cancer. The European population contains a much larger proportion of older people and therefore its cancer mortality is high relative to its population size. In addition, many cancers go unrecorded in African countries where there is a large rural population and limited cancer services to diagnose the disease.

Question 1.3

The European region with the best survival characteristics is Central Europe: Austria, Belgium, Switzerland, Germany, Netherlands and France all have five-year relative survival better than the European average. The worst region is Eastern Europe as represented by the Czech Republic and Poland, but there is an even lower five-year relative survival in two other countries in different regions: Denmark in Northern Europe and Slovenia in Southern Europe. The gap between the country with the lowest five-year relative survival from prostate cancer (Denmark at about 48%) and the highest (Austria at about 85%) is 37 percentage points.

Question 1.4

The period in which these data were collected spanned 24 years (1978–2002). The age-structure of Qidong could have 'aged' gradually during this period due to a falling birth rate (you may have heard of China's 'one child per family' policy), and also due to increases in life expectancy. Unless the data for each year were age-standardised to adjust for changes in the age-structure, the incidence rates for cancers collected at the beginning of the period could not be directly compared with those in later years, because of the distorting effect of a growing proportion of older people in the population who are more likely to develop cancers on account of their age.

Question 2.1

(a) 4; (b) 5; (c) 1; (d) 3; (e) 6; (f) 2; (g) 8; (h) 7.

Question 2.2

(a) Carbohydrates are themselves sugars or are formed by sugars (e.g. table sugar, starch), proteins are formed by amino acids (e.g. haemoglobin, keratin), nucleic acids are formed by nucleotides (e.g. DNA), and lipids are formed by fatty acids combined with other molecules (e.g. phospholipids, triglycerides).

(b) No. Macromolecules are formed by combinations of single molecule units. Fatty acids are long molecules that combine with other molecules to form lipid molecules which can then aggregate together into much larger structures. Therefore lipids are not long chains formed by combination of many single molecule units and so are not 'true' macromolecules.

Question 2.3

(a) False. Mutations in genes of tumour cells result in alterations in the nature of proteins they contain compared to the normal cells they derive from (Section 2.4).

(b) True. If you got this wrong, go back to Section 2.4.

(c) True. If you got this wrong, go back to Section 2.6.

(d) False. Many tumour cells produce an enzyme called telomerase that maintains the length of telomeres at the end of chromosomes, thereby allowing them to avoid cell senescence (Section 2.7.3).

(e) False. Although some properties of normal cells are maintained (e.g. in melanoma cells, production of pigment), most tumour cells lose the specialised structure and functions of differentiated cells (Section 2.8).

Question 2.4

Each daughter cell will contain the same amount of DNA, i.e. 46 chromosomes within one nucleus.

Question 2.5

(a) See Figure 2.21. (i) A normal cell responds to a growth-inhibitory signal binding its receptor and activating intracellular signalling molecules by terminating cell division. In tumour cells, there are four major cell-to-cell communication mechanisms involving mutations by which insensitivity to growth-inhibitory signals may arise: (ii) tumour cells show decreased production of growth-inhibitory signals, thereby activating receptors and intracellular signalling molecules to a reduced extent compared to normal cells; (iii) tumour cells produce lower levels of growth-inhibitory signal receptors or (iv) normal levels of a mutated receptor that is inactivated, thereby decreasing the activation of intracellular signalling molecules; (v) tumour cells produce normal levels of a mutated intracellular signalling molecule that is inactive.

(b) Tumour cells may become self-sufficient in anti-apoptotic (survival) signals by similar mechanisms to those leading to self-sufficiency in growth-inducing signals. Therefore, the changes in the levels and/or activity of the molecules involved would be similar to those in Figure 2.19, i.e. an increase in the activity or in the levels of the proteins involved.

Question 3.1

(a) 120 nucleotides would form 60 complementary base pairs.

(b) Since A always pairs with T, the number of T bases is the same as the number of A bases, i.e. 40.

(c) and (d) Eighty of the 120 nucleotides are formed by either A or T bases, so the remaining 40 nucleotides will contain either C or G bases. As C always pairs with G, then half this number, i.e. 20, are C and 20 are G.

Question 3.2

(a) Figure 3.15 (overleaf) is the completed version of Figure 3.14. Note that the sequences must be the same in the two replicating DNA double helices, so the bases can be deduced from the limited information provided in Figure 3.14. Here is one example. One member of the base pair at the bottom right is C. Since C always pairs with G, the missing base must be G. Because the two replicated double helices are identical, the missing pair at the bottom left must be CG.

(b) Since the DNA shown in Figure 3.14 is replicating, the cell must be at the cell growth stage (Section 2.7.1). This is the stage between successive cell divisions during which the DNA, and hence the chromosomes, becomes replicated.

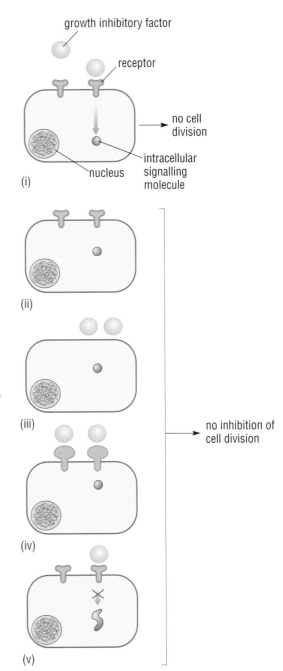

Figure 2.21 Abnormal responses to growth-inhibitory signals in tumour cells. (For the answer to Question 2.5.)

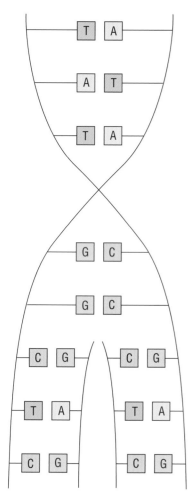

Figure 3.15 Completed Figure 3.14, showing base-pairing in part of a double-stranded DNA molecule during replication. (Answer to Question 3.2a)

Question 3.3

(a) Chromosome mutation

(b) Gene mutation

(c) Mutagen

(d) Gene mutation

Question 3.4

(a) A diagram is shown in Figure 3.16.

(b) Four clones of cells are depicted in Figure 3.11: one clone of cells that show no mutations with eight cells drawn, one clone of cells that have acquired one mutation with four cells drawn, one clone of cells that show two mutations with two cells drawn and one clone of cells that have acquired three mutations with only one cell drawn. Note that this figure is a simplified account and that each cell on the fourth column will continue dividing generating more progeny cells so that each of the four clones of cells depicted will be formed by many more cells.

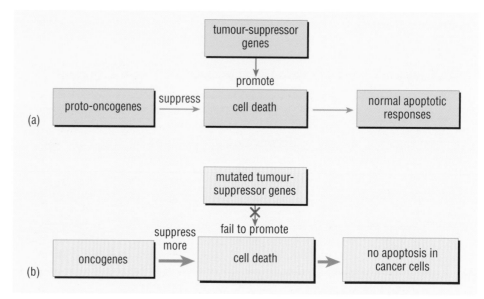

Figure 3.16 Schematic diagram to show the role of oncogenes and tumour-suppressor genes in cell death. (a) Normal cell death is controlled by the protein products of proto-oncogenes and tumour-suppressor genes. (b) Evasion from apoptosis is the result of mutations in both types of genes. (Answer to Question 3.4a.)

Question 3.5

Spontaneous errors occur all the time in cells that are replicating their DNA, but these errors are normally removed by DNA repair enzymes. If the repair system is defective, errors will go unrepaired and mutations will accumulate. The more frequent the mutations, the more likely that they will occur in proto-oncogenes and tumour-suppressor genes, increasing susceptibility to cancer.

Question 4.1

(a) 3; (b) 2; (c) 4; (d) 7; (e) 8; (f) 6; (g) 5; (h) 1.

Question 4.2

(a) Cancer of epithelial cells in the liver.

(b) Cancer of flat epithelial cells in the lung (Section 2.8.2).

(c) Cancer of immature red blood cells.

(d) Cancer of glandular epithelial cells in the prostate.

(e) Benign tumour of fat cells.

Question 4.3

Colon carcinoma is a solid tumour. Solid tumours require the formation of new blood vessels that provide oxygen and nutrients in order to become larger tumours. Leukaemia is a cancer of immune cells circulating in the blood which have all the oxygen and nutrients they require in order to proliferate. Therefore a drug that inhibits angiogenesis would not have any effect on neoplastic cells circulating in the blood.

Question 4.4

The adrenal glands are part of the endocrine system and as such secrete hormones that regulate many functions in the human body. If adenoma cells still secrete aldosterone, the number of cells in the adrenal glands that secrete aldosterone will be higher in individuals with adenoma than in individuals with a healthy adrenal glands. Therefore the levels of aldosterone in the blood will be higher and blood pressure may not be regulated appropriately. Failure to regulate blood pressure within certain limits may result in tissues and organs not functioning adequately. The imbalance of the endocrine system involving aldosterone production may thus result in the disruption of body homeostasis. *Note*: adrenal adenoma may result in increased blood pressure which may be fatal if left untreated.

Question 5.1

A case-control study is a study during which individuals that develop cancer are matched with healthy individuals that have similar age and lifestyle characteristics in an attempt to identify which differences between the two that have been responsible for the development of cancer. A prospective study is a study in which large numbers of healthy individuals are followed for many years.

Question 5.2

Young boys who swept chimneys contracted a cancer that was linked to their work.

Question 5.3

If pure chemicals that are known to be present in risky exposures cause the same cancer in animals as in humans this is strong evidence that the chemical may be a causal agent for human cancer.

Question 5.4

Some genes play a particularly crucial role in determining whether cells become cancerous or not. These are called cancer-critical genes and include proto-oncogenes, tumour-suppressor genes and genes that encode DNA repair proteins. For example, the *p53* gene is mutated in many human cancers. This is significant because one of the functions of the p53 protein is to decide whether cells with damaged DNA should divide or die.

Question 5.5

Discharges from nuclear power plants are responsible for only about 0.1% of the background radiation to which we are all subjected. Given that the risk of developing a radiation-induced cancer from all the background radiation is only about 1 in 10 000, the additional risks because of nuclear power plants are extremely small – about 1 in 10 000 000!

Question 5.6

1   Cancer risks change within one or two generations, suggesting that environmental factors must be major risk factors.

2   The changes in cancer risk in migrant populations often occur faster than those *within* countries.

Question 5.7

Pesticides can, at least in principle, be *removed* from our environment whereas dietary patterns can only be *altered*.

Activity 6.2

(a) At that time rates of cervical cancer were rising fast because of changes in sexual behaviour. The screening programme was able to prevent many deaths from the cancer.

(b) If women under 25 were screened a very large percentage of them would be found to have abnormalities. However, these would mostly be transient abnormalities that need not be treated. Not screening these women saves money and prevents unnecessary anxiety.

Question 6.1

The answer is (iii). Digital rectal examination is the only diagnostic technique out of the examples given that does not require specialised equipment.

Question 6.2

The attenuation coefficients of blood, fat and muscle are all very similar (around 0.2 cm^{-1}) so it will be hard to distinguish between them. Both bone and titanium will cause greater attenuation (coefficients 0.6 and 3.4 cm^{-1}, respectively) so are easily distinguishable from blood, fat and muscle. In addition, because the coefficient for titanium is much larger than for bone, it will be easy to distinguish it from bone. Air has a very much lower coefficient (at least 1000 times smaller) than all the other materials so is clearly distinguishable from each of them.

Question 6.3

Planar X-ray imaging and CT imaging both use X-rays which are a form of ionising radiation. In gamma camera imaging and PET imaging the patient is injected with a radiopharmaceutical which is taken up by the relevant organ so these will also expose the patient to ionising radiation.

Question 6.4

(a) Because activation of oestrogen receptor promotes cell proliferation in breast epithelial cells. If breast tumour cells express high levels of the oestrogen receptor, a good choice of therapy would be an inhibitor of the oestrogen receptor (e.g. tamoxifen), whereas if tumour cells do not express the oestrogen receptor, then inhibitors of the oestrogen receptor would have no effect on tumour cells.

(b) A biopsy of the tumour should first be obtained, either following surgery or during endoscopy. The tissue sample should then be fixed and cut into sections. The tissue sections are then incubated with antibodies specific for the oestrogen receptor. After a colour reaction, the tissue sections containing the tumour cells are visualised under the microscope by a pathologist.

Question 6.5

Possible advantages are:

- The prognosis is better because the disease can be detected either before it develops or at an early stage.
- Costs of caring for patients with the disease are reduced.
- People who do not have the disease are reassured.

Possible disadvantages are:

- Potential damage due to the screening process (e.g. by X-ray exposure)
- Costs of providing the screening
- Anxiety for people who receive a false positive result.

Question 7.1

Grading of a cancer is performed by a pathologist and is an assessment of how rapidly the cancer cells are changing. Staging, on the other hand, defines the spread of the cancer and is normally performed by a radiologist.

Question 7.2

The MDT has standardised the treatment and management of the cancer patient. The team meets twice to discuss the patient and treatment options (the make-up of a typical MDT is shown in Box 7.1). The role of the first meeting is to discuss the patient, the symptoms and the diagnosis. Often further tests, such as the staging of the cancer, will be ordered and a member of the team will discuss the possible treatment options with the patient. At the second meeting the results of any additional investigations are discussed together with the prognosis. The team then decides on the best course of treatment.

Question 7.3

The intent of a radical treatment is a cure whereas a palliative treatment ameliorates the symptoms or side-effects of the cancer. Palliative treatments are not curative.

Question 7.4

If a tumour is about to obstruct, for example, the gut or trachea, both life threatening events, then a palliative treatment that reduces the size of the tumour or removes the cause of the obstruction can be said to be life saving.

Question 7.5

Surgery: The main advantage of surgery is that it is rapid, often curative and local to the area of the cancer. The disadvantages are that (i) it can result in the loss or impairment of bodily functions that may have long-term consequences and (ii) can cause disfigurement.

Radiotherapy: The main advantage of radiotherapy is that it tends to preserve the affected organ. The main disadvantage is that it produces side-effects that, whilst local to the treatment site, can take many months to years to be fully manifest.

Chemotherapy: The advantage of chemotherapy is that it is a systemic treatment that can act as a 'catch-all' therapy for cancer cells in the body. The main disadvantage is the significant and widespread side effects associated with treatment.

Question 7.6

A phase I trial is designed to test the toxicity of a new treatment and involves a small number of healthy participants. A phase III trial involves a large number of participants with disease and tests the efficacy of a new treatment, normally against an established treatment. Often a phase III trial will include a placebo group and is randomised.

Question 8.1

An excisional biopsy is when a tumour is removed in its entirety together with a resection margin for diagnostic purposes. However, depending on the type of tumour and the quality of the margin, this intervention can be all that is needed to cure the cancer, and thus can be considered a surgery to treat primary disease.

Question 8.2

(a) A conservative surgical approach to treating breast cancer would involve removing the tumour lump together with a margin.

(b) A radical surgical approach would be to remove the entire breast, adjacent lymph nodes and connecting lymphatic vessels.

Question 8.3

Compared to open surgery, keyhole surgery offers the following advantages for the patient:

- it involves minimal trauma
- it is less disabling and disfiguring to the patient
- the patient recovers more quickly.

The limitations for the surgeon are:

- a requirement for considerable training
- lack of navigational aids
- poor assessment of depth of field
- no tactile feedback
- it is a time-consuming and complex procedure.

Question 8.4

The major side effects and risks associated with surgery are:

- choking (if the patient vomits during the operation)
- risk of haemorrhage
- anastomotic leakage (due to poor blood supply, tension or infection)
- deep vein thrombosis (resulting from immobility)
- infection at the incision wound
- organ-specific issues (such as diabetes after pancreas removal)
- postoperative pain
- nerve damage.

Activity 9.1

Prior to treatment the patient will have been imaged, most likely with a CT scanner (Section 6.5) and possibly on a simulator (not discussed in this course). Neither of these will have been an uncomfortable procedure – they will have involved lying on a couch while imaging takes place and, possibly, for the CT scan, the injection of a contrast medium. A patient who is having treatment for a head and neck cancer will have been fitted with the mask a few days before the beginning of the treatment.

When the patient arrives for treatment, depending on the part of the body to be treated, he will have to remove some of his clothes in order to expose the skin in the treatment region. This is essential to take advantage of the skin-sparing effect (Section 9.3). He will be given a gown to wear to go into the linac bunker.

When he is shown into the bunker the gown will be removed and the patient will be asked to lie on the couch while the radiographers carry out the procedures necessary to line up his tumour accurately with the beam. The couch may be rotated and moved backwards and forwards, and his position on the couch may be adjusted to align the tattoo marks with the laser beams. For a head and neck treatment the mask will be placed over the patient's head and clipped to the couch. During this process the lights may be dimmed which, combined with the experience of being in a windowless bunker, may make it a rather strange experience. When the radiographers leave the room the patient may feel rather isolated, although the radiographers will talk to him via the intercom and he will know that they can watch him via the CCTV.

During treatment the head of the linac will move to various different positions around the bed and he will hear the signal that indicates that the machine is on, but he will not feel anything. The treatment will only last a couple of minutes and then one of the radiographers will come back into the room to help him off the bed. He will then be free to leave but will return again the next day for more treatment.

Activity 9.2

The brachytherapy patient will, like the linac patient, have been imaged at some point before the treatment. On the day of treatment the applicator has to be inserted into the patient and this will be done outside the radiotherapy department and usually under general anaesthetic. For the patient this is probably the worst part of the procedure.

After the applicator has been inserted the patient will be wheeled into the windowless radiotherapy bunker and transferred to the treatment couch. The radiographers will then take over and will connect the applicator to the HDR equipment before leaving the room. At this point the patient will be on her own but will be able to speak to the radiographers via the intercom. They will tell her when the treatment is taking place and she will hear the warning signal when the radioactive source is outside the machine, but she will not feel anything.

After the treatment, which only lasts a few minutes, the applicator will be removed and the patient will be free to leave.

Activity 9.3

Method	Advantages	Disadvantages
Teletherapy	No overnight stay in hospital or general anaesthetic Patient is not radioactive at any time	In order to give sufficient dose to the tumour, other organs (e.g. rectum) will be irradiated. This can lead to some side effects Patient must attend every day for several weeks
Brachytherapy	Higher dose to the tumour and lower dose to other organs therefore fewer side effects Only one treatment	Treatment involves general anaesthetic and overnight stay in hospital Patient is slightly radioactive for a few weeks afterwards so has to avoid close contact with children, etc.

Activity 9.4

(a)   Iodine is excreted in the urine and sweat so the separate bathroom is necessary to avoid exposing other patients to unnecessary ionising radiation.

(b)   The gamma rays can be used for imaging. This is extremely useful because it allows the clinician to see whether there were any thyroid metastases. (As shown in Figure 9.16.)

Figure 9.16 Radionuclide images taken from a patient who has received treatment with iodine-131 for thyroid cancer. The scans show multiple areas of iodine-131 uptake in metastases in the neck, lungs, liver and abdomen about 10 days after treatment. (These are the dark patches.) (Source: University Hospitals Coventry and Warwickshire NHS Trust)

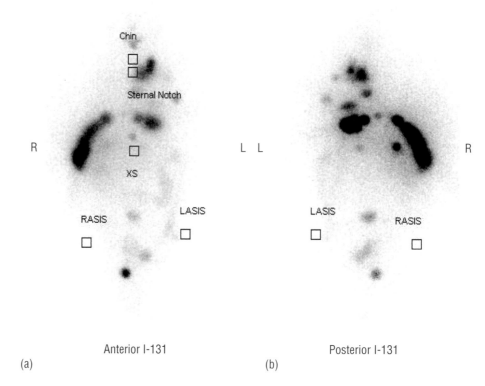

Question 9.1

Fractionation provides a time period between sessions of radiation treatment in which cells can attempt to repair the DNA damage caused by the ionising radiation. Since normal cells repair DNA damage more effectively than tumour cells, this time period makes good use of the difference in the response of normal cells and tumour cells to X-rays. More normal tissue cells can repair their DNA damage between radiation treatments and this gives rise to therapeutic window shown in Figure 9.3.

Question 9.2

The advantage of using more beams is that it should be possible to make the beams conform more precisely to the tumour, i.e. the tumour will be fully irradiated and the dose to normal tissue will be reduced. This is particularly important for organs at risk.

One disadvantage would be that, because more beams are used the treatment will take a little longer for each patient, so fewer patients will be treated in a day. Another one is that the treatment planning is more complicated and therefore more time-consuming. Both of these mean an increase in staff time and therefore cost per patient.

Question 9.3

Yes. Reading 25% of the prescribed dose from the horizontal axis, an imaginary line upwards will reach the brown line at about 25% of the tissue volume. So only about 25% of the normal tissue receives a dose that is more than 25% of the prescribed dose.

Question 9.4

Iodine-123 produces only gamma rays which makes it very suitable for radionuclide imaging because particle radiation is not wanted (see Section 6.5.6). (The energy of the gamma rays also happens to be well suited to the detectors used.) The half-life of 13 hours is also suitable – long enough to allow take-up by the organ, and short enough for the activity to fall quite rapidly once the procedure is over.

Iodine-125 could in theory be used for imaging as well but the half-life is too long (and in fact the energy of the X-rays produced is too low). However it is ideal for seed brachytherapy as the X-rays are emitted near the tumour. The half-life is also suitable – it allows treatment to continue over a period of months.

Iodine-131 emits beta radiation which does not travel far in tissue. It is therefore best suited for unsealed source therapy where it is used to kill thyroid cells which actually take up the iodine. As you can see in Figure 9.16, the gamma rays are also useful because they can be used to image the distribution of iodine in the patient's body after treatment.

Question 9.5

Teletherapy and intracavitary brachytherapy do not leave the patient radioactive as the source of ionising radiation is turned off or removed before the patient leaves.

Interstitial brachytherapy and unsealed source therapy do leave the patient radioactive and they will have to avoid air travel or will have to carry a letter as well as taking precautions to protect others for a few days.

Question 10.1

Treatment (iii) is a systemic therapy because the drug temozolomide, after absorption from the gut into the bloodstream, can travel to any location in the body.

Question 10.2

(i) Alkylating-like: although nedaplatin has no alkylating group in it, as a platinum-based drug it can link together bases in DNA strands in a similar way to an alkylating drug.

Question 10.3

Chemotherapy drugs are powerful medications that target rapidly growing cancer cells. Unfortunately, these drugs also kill other rapidly proliferating cells in the body – including those in hair follicles, resulting in loss of the hair.

Question 10.4

Herceptin is specific to HER2-positive breast cancers, i.e. those that overproduce the HER2 receptor. Less than 30% of breast cancers are HER2-positive, so 70% will not respond to Herceptin therapy.

Activity 11.1

Table 11.4 contains our suggestions for Activity 11.1; you may have proposed different but equally appropriate answers.

Table 11.4 Ways in which the needs of cancer survivors may be met. (Completed Table 11.2.)

Type of need	Example	A way in which this need may be met
Physical	Breathlessness as a result of surgery for lung cancer	Regular review by doctors/nurses who specialise in this area and can offer advice, treatment and follow-up, e.g. draining any fluids that build up in the lungs, prescribing antibiotics to prevent chest infections, or opioids to reduce the sensation of breathlessness
Physical	Colostomy following surgery for bowel cancer	Referral to nurse who specialises in management of colostomies and can give practical advice and support, e.g. on foods to avoid in the diet, returning to activities such as exercise, swimming
Psychological	Altered body image due to cancer surgery leads to depression	Evaluation of depression using a structured questionnaire, followed by antidepressant medication or access to group or one-to-one psychological therapies; referral to support groups with other survivors of this type of cancer
Social	Concerns about work colleagues avoiding contact after returning from cancer treatment	Discuss the situation with managers, or human resources department, or occupational health service where these exist
Financial	Inability to work full-time in previous occupation leads to financial difficulties	Easy access to advice about benefits available in the new financial situation
Information	Lack of knowledge about the possibility of recurrence of cancer	Routine provision of written information about the range of prognoses after the initial course of treatment; ability to discuss concerns with specialists at the follow-up appointments

Activity 11.3

Some people want to die at home with family present, whilst others want someone of their religion to be there, or they would prefer to die in a hospice with skilled professionals at hand. Some want to be alert until the very end and others would like to die in their sleep and know nothing about it. You may have considered other ideas of a good death.

Question 11.1

Polypharmacy is the use of multiple medications by the same person. It can cause additional health problems if two drugs interact with each other, producing enhanced side effects, or if a drug taken to counteract one symptom causes a new health problem. For example, opioid painkillers cause constipation, which is treated by prescribing a laxative, but this in turn may cause diarrhoea if the dose is not carefully controlled.

Question 11.2

The scale uses faces with different expressions to indicate different levels of pain. It would be appropriate to use this to estimate the level of pain experienced by someone who cannot speak the same language as the medical staff, or a person who could not complete a questionnaire like the Brief Pain Inventory in Figure 11.3 (e.g. a child, or someone with confusion or speech difficulties).

Question 11.3

Depression often goes undiagnosed in people with cancer because medical staff may be focused on physical rather than psychological symptoms and the patient may assume that feeling depressed is 'normal' and not worth mentioning.

Question 11.4

The completed Table 11.3 is shown in Table 11.5.

Table 11.5 Causes of nausea and vomiting and possible treatments. (Completed Table 11.3.)

Cause of nausea and vomiting	Possible treatment
Painkillers such as ibuprofen	Switch to an alternative analgesic, for example a weak opioid
Cancer in the brain	Steroids or radiotherapy to shrink the tumour and reduce intra-cranial pressure
Bowel obstruction	Surgery to relieve the obstruction
Constipation	Laxatives, increasing fluid intake, increasing fibre in the diet

Question 11.5

Palliative care teams in the UK typically include a social worker, who can advise the dying person and their family on sources of financial support such as additional benefits or tax credits. The team will also include someone with specialist training in treating psychological symptoms such as anxiety and distress, using medication and/or counselling techniques.

Question 11.6

Bob jk refers to his tiredness and how weak he feels (his 'get up and go had got up and gone'). He also refers to the touching quality of seeing newborn babies in the knowledge that he won't live long enough to watch them grow up. In Section 11.6 you learned that weakness is a very common symptom in people with terminal cancer, and that everyday experiences may take on an especially vivid character when a person knows that time is short and each day has to be lived fully, embracing whatever it brings.

APPENDIX

Throughout Chapter 10 you have been introduced to a number of anticancer drugs. Other examples (along with their trade names in some cases, and the names of the cancers they are used to treat) are given in Tables 10.2 to 10.5. *Note*: you do not need to remember any of these drug names nor the names of the cancers listed.

Table 10.2 Alkylating and alkylating-like chemotherapy drugs.

Class	Examples
nitrogen mustards	chlorambucil, chlormethine, cyclophosphamide, ifosfamide, melphalan
nitrosoureas	carmustine, fotemustine, lomustine, streptozocin
other alkylating drugs	busulfan, dacarbazine, procarbazine, temozolomide, thioTEPA, uramustine
platinum-based (alkylating-like)	carboplatin, cisplatin, nedaplatin, oxaliplatin

Table 10.3 Antimetabolite drugs.

Class	Examples
folate-like drugs	aminopterin, methotrexate, pemetrexed, raltitrexed
purines	cladribine, clofarabine, fludarabine, mercaptopurine, pentostatin, 6-thioguanine
pyrimidines	capecitabine, cytarabine, 5-fluorouracil, floxuridine, gemcitabine

Table 10.4 Cancer growth-inhibiting drugs and the types of cancer they are used to treat.

Drug name	Trade name	Treatment
dasatinib	Sprycel®	for chronic myeloid leukaemia (CML) after imatinib treatment
erlotinib	Tarceva®	for non-small cell lung cancer (NSCLC) and pancreatic cancer
gefitinib	Iressa®	for NSCLC and other cancers
imatinib	Gleevec®/Glivec®	for CML and gastrointestinal connective tissue tumours
lapatinib	Tykerb®/Tyverb®	for solid tumours such as breast and lung cancer
sorafenib	Nexavar®	for renal cell carcinoma (primary kidney cancer)
sunitinib	Sutent®	for renal cell carcinoma and imatinib-resistant gastrointestinal stromal tumour

Table 10.5 MABs in use: names, trade names and the types of cancer they are used to treat.

Monoclonal antibody	Trade name	Treatment
alemtuzumab	Campath®	chronic lymphocytic leukaemia
bevacizumab	Avastin®	colorectal cancer
ibritumomab	Zevalin®	non-Hodgkin's lymphoma
gemtuzumab	Mylotarg®	acute myeloid leukaemia
rituximab	Rituxan®	non-Hodgkin's lymphoma
tositumomab	Bexxar®	non-Hodgkin's lymphoma
trastuzumab	Herceptin®	breast cancer

ACKNOWLEDGEMENTS

Grateful acknowledgement is made to the following sources:

Cover

David Nunuk/Science Photo Library;

Text

Box 7.3: BBC News (2004) 'Ancient remedy shrinks cancer', 11 August 2004. BBC News Interactive;

Figures

Figure 1.1: Brando Quilici/AP/PA Photos; Figure 1.3: WHO and IUAC, (2005), '3 most common cancers in men and women per region' Global Action against Cancer'. World Health Organization; Figure 1.4c: Gang Wang/Panos Pictures; Figure 1.5: Levi, F. et al. (2007) 'Trends in lung cancer among young European women: The rising epidemic in France and Spain,' *International Journal of Cancer*, vol. 121. John Wiley & Sons Inc; Figure 1.6: Based on Bray, F. et al. (2006) 'Trends in testicular cancer incidence and mortality in 22 European Countries', *International Journal of Cancer*, vol. 118. Wiley-Liss Inc. A Wiley Company; Figure 1.7: 'Five year age standardised survival (%) adults diagnosed 1996–1999, England and Wales by sex and site,' (Data from Cancer Research UK website, http://info.cancerresearchuk.or/cancerstats/survival/latestrates, accessed February 2008); Figure 1.8: Based on Berrino, F. et al. (2007), 'Survival for eight major cancers and all cancers combined for European adults', *The Lancet Oncology*, vol. 8, September 2007. Elsevier; Figure 2.3: Edward L. Barnard, Florida Department of Agriculture and Consumer Services, Bugwood.org; Figure 2.7: Heather Davies; Figure 2.9: Steve Gschmeissner/Science Photo Library; Figure 2.12: © Biophoto Associates; Figure 2.14: Peter Lansdorp, Terry Fox Laboratories, B.C Cancer Research Centre UBC, Vancouver, Canada; Figure 2.16 (lung): CNRI/Science Photo Library, (liver): Astrid and Hanns-Frieder Michler/Science Photo Library, (kidney and stomach): Steve Gschmeissner/Science Photo Library; Figure 2.17: BSIP, GILLES/Science Photo Library; Figure 3.1: Courtesy of Professor Ferguson Smith; Figure 3.7a: Department of Clinical Cytogenetics, Addenbrookes Hospital/Science Photo Library; Figure 3.13: Robert W. Ginn/Alamy; Figure 4.6: Medimage/Science Photo Library; Figure 4.7: Cancer Research UK, 'Cancer – know the warning signs' http://www/info.cancerresearchuk.org/images/pdfs/rtr_sands_aug05.pdf (Accessed June 08) Cancer Research UK; Figure 4.8: Courtesy of Richard Wellings, University Hospitals Coventry and Warwickshire NHS Trust; Figure 4.9: Dr P. Marazzi/Science Photo Library; Figure 4.10: CNRI/Science Photo Library; Figure 5.1: Science Photo Library; Figures 5.2 and 5.4: *Cancer Trends in England and Wales 1950–1999. Studies on Medical and Population Subjects no 66.* Crown copyright material is reproduced under Class Licence Number C01W0000065 with the permission of the Controller of HMSO and the Queen's Printer for Scotland; Figure 5.5a: Rex Features; Figures 5.5b and c: The

Advertising Archives; Figure 5.6: http://www.deathsfromsmoking.net/countries. html. International Union Against Cancer (UICC), Geneva, Switzerland; Figure 5.8: 'Average annual dose from ionising radiation to the UK population from all sources', http://www.hpa.org.uk/webc/HPAwebFile_C/1194947372075, (Accessed June 2008); Figure 5.10: P. Hawtin, University of Southampton/ Science Photo Library; Figure 5.11: World Cancer Research Fund/American Institute for Cancer Research (1997) *Food, Nutrition and Cancer and the Prevention of Cancer: A Global Perspective*, WCRF/AICR; Figure 6.1: http://www.nice.org.uk/nicemedia/pdf/CG027fullguideline.pdf; Figure 6.2a: BSIP/Laurent/Trunyo/Science Photo Library; Figure 6.2b: CC Studio/Science Photo Library; Figure 6.3a and b: John Foster/Science Photo Library; Figure 6.3c: Dr P. Marazzi/Science Photo Library; Figure 6.4a: Deep Light Productions/ Science Photo Library; Figure 6.4b: David M. Martin MD/Science Photo Library; Figure 6.5: Duffy, Michael J. (2001), 'Carcinoembryonic antigen as a marker for colorectal cancer: Is it clinically useful?', *Clinical Chemistry*, vol. 47 (4), American Association of Clinical Chemistry; Figures 6.6, 6.8, 6.9, 6.11, 6.13, 6.17 and 6.19: Photograph supplied by Richard Wellings, University Hospitals Coventry and Warwickshire NHS Trust; Figure 6.12: Image supplied by University Hospitals Coventry and Warwickshire NHS Trust; Figure 6.14: Directorate of Radiology, Royal Berkshire NHS Foundation Trust; Figure 6.16a: Department of Medical Physics and Radiology, Oxford Radcliffe Hospitals; Figure 6.16b: University Hospitals Coventry and Warwickshire NHS Trust: Figure 6.18: Photo courtesy of GE Healthcare; Figures 6.23, 6.25 and 6.26: Photographs supplied by Nigel Williams, University Hospitals Coventry and Warwickshire NHS Trust; Figure 6.28: MK Breast Screening Unit NHS Trust; Figure 6.29b: Dr Tom Goodfellow, University Hospitals Coventry and Warwickshire NHS Trust; Figure 6.31: Paul Edwards, Department of Pathology, University of Cambridge; Figure 6.32a: CNRI/Science Photo Library; Figure 6.32b: Science Photo Library; Figure 6.33: Miettinen, M. et al. (2000), 'Immunohistochemical spectrum of GISTS at different sites and their differential diagnosis with a reference to GD117 KIT', *Modern Pathology*, vol. 13 (10), Nature Publishing Group. Figure 7.2: Cancer Institute New South Wales, Australia; Figure 7.3: Illustration by D.F. Gleason, taken from Humphreys, P.A. (2004) 'Gleason grading and prognostic factors in carcinoma of the prostate', *Modern Pathology*, vol. 17, 2002. Nature Publishing Group; Figure 7.4: Royal Berkshire NHS Foundation Trust; Figure 7.5: Mark Thomas/Science Photo Library; Figure 7.6: Larry Mulvehill/Science Photo Library; Figure 7.7: Simon Fraser/Royal Victoria Infirmary, Newcastle/Science Photo Library; Figure 7.8: Geoff Tompkinson/Science Photo Library; Figure 8.1: James Stevenson/Science Photo Library; Figure 8.2: Aletti, G.D. et al. (2007) 'Current management strategies for ovarian cancer', Mayo Clinic Proceedings, June 2007. Mayo Foundation for Medical Education and Research; Figure 8.3: Auro Fermariello/ Science Photo Library; Figure 8.4d: Science Photo Library; Figure 8.5: David M. Martin/Science Photo Library; Figure 8.6: AJ Photo/Science Photo Library; Figure 8.7: Mark Thomas/Science Photo Library; Figure 8.8: Science Photo Library; Figure 8.9: John Cole/Science Photo Library; Figure 8.10: BSIP/Platriez/ Science Photo Library; Figure 8.11: Royal College of Surgeons, Edinburgh; Figure 8.12: The Wellcome Library, London; Figure 8.13: Andrew Leonard/ Science Photo Library; Figure 9.9: Ralph Roberts, Oxford; Figures 9.11 and

9.14b: Directorate of Radiology, Royal Berkshire NHS Foundation Trust; Figure 9.15: Barton, M.B. (2006) 'Role of radiotherapy in cancer control in low-income and middle income countries', *Lancet Oncology*, vol. 7 (7). Elsevier Science; Figures 9.16 and 10.15: Images supplied by University Hospitals Coventry and Warwickshires NHS Trust; Figure 10.1: Syd Hoff/Cartoonbank/The New Yorker Magazine Inc; Figure 10.13: Ianni Dimitrov/Alamy; Figure 11.1: Developed by Drs Robert L. Spitzer, Janet B.W. Williams, Kurt Kroenke and colleagues, with an educational grant from Pfizer Inc. Copyright © 2005 Pfizer Inc. All rights reserved. Reproduced with permission; Figure 11.2: Richard Wellings, University Hospital of Coventry and Warwickshire; Figure 11.4: Owen Horn, The Open University; Figure 11.5a: Image Source/Rex Features; Figure 11.5b: Science Photo Library; Figure 11.6: http://www.mariecurie.org.uk/ whatwedo. Used with permission of Marie Curie Cancer Care; Figure 11.7: World Health Organization/Marko Kokic; Figure 11.8: Stock Connection Blue/Alamy; Figure 11.9: © Larry Williams/CORBIS; Figure 11.10: Scott Camazine/Alamy; Figure 11.11: © Richard Greenhill; Figure 11.12: St. Christopher's Hospice; Figure 11.13: Alex Bartel/Science Photo Library; Figure 11.14: © Paul Doyle/ Alamy; Figure 11.15: From Hockenberry M.J., Wilson D., Winkelstein M.L., *Wong's Essentials of Pediatric Nursing*, 7th edn, St. Louis, 2005, p. 1259. Used with permission. Copyright, Mosby; Figures 12.2 and 12.3: Bray, F. and Moller, B. (2006) 'Prediciting the future burden of cancer', *Nature Reviews Cancer*, vol. 6 (1). Nature Publishing Group; Figure 12.4: TEK IMAGE/Science Photo Library; Figure 12.5: World Health Organization and The International Union Against Cancer (2002) Global Action Against Cancer. World Health Organization and The International Union Against Cancer; Figure 12.6a: Hitachi Medical Systems Europe; Figure 12.6b: Professor Jem Hebden, University College London.

Every effort has been made to contact copyright holders. If any have been inadvertently overlooked the publishers will be pleased to make the necessary arrangements at the first opportunity.

INDEX

Entries and page numbers in **bold** are glossary terms. Page numbers in *italics* are entries mainly, or wholly, in a figure or table.

A

A (adenine) 56–**57**, 74, *260*

abdomen, images of *142, 144, 155,* 156

ABL region *63,* 64, 68

abnormal growth 2, 25, *46,* 50, 91, 132, 133, 134

accuracy, of screening 168, *169*

acquired resistance 278

activation 44–5, 271, 278

acute lymphoblastic leukaemia 163, 255, 263, 264–5, 279

acute side effects *188*

adenine *see* A

adenocarcinomas 42, 78, 99, *134, 149*
    prostate cancer 18–19

adenomas 78, 100, *165*

adjuvant treatment 189, 198
    chemotherapy 209, 220, 252, 279
    combination 279–80
    radiotherapy *185,* 187–8, 252, 279

adrenal adenoma 100

advertisements *107*

aflatoxins 121

Africa
    cancer incidence 9, 12
    cancer mortality 18
    diagnosis and treatment in 6
    Kaposi's sarcoma 11

age
    cancer in younger age-groups 12–14
    and cancer risk *104, 106,* 318–19
    in case studies *3*

age standardisation 12, 14

age-standardised data *10, 13,* 19, *106*

age-structures 12, 13–14, 318–19

airway management 218

albumin 135

alcohol 295–6

aldosterone 100

alkylating drugs 256–9, 278

alpha decay *151*

alpha particles 116, 239, 243

amino acids 28, *29,* 59, *252*
    and mutations *60,* 61

amoeba *22*

anaemia 95, 135, 290

anaesthetists 213, 215, 216, 219

analgesia 209, 215, **218**–20, 288–9, *292,* 309

anastomosis 221

anastomotic leak 221

anastrozole 275

angiogenesis 82, *83*
    anti-angiogenic drugs 100

angiogenic growth factors 83

animal cells *22*

animal models 104

anorexia 309, 310, 311

anti-angiogenic drugs 100

anti-apoptotic signals 49, 50, 54

anti-emetics 291, 293

antibodies 89, 167, 325
    monoclonal 269–72

antidepressants 285

antigen 89, **269**–70, 273

antimetabolite drugs 259–65

antimetabolite mechanism 255

antimicrotubule agents 266

antitumour antibiotics 265

anxiety 180, 284, **285**–6, 293, 307

apoptosis 49–50, 75

applicator, brachytherapy 240

'appropriate death' 311

arteries 80, *82*

ASA scoring system 216

Ashkenazi Jews 12, 170

Asia
    cervical cancer 9
    liver and oral cancers 11–12, 102, 121
    mortality and incidence *7*

Aspergillus 121

Astler–Coller staging system 88, *89*

astronauts 117

atomic number 150, 151, 153

atoms 24, **25**, 27, 115, 150–1

ATP 33, 34, 268

attenuation 140

attenuation coefficient 140–2, 143, 144, 146, *174*

auscultation 132

B

B cells 269, 270

background radiation *116,* 117

bacteria *22,* 66, 118, 119

ball-and-stick model *25*

barium 144

basal cell carcinoma *43,* 44, 49

base number 26

base-pairing 57, 59
    in DNA replication 64, *65*

bases **56**–8, 74, *252*
    chemical structures of *260, 261*
    and mutations 60–1

BCR–ABL fusion protein *63,* 64, 68, 268

benign tumours 2, 77–9

benzo[a]pyrene *67,* 109

beta minus decay *151,* 156

beta particles 241, 243

beta plus decay *151,* 156

bile *93,* 132

bilirubin *93,* 132

biological half-life 243

biological imaging 322

biological medicines 325

biological organisation, hierarchy of *24*

biological system 80, *92*

biological therapy 251, 267, 281
    adjuvant 279
    cancer growth inhibitors 267–9
    drug delivery 276

gene therapy 275–6
hormone therapy 274–5
see also immunotherapy
biology of cancer 319–20
biopsy 87, 145, **160**–7, 173, 209
excisional biopsy 162, 184, 202, 224
wedge biopsy 162, 202
see also tissue biopsies
bladder cancer *147, 149*
incidence and mortality *5, 9, 105*
blastomas 79
blood 80
complete blood count 135, 162
blood circulation 80, *82*, 84–5
blood pressure 218
blood tests 169–70, *171*, 298, 322
blood transfusion 120
body mass index 124
body size 122–3
bone marrow 278
biopsy 163
transplantation 222–3, 279–80
tumours 95, *141*
bones
metastasis in 87, 154, 244
myeloma *149*
scans *154, 184*
boron neutron capture therapy 239, 324
bowel
ultrasound scan of *148*
see also colorectal cancer
BRAC 112, 170
brachytherapy 192, **226**, 239–43, 324
activity 239
in the future 242–3
prostate brachytherapy 240–2, 249
Bragg peak *238*, 239
brain
imaging of *148, 149,* 184, *287*
metastasis in 87, 196
tumours *235, 236*
brand name *252*
breast cancer
biopsy 161, 167
chemotherapy 271–2
genetic testing for 112, 170
growth factors and 46

hormone therapy 274–5
images of *323*
incidence and mortality *5, 9, 105*
Japanese women *122,* 321
metastasis in 86, 87
mortality data 105
oestrogen and 94
reconstructive surgery 205–6
screening programme 147, 149, 169
surgery for 204, 224
survival rates *303*
susceptibility to 12
treatment 187–8, 189, 190
breathlessness 94–5, 289–90, 296, 311
Brief Pain Inventory *288*
bronchoscopy 133
Burkitt's lymphoma 111–12
bypass surgery 206

C

C (cytosine) 56–**57**, 74, *260*
cachexia 94
cancer cells *22, 23,* 25
adhesion in 48
forming larger tumours 80–3
growth-inhibitory signals in 54
mutations forming 69–70
new developments in studying 320
versus normal cells 32–3, 50
proliferation of 34, *35*
RAS in 46, 62, 68
senescence in 38–9
signals controlling 45–7
spread of 83–9, 184
structure of *32*
undifferentiated 42, 44, 78
cancer-critical genes 67–9, 276
Cancer Genome Atlas 319
cancer growth inhibitors 47, 50, 267–9
cancer nomenclature 78, 79
cancer prevention 123–4, 321–2
Cancer Research UK *91,* 194
cancer survivor 302–3
meeting needs of *304*
cancer therapy *see* chemotherapy; diagnosis; radiotherapy; surgery; treatments
cancer trend 7

cancer vaccine therapy 273–4
cancer vaccines 198, 321–2, 325
cancers
ancient and modern 1–3
biology of 319–20
definition 2
early detection and diagnosis 322–3
future global projections 317–19
global statistics 1
and imaging 138–9
and the immune system 89–90
inheritance of 71–3, 111
lifestyle, environment and 121–3, 294–7
long-term risk of developing 230
and mutations 60–4
screening 168–72, 175
staging of 87–9, *136,* 137, 144, 209
symptoms of 90–6
types of 42–4
see also tumours
capillaries 80, *82,* 86–7
carbohydrates 27, 28, *29*
carbon dioxide 80, 144
carbon isotopes 150–1
carboplatin 259
carcinogens 66, 67, 109, 121, 122, 256
carcinoma *in situ* 166
carcinomas 42, *43,* 79, *165*
basal cell carcinoma 43, 44, 49
diagnosis of 183
invasive carcinoma 166
see also adenocarcinomas
cardiopulmonary exercise testing 216
cardiovascular system 80, *82, 92,* 96
case-control study 106
case studies *3*
Anneke de Groot 110, 172–3, 220, 305, 307, 309, 311
Dave Bayler 72–3, 134–5, 167, 209, 294–5, 297–8
Jôao Rodrigues 171–2, 192, 242, 302, 305
Julie Simpson 97, 204–5, 244–5, 300
Lin Ming 120, 145, 277, 308
Naheed Jones 95, 212–13
Terri Moloney 49, 86, 184, 197–8, 274

Trupti Shah 40, 96, 162–3, 264–5, 279–80

causal link 101, 102, 109

CEA blood levels 136, 137

cell adhesion molecules 47

cell cycle 35–7, 113

cell division 36–7
cancer-critical genes and *68*
cancer development and 69–70
in RAS *62*
sequence of *35*
timing of 37–8

cell growth 36, *37*

cell membrane 30–1, *32*, 44–5

cell metabolism 33–4, 259

cell proliferation 22, 25, 34–9
signals controlling 45–7, 78
see also cell division

cell senescence 38–9

cell survival curve 227–8

cell-to-cell communication 45, 47

cells
adhesion 47–8, 83
B cells 269, 270
chemical composition of *29*
'clones' of 69–70, 75, 269
communication in 44–5
composition of 25–9
death of 48–50
definition 21–5
differentiation 39–44
diversity *22*
examples of human *40*
properties of normal and neoplastic 32–3, 50
a 'typical' human cell 30–2

cervical cancer
incidence and mortality 5, *8*, 9, *105*
survival rates *303*
treatments *211*, 273, 321–2

cervical screening 119, 124, 161, *166*, 169, 171

chaparral 193, 194, 195

chemical elements *24*, **25**, 27, 115, *150*

chemical fixation 163, *164*, 167

chemical symbols 27

chemo-radiation 252

chemotherapy 186, 251–2, 280, 281

adjuvant 209, 220, 252, 279

alkylating drugs 256–9, 278

antimetabolite drugs 259–65

antimicrotubule agents 266

antitumour antibiotics 265

case studies 264–5, 271–2, 274, 279–80

chemotherapy drugs 253–6

combination chemotherapy 279–80

in the future 325

issues considering 191

in low-income countries 6

palliative 190, 277

radical treatments 188–9

side effects 277–8, 280

see also biological therapy; drugs

chest infections 221, 290, 296

chest X-ray 130, *131*, *139*, 141, 173

childhood cancers 12

chimney sweeps 103

China *10*, 17, 117–18

chloro groups 258

chondromas 78

chondrosarcomas 78

chromosomal translocation 63–4, 268

chromosomes 31, 56–8
in cell ageing 38, *39*
in the cell cycle 36, *37*
and mutations 62–4

chronic myeloid leukaemia (CML) 63–4, 263, 268

circulation 218

cisplatin 220, 257–9, 262–3, 277, 325

clinical evaluation 88

clinical examination *178*

clinical nurse specialist 181, 183, 193, 209, 212

clinical target volume *233*, 234

clinical trials 193–8, 199
case study 197–8, 274

clinically significant 196

'clone' of cells 69–70, 75, 269

close margin 203

'co-pathology' 138, 141

codons 59, 61

cohort 107–8

colonoscopy 133, *134*, 212

colorectal cancer
biopsies *165*
case studies *3*, 72–3, 167, 209, 212–13
CEA levels in 136, 137
drug treatment 100
growth factors and 46
incidence and mortality 5, *8*, 9, *105*
inheritance of 71–2, 73, 111
reconstructive surgery 205–6
and red meat 121, 321
staging systems 88, *89*, *136*, 137
surgery 203, 206, *207*, *208*, 209, 222
survival rates *303*
tests for 135, 169–70

colostomy 206, *207*, 209, 221, 294, 295

combination chemotherapy 279–80

complete blood count 135, 162

'complete remission' 303

compounds 25, *253*

computed tomography (CT) 141, **142**–5, *159*, 173, *287*
in diagnosis 184, 185, 212, 322
PET/CT 157, *158*, 184, 322
SPECT/CT 155, 156, 322

concentrations 137

connective tissues 41–2, 43

consent 130, 192–3, 199, 220

conservative surgery 204, 224

consolidation therapy 264

constipation 289, 291, 293

contrast agents 143–4, 221

coping with cancer 177, 178–80, 283–6

core biopsy 161, 202

cosmic rays *116*, 117

cost-effectiveness 246, 324

costs, cancer screening *159*, 168

counsellors 192, 302, 307

craniotomy 208

crown galls *23*

cryosurgery 211

CT *see* computed tomography (CT)

cumulative dose–volume histogram *236*, 237, 249

curative surgery *see* radical treatments

cyclophosphamide 256, 264

cyclotrons 157

cytarabine 264

cytokines 89, 93–4, 198, 273

cytosine *see* C

cytoskeleton 31

cytosol *30*, **31**, *32*

cytotoxic 251

D

daughter cells 36, *37*

daunorubicin 264

death *see* mortality

death certification 16–17

debulking surgery 206

deep vein thrombosis 219, 221

deletion of nucleotides *60*, 61, 64, 73

deoxyribonucleic acid *see* DNA

depression 180, **284**–6, 293

depth–dose curves 232, *238*

diabetes 216, 222

diagnosis 177–80

    case study 184

    in the future 322–3

    manner of delivering 178, 179–80

    'patient journey' to treatment *178*

    reactions to 179, 180

    surgery used in 202

diagnostic process 129

    biopsies 160–7

    imaging tests 138–60

    laboratory tests 135–8

    overview of 130–1

    physical examination 130, 132–5

diagnostic tests

    imaging used in 138

    initial 130, 131, 134–5

diet 295, 309, 310

    and cancer 72, 321

    carcinogens in 121

    and global incidence 9

differentiation 39–44

digestive system *92*

dimethylnitrosamine 120

dirty margin 203, 221

Disability Discrimination Act (2005) 301

disease-free survival 15

distance, radiation protection and 246

DNA **28**, *29*, 31, *32*, *252*

    cross-linking 254, *255*, 256

    damage to 116, *117*, 226, 227–8

    decoding information 59

    intrastrand links 258

    microarrays 320

    mutations in 110

    sequencing 320

    structure of 56–8, 260

DNA polymerase 64, 65–6

DNA repair proteins 66, 68, 72, 75, 111, 112

    mismatch in 263, *264*

DNA replication *36*, *37*, 51, **64**, *65*, 74

    errors in 38, *255*, 256, 261

    repair in 65–6

docetaxel 266

Doll, Sir Richard 108

Doppler effect 147–8

dose

    dose–volume histogram *236*, 237, 249

    drug dose 277

    largest dose, radiotherapy 232, *233*, 238

    onset dose *229*

    tolerance dose 187, 188

    treatment planning and 234

    units of 226–7

dose–response curve 228, *229*, 230

dosette box *292*

double-blind studies 196

'double' chromosomes 36, *37*

double helix 56, *57*, 64, *65*, 226, 228

doxorubicin 277, 278

draining lymph nodes 204

drug delivery 276

drug interactions 292

drug resistance 263, 277, **278**, 279

drugs *252*

    anti-angiogenic 100

    anti-cancer 194–5

    anti-emetics 291, 293

    antidepressants 285

    antimetabolites 259–65

    difficulties in taking 292–3

    dosage 277

    in the future 325

platinum-based 257–9, 282

polypharmacy 292–3, 312

    side effects 198, 265, 271

    see also analgesia; chemotherapy

Dukes staging system 88, *89*, 209

dyes 103, 161, 163, *164*, *165*

dysplasia 166

E

E-cadherin 48, 84

elastography 160

electromagnetic radiation 113–14, 116

electrons 115, 116, 150–1, 156, 231

electronvolts *114*, 231

endocrine system *92*, **94**, 274

endoluminal endoscopy 210

endoplasmic reticulum *30*, 31, *32*

endoscope 133, *134*, 135, 162, 207, *208*, 210

endoscopic robotic techniques 211, 324

endoscopy 133, *134*, 135, 162, 207, *208*, 210–11

    NOTES technique 212

endothelial cells 83

environmental agents, mutations caused by 66–7

environmental carcinogens 122

environmental risk 102, 113–21

    lifestyle and 121–3

enzymes 34, *252*, 255

eosin 163, *165*

epidemiological data in graphs 9–12

epidemiology 4

epidermis *43*, 49

epidural block 220

epithelial cell 38, 40, *166*

    forming carcinomas 42

    in the skin *43*

epithelial tissues 42

erythroblastoma 99

ethanol *27*

ethnicity *3*, 12

Europe

    cancer mortality 18

    five-year relative survival *16*, 18–19

excisional biopsy 162, 184, 202, 224

exercise 296, 321
extracellular matrix 47, 84

F

faecal occult blood (FOB) test 135, 169–70
false negatives 169, 170
false positives 136, 169
familial 71
familial adenomatous polyposis 71
families 294–5, 301–2, 306, 307, 308, 311
fatty acids 28, 30
fertilised egg 34, *35*, 39
fever 95
fine needle aspiration 161, 202, 204
five-year relative survival 14, *15*, 16, 18–19
    and cancer therapy success 214
    clinical trials and 196
    in high-, middle-, and low-income countries *303*
    and staging *186*
flu vaccine 273
fluid loss 218
fluorine-18 157
5-fluorouracil 209, 261–3, 278
folate (folic acid) 255
follow-up appointments 297–9, 300, 302, 305
food *see* diet
fractions 228, 230, 249
France 9, *11*
free radicals 116
frequency, ultrasound pulse 146, 147–8
friends 301, 306
fructose 27, 28

G

G (guanine) 56–57, 74, *260*, 263
gamma camera imaging 152, 153–6, *159*
gamma decay *151*, 154
gamma knife 236, 324
gamma rays 113, 114, 116, *153*, 154, 156, 232
gastroscopy *134*, 174

Geiger–Müller counter 152, 161, 244, 245
gender
    and age-specific mortality *104*, 105
    in case studies *3*
    and five-year relative survival *15*
    and global incidence *8*
    and incidence rates in China *10*
    and lung cancers 7, 9, 108, *109*
    and mortality data 4, *5*, *105*
    see also men; women
gene product 58
gene therapy 275–6
gene variants 71, 110–11, 112, 170
generic name *252*
genes 28, *29*, 32, 50
    cancer-critical 67–9, 276
    mutations and 51, 60–2, 110, 111
    and proteins 58–9
    tumour-suppressor 68, 276
genetic instability 68, *70*
genetic risk 103, 110–13, 170
genetic screening 111, 112, 170, 297–8
genetic variability 73, 112
genome 58, 113, 319, 322
germline cells 23
germline mutations 71, 111
Gleason score 182, *183*
'Global Action Against Cancer' initiative 321, 327
global statistics 1
    accuracy of 16–17
    age, poverty, geography and gender 6–12
    cancer surgery 223
    cancers in the future 317–19
    pain 289
    prevalence, mortality and incidence 4–5
    radiotherapy 246–7
    survival rates and disease-free statistics 14–16
    in younger age-groups 12–14
glucose *27*, 28
glycine 59
good death 310–11
goserelin acetate 275
grade 182

grading 88, **166**, 182, *183*
graphs, interpreting data from 9–12
grays 227, *229*, 230
gross tumour volume *233*, 234
growth factors 45–7, 50, 68, 83
growth-inducing signals *46*, 267–8
growth-inhibitory factors 47, 50, 267–9
growth-inhibitory signals 47, 50, 54
guanine *see* G
'guardian of the genome' 113

H

haematoxylin 163, *165*
haemoglobin 80, 135
haemorrhage 220
hair loss 258, 278, 280, 282
half-life 152–4, *157*, *241*, *242*, *243*, 249
HCV 120
health, definition of 77
health care, levels of 130
health insurance 192, 209, 242, 277, 294
health services, lack of 6, 16–17
healthcare professionals 17, 130, *178*, 217
    patient consent 192–3
    physical examinations 132–3, 134
    support from 293, 326
    see also multidisciplinary team (MDT)
healthy margin 203, 221
heart function 271–2
heavy-ion radiation *227*, 231, 238–9
HeLa cells 39
Helicobacter pylori 119
help, sources of 293–4
heparin 221
hepatitis virus 11–12, 66, 118, 120–1, 145, 273
HER2 46, 68, 167, 271
Herceptin 46, 167, 271–2, 282
hereditary non-polyposis colorectal cancer 71–2, 73, 111
high dependency unit (HDU) 213, 215, 217–18
high dose rate (HDR) therapy 240, *241*, 242–3

high grade cancer *182, 183*

high-income countries 6, 7
    diagnosis and screening in 169, 172
    five-year relative survival *303*
    follow-up appointments 297–8, 299
    future screening 323
    life expectancy in 13
    multidisciplinary teams in 198
    numbers of smokers *321*
    perception of cancer 177
    projected cancer incidence *318*

'high-risk' populations 102, 170

Hippocrates 2

histopathological assessment
    163–7

histopathology report 165–6

HIV/AIDS 11, 118

homeostasis 96–7, 100

homologous chromosomes 56, 58

hormone therapy 274–5

hormones 94, 244

Hospice Care 293

hospices 306–7, 309

'hot spots' *154*, 156, 160, 184

Hounsfield number 142, *143*

human papilloma virus (HPV) 118, 119,
    124, 273, 321–2

humanised MABs 271

hybridomas 270–1

hyperplasia 166

hypertrophy 166

hypoxia 80

I

ibuprofen 288, 289, 291

identical twins *71*

ifosfamide 19, 220

**image guided radiotherapy (IGRT)
    236**, 324

imaging tests 138–60, 322
    in the future 159–60
    magnetic resonance *93*, 148–9,
        159, 185
    positron emission tomography *151*,
        156–7, *158*, *159*
    pros and cons of methods *159*
    radionuclide imaging 149, 151–7,
        158, *159*

see also computed tomography (CT);
    ultrasound imaging; X-ray imaging

imatinib *252*, 268

immediate referral 131

immune cells cancer *3*, 274

immune system 85, **89**–90, *92*, 95
    boost to 198
    response to pathogens 270
    and vaccine therapy 273

immunohistochemistry 167

immunosuppression 118

immunotherapy 90, 251
    cancer vaccine 273–4, 325
    monoclonal antibodies 269–72

implant therapy 192

**IMRT (intensity modulated
    radiotherapy) 235**

incidence 4
    future global projections 317–19
    global *8*, *9*
    and life expectancy 6
    regional variations 11–12
    stomach cancer *106*
    testicular cancer 12, *13*, 14

incidence rate 5, 6, 7
    among children 12
    trends in China *10*, 19

incisional biopsy 162

indium-111 pentetreotide 156

industrial chemicals 103–4, 120

infections 221, 321

infectious agents 118–20

infertility 188

inflammation 118, 119, *188*

information
    about cancer 90, *91*
    and consent 193
    importance of 219
    manner of imparting 178–80, 326

infrared radiation 114, 160

inheritance of cancers 71–3, 111

inhibitors *253*, 267–9
    growth-inhibiting drugs
    growth-inhibitory signals 47, 50, 54

insertion of nucleotides *60*, 61, 64, 73

integumentary system *92*

**intensity modulated radiotherapy
    (IMRT) 235**

interferon 198, 273

interleukin-2 273

intermediate grade cancer *182, 183*

internal examination 133

interstitial brachytherapy 240, *241*, 242

interstitial fluid 85, 161

intracavitary brachytherapy 240, *241*

intracellular signalling molecules 44,
    45, 62

intrastrand links 258

intravenous injection *189*, 219, 271,
    276, 277

invasion 48

invasive carcinoma 166

inverse square law variation 246

iodine 144, 189, 241–5, 249, 300

ionisation 115

ionising radiation 115–17, *159*,
    225, 226

ions 115

isodose lines 234

isotopes 149, **150**, 151

J

Japanese migrants 122, 321

jaundice *93*, 132

K

Kaplan–Meier survival plot 196

Kaposi's sarcoma *8*, 11, 12, 118

keratinocytes *43*

keyhole surgery 210–11, 212–13, 224

L

laboratory tests 135–8

laparoscopy 210, 212–13

laparotomy 208

laryngeal cancer 187

laser surgery 211

late side effects *188*

laxatives 289, 291, 293

leukaemias 25, **43**
    acute lymphoblastic 163, 255, 263,
        264–5, 279
    case study 264–5, 279–80
    chronic myeloid 63–4, 263, 268

drug treatment 100, *189*, 195, 263, 268, 279
mortality *5, 105*
signs 92
survival rates *303*
tissue transplantation 222–3
leukocytes 40, 89, 135, 222
leuprorelin 275
life expectancy 6
    in high-income countries 13
    in middle and low-income countries 14
life-saving treatment 211
lifestyle 121–3, **294–7**
    returning to normal life 297–305
    see also quality of life
Li–Fraumeni syndrome 113
light micrographs *166*
linacs 231–2
linear accelerator 231–2, 237
lipids 27, 28, *29*
lipoma 99
liposarcoma 43
liquid nitrogen 211
liver
    biopsy 145, 202
    metastasis in *86, 87, 142*, 144, 205
liver cancer 84–5, 99
    in Asia 11–12, 102, 121
    in case studies *3*, 145, 277
    incidence and mortality *5, 8*, 11–12, *105*
    signs 92
    treatment 273, 277
local anaesthetics 220
local signs and symptoms of cancer 91–3
    origins of 94–6
low dose rate (LDR) therapy 240
low grade cancer *182, 183*
low-income countries 6, *7*
    cancer care and support 294
    five-year relative survival *303*
    and infections 118
    life expectancy in 14
    numbers of smokers *321*
    projected cancer incidence *318*
    radiotherapy and 247

and smoking 117–18
    surgery in 223
    survival data 17
lumbar puncture 163
lumpectomy 187–8, *189*
lung cancers
    biopsy 173
    breathlessness 290
    case studies *3*, 172–3, 220, 305, 307, 309, 311
    CT image of *143, 145*
    diagnosis 184, *185*
    global incidence *8*
    mortality and *5, 11*, 105, 108
    NICE guidelines for patient referral *131*
    origins of 99
    PET/CT image of *148*
    signs and symptoms of 94
    and smoking 106, 108–9, 117–18, 123
    treatment for 187, 220, 240
    trends in *7, 9*
lung collapse 221
lungs 86–7, *166*
lymph 85
lymph glands 86, *144*
lymph nodes 77, **85**, 86, 88, 132
    biopsy 161, 209
    and cancer spread 185
    draining 204
lymphatic system 85–6, *92*, 204
lymphocytes 89, 90
lymphoedema 85, 298
lymphomas *5*, **43**, 119
    Burkitt's lymphoma 111–12
    diagnosis of 183
Lynch syndrome 110, 111

M

M4N 194, 195
MABs (monoclonal antibodies) 269–72
Macmillan Cancer Support 293, 300, 302
macromolecules 27–8, 53
magnetic resonance imaging (MRI) *93*, 148–9, *159*, 185
major surgery 215–20
malignant tumours 2, 77–9

see also cancers
malnutrition 122
MALT lymphoma 119
mammography 147, 149, 169
margin, tissue **202**–3, 221
Marie Curie Cancer Care *293*
mass number 151, 153
mastectomy 187–8
MDT *see* multidisciplinary team (MDT)
medical check-ups 297–9, 300, 302, 305
medication patch *292*
melanin 43, 49
melanocytes *43*, 44, 49
melanoma 43–4, 49, 115, 123
    case study *3*, 49, 86, 184, 197–8, 274
    incidence and mortality *5, 8, 105*
    radiotherapy for 232
    treatment options 197, 202, 205
membrane proteins 30, *31*
men
    chromosomes in *56*
    prostate cancer survival *16, 303*
    testicular cancer trends 12, *13*, 14
    see also gender
metabolic activity 33, 157
metabolites 260–1
metastasis 48
    via the blood circulation 84–5
    in bones 87, 154, 244
    in the liver *86, 87, 142*, 144, 205
    via the lymphatic system 85–6
    PET scanning and 157, *158*
    tumour cells and 86–7, *142*, 144, 154, 196
methotrexate 255, 259, 265
methyl group 256–7
'microevolutionary' process' 70
microtubules 36, 266
middle-income countries 6, *7*
    five-year relative survival *303*
    life expectancy in 14
    numbers of smokers *321*
    projected cancer incidence *318*
    radiotherapy and 247
    survival data 17
migrant populations 122
minimally invasive surgery *see* keyhole surgery

mitochondria *30*, 31, *32*, 33

mitomycin C 220, 277

MLCs (multileaf collimators) 235

molecules *24*, **25**, 27, 115, *253*

monitoring treatment 139

monoclonal antibodies (MABs) 269–72

morphine 209, 219, 289, 311

mortality 305–6, 307

    age-specific *104*, *106*, 318–19

    death certification 16–17

    gender differences *105*

    global projections of *317*, 318

    a good death 310–11

    lung cancers *11*, *109*, 118

    in smokers 108

    testicular cancer 12, *13*

mortality data 1, **4**, *5*, 7, *105*

mortality rate 5, 6

mould brachytherapy 240

MRI (magnetic resonance imaging) *93*, 148–9, *159*, 185

mRNA (messenger RNA) 58

multicellular organisms 21, *22*, 23, *24*

multidisciplinary team (MDT) 131, *178*, **180**–6, 198

    core members 181

    first meeting 182–4

    palliative care 308

    second meeting 184–6

    and tumour operability 214

multileaf collimators (MLCs) 235

muscular system *92*

mustard gas 254

mutagens 66, 67

mutation 34–5

    in cancer cells 46

    chromosomes and 62–4

    environmental agents and 66–7

    forming cancer cells 69–70

    genes and 51, 60–2, 110, 111

    occurrence of 64–70

    repair of 65–6

myeloma *5*, 95, *141*, *149*

N

N-nitrosonornicotine 109, 120

natural orifice transluminal endoscopic surgery (NOTES) 212

nausea

    causes and treatment 291, *313*

    chemotherapy and 258, 259, 277, 278, 280, 291

    painkillers and 289, 291

nedaplatin 282

negative powers of ten 26, 137

neoadjuvant 252

neoplasia 25

neoplasm 25, 166

nervous system *92*, **93**

nervous-tissue cancers *43*

neuroblastoma 43

neurons 93

neutron therapy 239

neutrons 115, 150–1

NICE guidelines, patient referral *131*

nicotine 109, 110

nitrogen mustards 254, *255*, 256, 258, 264

normal life, returning to 297–305

normal tissue complications probability (NTCP) 229–30

NOTES (natural orifice transluminal endoscopic surgery) 212

nuclear magnetic resonance (NMR) 148

nuclear membrane 36, *37*

nuclear power industry 126, 152, 153

nucleic acids 27, 28, *29*

nucleotides 28, *29*, 32, **56**–8, 59–61, *252*, 260

nucleus (atomic) **115**, 148, 149, 150–1, 152

nucleus (cellular) *30*, **31**, *32*

O

obesity 123, 124

occupational cancers 103–4, 120

occupational therapist 309–10

Octreoscan 156

oesophageal cancer *5*, *105*, 202–3, *208*

oestrogen 94, 167, 274, 275

oncogenes 67–8

oncogenomics 319

oncologist 181, 183, 187, 188, 193, 204

    treatment options 190–2

oncoproteomics 320

open surgery 208–9, 224

opioids 288, 289, 290, 291, 293, 309

opportunistic 168

optic fibres 211

optical tomography 160, 322, *323*

oral cancers *5*, *8*, 12, *105*

oral thrush 310

organ system *24*, 80

organelles *24*, **31**

organs 23, *24*, 41–2, *92*

    gamma camera imaging of *153*

    homeostasis in 96

    see also specific organs

organs at risk 234

osteosarcoma 43, 93, *148*

ovarian cancer *5*, *105*

    genetic testing for 170

    signs and symptoms 94–5

    surgery for 186, 203

    treatment 190, 240

overflowing bath 111–12

overweight 123, 124

oxaliplatin 259

oxygen 80, 151, *290*, 311

P

p53 protein 113

paclitaxel 266

pain 93, **218**–19, 221

    levels of 287–8

    management of 326

    statistics 289

    in terminal cancer 309

pain control *see* analgesia

pain scale *288*, *313*

palliative care 3, **306**–8, 309, 326

palliative care specialists 307

palliative care team 308, 309, 314

palliative treatment 186, 189–90, 198

    chemotherapy 277

    radiotherapy *190*, 196, 289

    surgery 189, 206–8

palpation 132, 134, 184, 298

pancreatic cancer *5*, *93*, *105*, *155*, 156, 222

Pap smear test 161, *166*, 169

paracetamol 288, 289

parent cells 35, 36

pathologists 87–8, 163, 167, 181, 182, 185, 203, 323

patient-controlled analgesia 219–20

patient health questionnaire *286*

patients
   brachytherapy 239
   in clinical trials 195–6
   consent 130, 192–3, 199, 220
   in decision-making 326
   'patient journey' *178*
   postoperative care 217–18
   preoperative preparation 215–17
   referral 131
   teletherapy treatment 237–8
   treatment options 190–2

PDGF (platelet-derived growth factor) 46, 68

pelvic examination *133*

penetrance 112

percussion 132

peripheral stem cell donation 223

perivisceral endoscopy 210

personal risk 102

PET/CT 157, *158*, 184, 322

pharynx cancer *8*, 206

phase I trials 195

phase II trials 195

phase III trials 195–6

'Philadelphia' chromosome 63, 66, 268

phospholipids 28, 30

photons 113, *114*, 140, *151*, 232, *238*

physical examination 130, 132–5

physiotherapy 213, 220, 309

pie charts 5, *116*

pituitary downregulators 275

placebo group 195, 274

planar X-rays *139*, 141, *159*

planning treatment volume *233*, 234

plant cells *22*

plasma 80

platelets 135

platinum-based drugs 257–9, 282

Poland 9, *11*

polypharmacy 292–3, 312

polyps 78, *133*, *165*

POMP regimen 279

positron emission tomography (PET) *151*, 156–7, *158*, *159*

positrons *151*, *156*

postoperative care 217–18

Pott, Sir Percivall 103

poverty 6, 7
   see also low-income countries

powers of ten 26–7, 81, 137

preoperative check clinic 212, 215

preoperative preparation 215–17

prevalence 1, **4**, 6
   testicular cancer 18

prevention, cancer 123–4, 321–2

preventive vaccine 273, 321–2

primary healthcare 130

primary healthcare professionals 130, 132–3, 134

primary resistance 278

primary tumours 2, 3, 84
   curative surgery for 202–5

pro-apoptotic signals 49, 50

probability 71, 228, 229–30

prodrug 257

progeny 35

progesterone 274

prognoses 2, 87, *186*

programmed cell death 49

prophylactic radiotherapy 184

prospective studies 107–8

prostate cancer 87
   adenocarcinoma 18–19, 99
   biopsies 161, *162*
   brachytherapy 240–2, 249
   case study *3*, 171–2, 192, 242, 302, 305
   global incidence *8*, 9
   grading of 182
   hormone therapy 275
   mortality data 5, 105
   PSA blood test for 170, 171, 302
   spread of 184, 185
   staging in 88
   survival rates *16*, *303*
   treatment options 190, 192

prostate-specific antigen (PSA) 138

proteases 84

proteins 27, 28, *29*, *252*

BCR–ABL fusion protein *63*, 64, 68, 268
   during cell differentiation 40
   and genes 58–9
   membrane proteins 30, *31*
   p53 protein 113
   role in cancer cells 50, 270
   see also DNA repair proteins; enzymes; signalling molecules

proto-oncogenes 67–8

proton therapy 238–9

protons 115, 150–1

PSA blood test 170, 171, 302

psychological effects 180, 205, 284–6

psychotherapy 285

pulmonary embolism 221

purines *260*

pyrimidines *260*, 261

quality of life 3, 198, 284–6, 289, 326

R

radiation 113–17, *159*, 225, 226

radiation protection 226, 245–6

radical surgery 204

radical treatments 186–90, 198
   chemotherapy 188–9
   radiotherapy 187–8
   surgery 186, 202–5, 224

radioactive decay 149, 151, 152, 156

radioactive materials 116, 152

radiobiology 116, **226**

radiologists 181, 182, 185

radionuclide 149, 152, 153–4, *159*
   in brachytherapy *241*
   for PET imaging 156–7
   in unsealed source radiotherapy *243*

radionuclide imaging 149, 151–7, *158*, 272

radiopharmaceutical 153, 156–7, 243, *272*, 325

radiotherapy 186, 225–6
   adjuvant *185*, 187–8, 252, 279
   advances in 324–5
   case studies 242, 244–5
   global differences 246–7
   image guided radiotherapy 236, 324
   issues considering 191
   in low-income countries 6

method of working 226–30
palliative *190*, 196, 289
prophylactic 184
radiation protection 245–6
radical 187–8
side effects *188*
total body irradiation 222
treatment planning 139, 144, *145*, 232, 234
see also brachytherapy; teletherapy; unsealed source radiotherapy
radon gas *116*
raltitrexed 263
randomised controlled trials 195–6, 274
RAS 46, 62, 68
reactive nitrogen species 118
reactive oxygen species 116, 118
reassurance 298
receptors 44–5, 46, 270, 272
hormone 274–5
recombinant human thyroid-stimulating hormone 244
reconstructive surgery 205–6, 220–1
recovery period 217–18
rectal examination 133
recurrence 297, 298, 299, 303–4, 305
red cells 80, 95, 135
red meat 121, 321
reflection, tissue interfaces *146*, 147
regimen 190
Rehn, Ludwig 103
relative risk 108
renal cancer 87, 96, *105*
replicative senescence 38
reproductive system *92*
resection margin 202
respiratory system 80, *92*, 96
retinoblastoma gene (*Rb*) 68, 71
retrospective 106, 108
ribosomes *30*, 31, *32*
risk 101
assessment 215, 216
long-term risk of developing cancer 230
surgery 220–2, 224
risk factor 2, 102–4
and age 318–19

environmental 113–21
genetic 103, 110–13, 170
identifying and quantifying 104–10
lifestyle, environment and 121–3

S

safety of treatments 195
sarcomas 43, 78, 79, 183
Kaposi's sarcoma *8*, *11*, *12*, 118
osteosarcoma 43, 93, *148*
Saunders, Dame Cicely 306–7
scientific notation 26–7, 81
screening 168–72
breast cancer 147, 149, 169
cervical cancer 119, 124, 161, *166*, 169, 171
in the future 322–3
pros and cons 175
secondary health care 130
secondary tumours 2, 84–5
chemotherapy of 188–9
CT scan of 184
curative surgery for 205
self-sufficiency in growth signals 47
sentinel lymph node biopsy 161
sex chromosomes 56
shielding 245–6
SI units 81
side effects
cancer, management of 286–94
chemotherapy 277–8, 280, 291
drugs 198, 265, 271, 291
pain control 289, 291
radiotherapy *188*, 291
surgery 224
X-ray imaging *229*
signalling molecules 44–5, 46, 62
growth-inducing and growth-inhibitory *46*, 47, 50, 54
signs 90
local 91–3
origin of 94–6
systemic 93–4
silent mutation 61
skeletal system *92*
skin cancer *see* melanoma
skin cells 37, *40*, *43*

smoking 106, *107*, 108–9, 117–18, 123, 296–7
carcinogens in 67
case study 110
gender and 4, 7, 9
numbers of smokers *321*
somatic mutations 71, 111
somatostatin 156
Spain 9, *11*
specialist clinics 298
specialists 131, 173, *178*, 307, 326
SPECT 155
SPECT/CT *155*, 156, 184
spectrum 113, *114*
sporadic 71
squamous cells 42, *43*, 49, 99
stable isotopes 149, 151
stage grouping 88–9
staging 87–9, *136*, 137, 144, 209
and diagnosis 182, 185
imaging used in 138
and prognosis *186*
surgery used in 202
staining 163, *164*, *165*, 167
start codon 59
statistically significant 196
statistics *see* global statistics
stem cells 42, 222–3, 280
stent 206–7, *208*
stereotactic radiosurgery 236
steroids 289, 307, 310
stoma 206, *207*, 209
see also colostomy
stomach cancer 208
adhesion and 48
caused by bacteria 119
global incidence *8*, 9
Japanese women *122*
mortality from *5*, 105, *105*, *106*
stop codons 59, 61
Sub-Saharan Africa
cancer incidence 9, 12
Kaposi's sarcoma 11
substitution of nucleotides *60*, 64, 73
sucrose *27*, *28*
sugar–phosphate backbone *57*, 260
support, sources of 293–4

surgeons 193, 202–3, 209, 212, 218
   lack of in low-income countries 6, 223
surgery 186
   adjuvant treatment and *185*, 187–8, 189, 220
   advances in 324
   approaches in 201–8
   case study 220
   debulking 206
   as a diagnostic and staging tool 202
   effects on the human body 215, 224
   issues considering 191
   in low-income countries 6, 223
   open or minimal 208–11, 224
   palliative 189, 206–8
   postoperative 217–20
   preoperative preparation 215–17
   for primary disease 202–5
   process in cancer treatment 214–20
   radical treatment 186, 202–5, 224
   reconstructive 205–6, 220–1
   review of 185
   risks of 220–2, 224
   special techniques in 211–13
   see also biopsy
survival rates *see* five-year relative survival
'survival' signals 47, 48, 49, 50
symptoms 90–6
   cancer, management of 286–94
   local 91–3
   origin of 94–6
   and patient referral 131
   systemic 93–4
   in terminal illness 309–10, 314
syringe driver *309*, 311
systematic screening 168
systemic signs and symptoms 93–4
   origins of 94–6
systemic therapy 251–2, 282

T

T (thymine) 56–**57**, 74, *260*, 261–2, 263
T cells 269
TACE 277
tamoxifen 94, 167, 275
target volumes *233*, 234

'targeted radiotherapy' 244, 325
targeted therapy 251, **269**, 325
taxanes 266
Taxol 194, 266
TCP (tumour control probability) 228, 230
technetium-99m 152, 153–4
teletherapy 226, 324
   activity 237–8
   assessing the plan 236–8
   fractionation 249
   global differences and *247*
   linear accelerator 231–2, 237
   multileaf collimator and image-guided therapy 235–6
   treatment planning 232–4
   using heavy particles 238–9
telomerase 38, 39
telomeres 38, *39*
temozolomide 256–7, 278
temperature regulation 97, 218
terminal illness 305–6, 307, 311
   symptoms in 309–10, 314
tertiary health care 130
testicular cancer 12, *13*, 14, 18, 188, 318
testosterone 275
TGN1412 195
therapeutic window 229–30
6-thioguanine 263–5
thoracoscopy 210
thoracotomy 208
'three-step ladder' 289, 309
thromboembolism deterrent stockings 221
thymidylate synthase (TS) 261–2, 263
thymine *see* T
thyroid cancer
   case study *3*, 204–5, 244–5, 300
   treatment 189, 244
thyroidectomy 189, 204
thyroxine 300
time, radiation protection and 246
tissue biopsies 161–3, 202, 210
   histopathological assessment of 163–7
tissue interfaces *146*, 147
tissue transplantation 222–3

tissues 23, *24*, 41–2
   attenuation coefficients 140–2, 143, 144, 146, *174*
   normal tissue response 229–30
   paths of X-rays through *140*
   ultrasound imaging and 146–7
TNM staging system 88–9, 138, 144, 182, 209
tolerance dose 187, 188
tomographic 141
Tomotherapy 236
total body irradiation 222
tracheotomy 189
transcription 58
transducer 146
translation 58, 59
transport protein 278
transrectal ultrasound biopsy *162*, 171–2
trastuzumab *see* Herceptin
treatment plan 139, 144, *145*, 232–**4**, 249
   assessing 236–8
treatments 3
   advances in 324–6
   case study 192
   choosing options 190–2
   effectiveness of 193–8
   global 6
   high dose rate (HDR) therapy 240, *241*, 242–3
   monitoring of 139
   'patient journey' to *178*
   process of surgical therapy in 214–20
   surgical approaches in 201–8
   see also adjuvant treatment; palliative treatment; radical treatments
triglycerides 28
true negatives 169
true positives 169
tubulins 266
tumour cells *see* cancer cells
tumour control probability (TCP) 228, 230
tumour growth 21
tumour markers 135–8, 298
tumour-suppressor genes 68, 276
tumours 2, 25
   benign and malignant 77–9

bone marrow tumours 95, *141*
brain tumours *235*, 236
evolution of a *70*
operability of 214
from tumour cells 80–3
see also primary tumours; secondary tumours

U

ultrasound elastography 322, *323*
ultrasound imaging 145–8, *159*, 160
in biopsies 161, *162*
in brachytherapy *241*
in surgery 211
ultrasound pulse 145, *146*, 148
ultraviolet rays 113, 114–15, 123
uncertainty, living with 303–5
undifferentiated cells 42, 44, 78
United Kingdom
background ionising radiation *116*, 117
cancer diagnoses 17
cancer therapy *178*, 180–1
cervical screening programme 171
consent form 193
five-year relative survival *15*, 16
lung cancer mortality 9, *11*, 108, *109*
NICE guideline for referring patients *131*
radiotherapy and 247

risk factors for cancers 104, *105*, 121
UK Cancer Research *91*
United States 16, 17
unsealed source radiotherapy 226, 243–5, 325
unstable isotopes 149, 151
uracil 261–2, 263
urgent referral 131, 134
urinary system *92*, 96
urine tests 135, 322
uterine cancer *167*, *303*
see also cervical cancer
UVA 114–15
UVB 114
UVC 115

V

vaccine 198, **273**–4, 321–2, 325
variant 71
VEGF 83
veins 80, *82*
deep vein thrombosis 219, 221
vinblastine 194, 266
vinca alkaloids 266
vincristine 194, 264, 265, 266
viruses *22*, 23, 90, 118, 273, 321–2
mutations caused by 66, 67
see also hepatitis virus; human papilloma virus
visual inspection 132

vomiting *208*, 259, 277–8, 289, 291
causes and treatment *313*

W

ward, care on 213, 218
water molecule *25*, *27*, *29*
weakness 309
wedge biopsy 162, 202
women
Japanese migrants *122*, 321
mortality from lung cancer *11*, 108
see also gender
Wong-Baker 'faces' pain scale *313*
work, returning to 299–301

X

X-ray imaging 139–41
cell survival curve *227*
mammography 147, 149, 169
side effects *229*
in surgery 212
using linear accelerators 231–2
see also chest X-ray; computed tomography (CT)
X-rays 113, 114, 116, 140, *159*, 226

Y

'yellow finger' hypothesis 109